INTERNATIONAL CHEMICAL SERIES

JAMES F. NORRIS, Ph.D., Consulting Editor

SOLUTIONS OF ELECTROLYTES

SOLUTIONS
OF ELECTROLYTES

WITH PARTICULAR APPLICATION TO
QUALITATIVE ANALYSIS

BY

LOUIS P. HAMMETT, Ph.D.

Professor of Chemistry in Columbia University

SECOND EDITION
FIFTH IMPRESSION

McGRAW-HILL BOOK COMPANY, Inc.

NEW YORK AND LONDON

1936

THE MAPLE PRESS COMPANY, YORK, PA.

PREFACE TO THE SECOND EDITION

I have been led to this revision partly by experience in the use of the text, which has shown many ways in which the presentation could be improved, and partly by the constant pressure that the progress of science exerts upon the writer of a textbook. The most important effect which the latter influence has had is the incorporation of the theory that acids and bases ionize not by a dissociation but by a transfer of hydrogen ions to or from molecules of the solvent. The dissociation idea, it is true, can give a satisfactory account of most of the phenomena treated in this book. But the newer theory has so liberated thought and stimulated investigation into the kinetics of acid and base catalyzed reactions and the properties of nonaqueous solutions that it seems undesirable to teach the older one any longer. Fortunately the newer theory is at least as simple and teachable as the older one.

It is a pleasure to acknowledge the valuable advice of Professor J. K. W. Macalpine of Washington Square College, New York University; the many contributions of Dr. H. L. Pfluger, Dr. L. A. Flexser, Mr. H. P. Treffers, and Mr. J. Steigman, assistants in chemistry in Columbia University; and the kindness of Professor C. D. Carpenter, whose form of the periodic table I have used.

L. P. HAMMETT.

NEW YORK, N. Y.,
February, 1936.

v

PREFACE TO THE FIRST EDITION

This book is based upon the belief that a course in qualitative analysis is an ideal method of presenting and of illustrating by copious examples the general principles relating to the behavior of solutions of electrolytes; and that this part of physical chemistry is an indispensable part of the preparation for advanced work in chemistry and for the study of medicine and engineering. It is an attempt to make the fullest use of qualitative analysis as a means of teaching chemistry.

The book is not an attempt to teach an immediately useful practical art. A properly conducted course of qualitative analysis does teach much valuable analytical chemistry, in the sense of general principles, typical methods, and some experience in technique. But this is not a practical art, and cannot be so long as we must exclude elements as common as tungsten and vanadium lest the course become too time consuming.

The most valuable thing to be gained from a scientific education is the ability to find things out by experiment. Descriptive experiments whose results can be foretold by reference to the text book are not good examples of scientific method, and it is precisely to the most intelligent students that they are most tiresome. Such instruction is only too likely to produce students who have spent so many years accumulating facts that they have forgotten how to be either original or critical. It is the great virtue of analytical chemistry as a teaching instrument that it sets problems which can only be answered by experimentation. Yet this value can be curtailed or lost if the work is driven into a hard and fast routine by purely traditional ideas of the material which must form part of every course in qualitative analysis.

The laboratory exercises which form the second part of the book are intended to illustrate by sound examples of experimental method the principles discussed in the first part rather

vii

than to teach a definite scheme of analysis.   This work should require one term, and can be so carried out that the laboratory work is closely related to the principles being discussed at the same time in the classroom.   Where more time is available the further work should be based upon the principle that the student now understands how to use an analytical method, and that he needs little further instruction or practice in order to learn from reference or text books the methods of analysis for the anions and for other common metallic ions, and the methods of preparation of the solution.

It has seemed to me particularly important to capitalize in our instruction in chemistry the great advance in clarity and simplicity to which our views on the nature of solutions of strong electrolytes have recently attained.   Most of us who are now teaching chemistry struggled through the confusion of "anomalous strong electrolytes," but that should be all the more reason why we should not first teach the ionization theory of 1885, then unteach part of it to reach a new theory which is simpler than the old as well as apparently more nearly correct.

All who have to do with the teaching of qualitative analysis owe a great debt to the genius and effort which A. A. Noyes and his co-workers have devoted to the improvement of its methods.   My own debt will be obvious from a perusal of the book.   I am further indebted to other texts on qualitative analysis, notably to those of Stieglitz, of Treadwell and Hall, and of Böttger.   I have also made much use of the reference works on inorganic chemistry of Mellor, of Abegg, and of Gmelin-Kraut, of the Elektrochemie of Foerster, and of the Landolt-Börnstein Tabellen.

It has been my great good fortune to have studied with Professor H. T. Beans, to have been introduced to the teaching of qualitative analysis by Professor J. E. Zanetti, and to have enjoyed years of congenial association with both.   What there is new and valuable in the spirit of this book, and in many details of the presentation arises directly from this association, and I here gladly recognize the indebtedness.

L. P. Hammett.

New York, N. Y.,
August, 1929.

CONTENTS

PART I
PRINCIPLES

CHAPTER I

INTRODUCTION

Introductory.—A working knowledge of the general principles and laws describing the behavior of solutions of electrolytes and of the descriptive chemistry of ionic substances is a fundamental part of the scientific equipment of anyone who is to study the science of chemistry or the applications of chemistry to medicine and in industry. Important parts of physical chemistry and electrochemistry are concerned with these general principles and laws; inorganic analytical chemistry is based almost entirely upon the reactions of electrolytes; biological chemistry and physiology can no longer be studied without an extensive knowledge of the properties of these solutions; and the chemical engineer must use the same reactions and apply the same principles when the container is the huge reaction vessel of chemical industry instead of the test tube of the laboratory.

In this book the reactions of inorganic qualitative analysis will be used to illustrate the properties of electrolytes and the application to special cases of fundamental generalizations and methods of reasoning. There is no other laboratory study which touches so completely the whole range of the behavior of solutions of electrolytes and offers so satisfactory a means of becoming familiar with the descriptive and theoretical chemistry of this important field. In itself, moreover, the subject is a valuable introduction to the subject of analytical chemistry. This leads easily into the more precise methods of quantitative analysis, or into the more comprehensive methods of the qualitative analysis of natural and industrial products.

Some Considerations about Atomic Structure.—The properties of electrolytes are most easily correlated and remembered in the light of the picture of the structure of atoms and of the behavior of atoms when they take part in chemical reactions, which is generally used by both physicists and chemists. Like all the

3

pictures which science uses for the correlation and organization of known facts and for guidance in the search for new facts, this one has no claim to absolute truth.   It cannot be proved, but it can be shown to be extremely useful in describing and predicting the behavior of nature.   Some phases of this usefulness will be illustrated by our discussion of the properties of electrolytes. It is important, however, to realize that the picture is the result of a long evolution, that it has developed by a process of constant revision, and that there is every reason to expect the process to continue.

According to this picture, the atoms of the chemical elements consist of assemblages of particles of electricity, each kind of atom possessing its own characteristic number and arrangement of particles.   The most familiar of these particles is the *electron*, which has a negative charge of 1.592×10^{-19} coulombs, and a mass equal to $\frac{1}{1850}$ of the mass of a hydrogen atom.   The electrical charge possessed by the electron is the fundamental indivisible unit of electricity.   No quantity of electricity smaller than this has ever been observed and all electrical charges are integral multiples of it.   Atoms consist of electrons and a *nucleus*.   The latter is concentrated within a very minute fraction (about 10^{-15}) of the volume of the atom; it carries practically the whole mass of the atom; and it has a positive charge equal in magnitude (but opposite, of course, in sign) to the product of the electron charge by a quantity called *the atomic number*, which is characteristic of the kind of chemical element.   With a few exceptions the atomic numbers may be obtained by writing down the symbols of the elements in the order of increasing atomic weight and then numbering them according to this order.   They may be more accurately determined from the way in which high-speed positively charged particles are deflected by the nucleus or from the frequencies of the X-ray spectra of the elements. The nuclei are no doubt themselves complex assemblages of particles, including electrons, but neither the mass nor the charge of the nucleus changes during ordinary chemical reactions.

The major portion of the volume of the atom is occupied by the paths or orbits of the extranuclear electrons, which make up nevertheless a very minor portion of the mass of the atom.   In the electrically neutral atom their number is necessarily equal to the atomic number, because this is the number of equivalent positive charges on the nucleus. An atom may, however, lose one or more electrons, in which case it becomes a positively charged *ion*, a *cation*, or it may gain additional electrons which make it a negatively charged ion, an *anion*. The relative ease with which electrons are lost or gained is one of the most characteristic of the chemical properties of an element. It is determined in many cases by the fact that the number and arrangement of electrons which is found in the inert gases (He 2, Ne 10, A 18, Kr 36, Xe 54, Rn 86) has an especial stability. As a result the alkali elements (Group Ia of the periodic table; see inside back cover), which contain one more electron than the next preceding inert gas, lose one electron easily and form thereby an ion with a single unit of positive charge (Li^+, Na^+, K^+, Rb^+, Cs^+). The remaining electrons are too firmly held to be removed during a chemical reaction, and no ions of greater charge than this are formed. On the other hand, seven or more additional electrons would be needed to reach the next higher stable configuration, and this is too many to be held firmly by the nuclear positive charge. For this reason the alkalis do not appear as anions. Similarly the alkaline earths can easily lose two electrons to form Be^{++}, Mg^{++}, Ca^{++}, Sr^{++}, Ba^{++}, Ra^{++}, but do not appear as cations of larger charge than two or as anions of any charge. (The fact that singly positive ions of these elements appear only under exceptional circumstances can be accounted for, but the explanation is much too complicated to discuss here.)

The halogens on the contrary have a large tendency to add one electron to form the singly charged negative ions, F^-, Cl^-, Br^-, I^-. Anions of greater charge than this are not known, nor do these elements exist in solution as cations to any demonstrable extent. They do, however, form complex ions (see page 13), which may in some ways be considered as derived from positively charged halogen ions with charges up to seven units. Similarly sulfur and its analogues in Group VIb easily gain two additional electrons to form such ions as $S^=$, and also form complex ions like $SO_4^=$ and $SO_3^=$, which may be considered as derived from sulfur ions with six and four positive charges, respectively. The situation is more obscure with elements which are more widely removed from the inert gases.

The Nature of Salts.—In terms of this picture the reaction of sodium and chlorine appears to be primarily a transfer of the loosely bound electrons of the sodium atoms to the chlorine atoms, which have a large affinity for them. The equation is

$$Na + Cl \rightarrow Na^+ + Cl^-. \tag{1}$$

Following this, various things may happen according to the conditions. At very high temperatures the sodium and chloride ions pair off into electrically neutral NaCl *molecules*. (This is known to be the case from measurements of the density of sodium chloride vapor, which lead to a molecular weight of 58.45.) At lower temperatures and in the absence of a solvent they form crystals of sodium chloride.

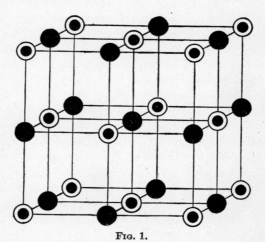

Fig. 1.

Somewhat surprisingly we find that the molecules which exist in the vapor have lost their identity in the crystalline salt. The arrangement of the atoms is that shown in Fig. 1. This represents a small portion of the crystal which may be thought of as formed by an almost infinite repetition in three dimensions of this unit. The ions making up the crystal are to be thought of as spheres with surfaces in contact, or nearly so, and with their centers at the positions indicated by the circles in the figure. The solid black circles may be taken as the sodium, the ringed circles as the chloride ions. If it is kept in mind that this is only part of the crystal, that similar cubes are in front of, in back of, on each side of, above, and below the cube pictured, it will easily be seen that each sodium ion is surrounded by 6 equidistant chloride ions, and each chloride ion by 6 equidistant sodium ions. Sodium and chloride ions alternate in a sort of three-dimensional chessboard. There are no molecules of NaCl in such a structure; any attempt to pair off the sodium and chloride ions into molecules would be purely arbitrary and meaningless.

This arrangement has been established by the methods of X-ray structure analysis which we owe to the discoveries of Laue and of W. H. and W. L. Bragg in 1912. The principle of the method is this, that X-rays, being light of a wave length comparable with the distance between the atoms in crystalline substances, interact with crystals in a manner similar to, but more complex than the way in which visible light interacts with a ruled diffraction grating. From the diffraction effects produced it is possible to reason back to a determination of the arrangement of the atoms in the crystal.

An arrangement of this sort, which is called an *ionic lattice*, has also been found to exist in the crystals of almost all of the substances which chemists have usually called *salts*, and certainly in all which would be considered typical salts. Thus calcium carbonate is built up of Ca^{++} and $CO_3^=$ ions, the carbonate ion having a triangular shape with the carbon surrounded by the three oxygens. This triangular shape of the carbonate ion results in a distortion of the crystal from the cubic to the rhombohedral type, but it still remains true that each calcium ion is surrounded by six equivalent carbonate ions, and that each carbonate ion is surrounded by six equivalent calcium ions. In ammonium chloride each ammonium ion is surrounded by eight instead of six chloride ions, and each chloride ion by eight ammonium ions; this is a different type of cubic structure. In neither case is there evidence of the existence of molecules. Although it is not always done, it is probably desirable to restrict the name salt to substances which crystallize in ionic lattices. On this basis stannic iodide, whose crystals contain easily recognizable molecules of SnI_4, is not a salt.

Both gaseous and solid sodium chloride are poor conductors of electricity. Liquid sodium chloride by contrast is an exceedingly good conductor, and thus betrays the essentially ionic nature of the substance in a way which the other forms do not. Apparently the solid structure is too rigid to permit motion of the ions, the gas contains the ions completely paired off into widely separated neutral molecules, the liquid suffers under neither disadvantage.

The Laws of Definite Proportion and of Combining Weights.— In the light of this picture these laws do not necessarily depend upon a combination in constant proportions of the different kinds of atoms into molecules. In the case of salts they depend upon the fact that the compound consists of sodium and chloride ions which possess equal but opposite charges and which are formed by the transfer of an electron from each sodium atom to each chlorine atom reacting. The number of chloride ions formed is therefore necessarily equal to the number of sodium ions. Given the constancy of the average atomic mass of an element (average because of the existence of isotopes) the law of definite proportions is a simple and necessary consequence, which is independent of the fact that sodium chloride molecules are formed under certain conditions and are not formed under others.

There is some confusion possible in using the terms *mole* and *equivalent weight* for substances of this sort. A mole is a weight in grams equal numerically to the molecular weight of the substance. What, then, is a mole of solid sodium chloride or of liquid sodium chloride if these substances do not contain any simple molecules? We might say with some justification that the molecule of solid sodium chloride is the whole crystal, in which case we should have to admit that we could change the molecular weight with a mortar and pestle. In order to avoid this kind of reductio ad absurdum and to preserve the values which the terms still possess, chemists have generally agreed to calculate the mole and the equivalent weight of salts in terms of the simplest possible formula. Thus the mole of sodium chloride is 58.45 corresponding to the formula NaCl.

The Solution of Salts.—In spite of their importance in practice, solutions of salts are really exceptional and specialized compositions of matter. Solution must represent a breaking down into smaller units of the large and complex structure of the ionic lattice. These smaller fragments cannot be molecules such as NaCl because there is little if any more occasion for the evaporation of such molecules into the solvent than there is into a vacuum. But it is one of the most characteristic properties of a salt that its vapor pressure is extremely low at ordinary temperatures, that its boiling and melting points are high. (Substances like ammonium chloride which break up into the nonsalt-like fragments, NH₃ and HCl, are exceptions to this rule.) This means that the forces holding the ions together in the lattice are so strong that the disrupting influence of heat does not have an important effect in breaking up the lattice into simple molecules until the temperature is very high.

In accord with these ideas we find that solutions of salts are always good conductors and further that the only liquids which have a generally high solvent action on salts are those which have high *dielectric constants*. By the very definition of the term dielectric constant this means that these are media in which the forces acting between charged particles are relatively weak. Thus the statement that water has a dielectric constant of 80 implies that the amount of work required to separate two oppositely charged bodies from a distance a to a distance b is $\frac{1}{80}$ as great when they are immersed in water as it is when they are in a vacuum. But the number of such solvents is restricted. Water is not only the most familiar solvent for salts, but it has also the largest solvent action without decomposition on the widest range of salts of any substance known. Liquid ammonia is nearly as good. Sulfuric and hydrofluoric acids are extremely powerful solvents but convert all other salts into bisulfates and fluorides, respectively. The solvent power of organic liquids varies greatly. Methyl alcohol, formic acid, and formamide approach fairly closely to water in this respect. At the other extreme benzene and the paraffin hydrocarbons dissolve to a measurable extent only certain specialized types of organic salts. There is a very rough parallelism between the solvent power on salts and the dielectric constant. It should be reiterated that even the poorest solvents dissolve salts to form conducting solutions when they dissolve them at all.

On this basis it is hardly to be expected that solutions of a salt in a solvent of high dielectric constant like water should contain more than vanishingly small traces of molecules. The salt dissolves only because the solvent is one which favors the separation of individual ions; if molecules were formed in the solution, they would be expected to crystallize out as completely or nearly as completely as they would from the vapor of the salt at ordinary temperatures.

Additivity of Properties.—The behavior of dilute aqueous salt solutions is entirely in agreement with this prediction. Their most striking property is the one called *additivity*. By this is meant the fact that a solution of potassium chloride has certain properties which it shares with all other potassium salts and which are therefore the properties of potassium ion. It also possesses properties which can for a similar reason be called the properties of chloride ion. The summation of the properties of potassium ion and of chloride ion gives the totality of the properties of the potassium chloride solution. There is nothing left that may be considered a property of potassium chloride molecules, no definite or obvious reason therefore to concern ourselves with their possible existence. Of course, it would be entirely foolish and unwise to say that the molecular substance is completely absent; we are concerned merely with the question whether it is present in an amount large enough to have any significant influence on the properties of the solution.

As an example let us consider the familiar blue *color* of cupric salts: cupric sulfate, cupric nitrate, cupric chloride, and many other cupric salts have in dilute solution an identical color. But solutions of cupric dichromate and permanganate have colors very different from this blue. It is not very difficult however to show that the color of a cupric dichromate solution is in a way the sum of the colors characteristic of cupric salts and of dichromates.

A colored substance is one which selectively absorbs certain frequencies of visible light. The blue color of cupric salts represents the abstraction from transmitted white light of a certain amount of red and violet light, the orange of dichromates represents the absorption of blue and violet. The absorption of a cupric dichromate solution is the sum of these two absorptions, that of cupric salts and that of dichromates. To show this qualitatively it is only necessary to compare the color sensation produced by light which has traversed a solution of cupric dichromate with that produced by light which has traversed successively a solution of cupric sulfate and one of potassium dichromate. The identity of the observed colors is very clear evidence of the additive effect. The method of investigation may be made quantitative, and may be extended to substances which are colorless in the ordinary sense, but which absorb in the ultraviolet. The same result is obtained; the light absorption of a solution of a salt is almost exactly the sum of the absorptions of the metallic part and of the acid radical.

Color is a particularly obvious physical property, but what is true of color is true of practically all the other physical properties of such solutions. Specific volumes, heat capacities, viscosities, refractive indices, heats of reaction may all be represented as the sum of two parts, one characteristic of all salts with the same metallic radical, the other characteristic of all salts with the same acid radical (see page 59).

Chemical properties too are additive. Copper sulfate, like other copper salts, reacts with zinc or iron to give metallic copper and with hydrogen sulfide to give cupric sulfide; like other sulfates it reacts with barium chloride to precipitate barium sulfate. There are no properties of cupric sulfate solution which it does not share either with other cupric salts or with other sulfates.

Freezing points also offer evidence that the ions of a salt are not associated into molecules in dilute aqueous solutions. Solutions have lower freezing points than the solvent, and the difference between the freezing point of water and that of a solution of a nonelectrolyte is proportional to the molar concentration of the solute. The depression of the freezing point is in the proportion of 1.860°C. for each mole per liter in water. But uni-univalent electrolytes depress the freezing point nearly twice as much as do nonelectrolytes at the same molar concentration; uni-bivalent electrolytes give nearly three times the depression of a nonelectrolyte, and so on. (The fact that these depressions are not quite two or three times the depression produced by a nonelectrolyte has been satisfactorily explained by the theory of Debye and Hückel as a result of electrical forces acting between the ions.)

Homopolar Combination.—The saltlike kind of combination typified by sodium chloride is not the only way in which atoms may react. There is an entirely different kind, of which H_2, O_2, and the other diatomic elementary gases are the perfect examples. These are low-boiling, low-melting substances, which exhibit the same molecular weight in solution as in the gaseous form and do not conduct electricity as solids, liquids, gases, or in solution. In fact, their properties are in every way in complete contrast to those of salts. While it is conceivable that two hydrogen atoms might react by the transfer of an electron from one to the other

$$H + H \rightarrow H^+ + H^- \qquad (2)$$

after which the positive and the negative hydrogen ions might combine to form the molecule, such a molecule would necessarily have much the same properties as the sodium chloride molecule. It would condense easily to a conducting liquid, and freeze to a crystal having an ionic lattice: it could not conceivably have the properties of the actual hydrogen molecule, whose behavior is that to be expected of a molecule in which the distribution of electric charges is very symmetrical.

This hydrogenlike kind of combination is called variously *homopolar, nonpolar,* or *covalent* in contrast to the sodium chloride kind which is called *heteropolar, polar,* or *electrovalent.* The homopolar or covalent linkage is generally considered to involve the sharing of electrons between the atoms linked, a pair of electrons (four or six in the case of the double and triple bonds of the organic chemist) being shared by each pair of atoms linked.

The atoms held together by this kind of linkage need not be of the same kind, the C—H linkages in methane, CH_4, and indeed in most organic compounds are very closely similar to the H—H linkage in H_2. There are also many linkages which partake to a greater or lesser extent of both forms. This is because the homopolar form of combination may be entered into by atoms which have previously lost or gained electrons, and have therefore become ions. Sulfate ion, for instance, has some properties which would lead us to consider it a homopolar compound of sulfide ion, $S^=$, with electrically neutral oxygen atoms. From this point of view it resembles methane, CH_4, except that the central sulfur atom in sulfate ion has gained two electrons before it entered into combination. In other important respects, however, sulfate ion behaves like a combination of a sulfur atom which has lost six electrons with four oxygen atoms, each of which has gained two electrons

$$S^{++++++} + 4O^= \rightarrow SO_4^=. \tag{3}$$

This combination, while it may depend partly upon electron sharing, must also be largely affected by the fact that the atoms entering into combination are oppositely charged and are attracted to each other by electrostatic forces. To this extent the combination is sodium chloride-like or heteropolar. The actual sulfate ion is to be thought of as something in between, to whose great stability several kinds of linkage simultaneously contribute. These include not only the homopolar linkage between $S^=$ and O, and the mixed-type linkage between S^{++++++} and $O^=$, but also the mixed-type linkage between S^{++} and O^-, and possibly other forms.

Sulfate ion is a *complex ion*, specifically an *oxygen complex ion*, because it is formed from a central atom surrounded by oxygen atoms. There are many other types of complex ions, sulfide complexes, such as $AsS_4^=$, chloride complexes, such as $SnCl_6^=$, cyanide complexes, such as $Fe(CN)_6^{\equiv}$, ammonia complexes, such as $Ni(NH_3)_6^{++}$, and many others. Complexes may also be of mixed type, as $AsSO_3^=$, or $Co(NH_3)_5Cl^{++}$ (see Chap. V).

Acids and Bases: Protolytic Reactions.—Ammonium ion, NH_4^+, is an example of an extremely important type of complex ion, for it is upon the formation of ions of this sort that the ionization of acids and bases seems to depend. Consider the substance hydrogen chloride, HCl. It has a low melting and boiling point, the pure liquid is a poor conductor of electricity, it dissolves easily in liquids like benzene, which have little solvent action on salts, and the solutions in such solvents are likewise very poor conductors. In all these respects the substance seems homopolar, hydrogenlike, nonsaltlike. Yet its solutions in a few solvents, notably water and ammonia, have a saltlike

conductivity.   In the ammonia case the reason is clear; the
hydrogen chloride has reacted with the ammonia

$$HCl + NH_3 \rightleftarrows NH_4^+ + Cl^- \tag{4}$$

and we have the typically saltlike substance NH_4Cl, in the form
of its ions NH_4^+ and Cl^-.   Indeed solid ammonium chloride
can be obtained from the solution simply by allowing the ammonia
to evaporate.   We can account for the otherwise puzzling
contrast between the generally homopolar properties of HCl and
its strong electrolyte properties in water if we assume that a
similar process occurs in that solvent also

$$HCl + H_2O \rightleftarrows OH_3^+ + Cl^-. \tag{5}$$

The substance OH_3^+ is called *oxonium ion* (also *hydroxonium ion*,
or *hydronium ion*).

The evidence for this interpretation of the ionization of acids
in water is overwhelming and so varied that we can mention only
a few points.   An important one is the similarity of solutions
of electrolytes in water to solutions of electrolytes in liquid
ammonia, and especially the great similarity between the properties of acids in water and their properties in ammonia, in
which they unquestionably exist as ammonium salts.   In liquid
ammonia ammonium salts dissolve metals with evolution of
hydrogen, they dissolve difficultly soluble salts of weak acids,
and they neutralize amides.   These reactions are the exact
analogues of the reactions of aqueous acids with metals, with
salts like calcium carbonate, and with hydroxides (amide ion,
NH_2^-, bears the same relation to the solvent ammonia that
hydroxyl ion does to water).   It is inconceivable that the ionization of the acid should take place by the proton transfer of
Eq. (4) in liquid ammonia and should depend upon an entirely
different process, a simple dissociation of HCl into H^+ and Cl^-, in
water.

The existence of the substance OH_3^+ is not a matter of pure
theory, there is ample direct experimental evidence for it.   X-ray
crystal structure methods show that the hydrate of perchloric
acid is composed of OH_3^+ and ClO_4^- in exactly the same way that
ammonium perchlorate is composed of NH_4^+ and ClO_4^- ions;
the substance is really oxonium perchlorate.   Oxonium ion is

unquestionably present in the solutions obtained by dissolving a small amount of water in the solvent H_2SO_4. In this medium water has the same molar conductivity as $NaHSO_4$, NH_4HSO_4, and other strong electrolytes, and the freezing point of the solvent is lowered twice as much by a given concentration of water as it is by the same concentration of a nonelectrolyte (see page 11). The ions must be formed by the reaction

$$H_2O + H_2SO_4 \rightleftarrows OH_3^+ + HSO_4^-. \tag{6}$$

They certainly do not result from a dissociation of water into hydrogen and hydroxyl ions. Similar results have been obtained in the solvent HF, which is also a very highly acid medium. The existence of oxonium ion has also been demonstrated in solutions in liquid sulfur dioxide. In this solvent neither water nor HBr is an electrolyte, but a solution containing both of these solutes is an excellent conductor. When such a solution is electrolyzed, bromine is formed at the anode, hydrogen at the cathode, and water gathers in the cathode compartment at the rate of 1 mole of water for every gram atom of hydrogen discharged. These phenomena obviously result from the presence in the solution of the ions OH_3^+ and Br^-.

Since in all these solutions, and in many others that might be cited, hydrogen ions appear combined with water molecules to form oxonium ions, it is altogether improbable that they should exist free and uncombined in solutions in the solvent water itself. And indeed the properties of acids in aqueous solution bear out this conclusion (this is especially true of the behavior of acid catalyzed reactions). Unlike any other ion a hydrogen ion is a bare nucleus, because a hydrogen atom contains only one electron, and all other atoms contain more. A free hydrogen ion would therefore have properties of a completely different sort from those possessed by other ions. Actually the cation produced by the ionization of acids in water differs no more from other ions than the latter differ among themselves.

The meanings of the words *acid* and *base* have varied somewhat from time to time. The best modern usage is that proposed by Brönsted and by Lowry. It defines an acid as a substance which can lose hydrogen ions, and a base as one which can add hydrogen ions. The definitions are independent of the electrical charge of the substance concerned.   Typical acids include: hydrogen chloride, HCl; acetic acid, $HC_2H_3O_2$; oxonium ion, OH_3^+; ammonium ion, NH_4^+; and bicarbonate ion, HCO_3^-.   Typical bases include: ammonia, NH_3; hydroxyl ion, OH^-; carbonate ion $CO_3^=$.   In aqueous solution all other acids but oxonium ion give rise to this substance, for instance

$$HCl + H_2O \rightleftarrows OH_3^+ + Cl^- \tag{7}$$
$$NH_4^+ + H_2O \rightleftarrows OH_3^+ + NH_3. \tag{8}$$

Therefore all acids have the properties of oxonium ion in aqueous solution.   The concentration of this ion may, however, be so small in the case of weak acids that it is difficult or impossible to detect directly.   Oxonium ion has the properties of sourness, effect upon indicators, and so forth, with which the name acid has always been associated.

Aqueous solutions of bases contain hydroxyl ion, more or less according to the strength of the base.   With other bases than hydroxyl ion itself this arises from reactions of the type

$$NH_3 + H_2O \rightleftarrows NH_4^+ + OH^- \tag{9}$$

or

$$CO_3^= + H_2O \rightleftarrows HCO_3^- + OH^-. \tag{10}$$

In the same way, solutions of acids in liquid ammonia contain ammonium ion, solutions of bases contain amide ion, NH_2^-. Similarly, solutions of acids in acetic acid contain the ion $H_2C_2H_3O_2^+$ solutions of bases contain acetate ion

$$H_2SO_4 + HC_2H_3O_2 \rightleftarrows H_2C_2H_3O_2^+ + HSO_4^- \tag{11}$$
$$NH_3 + HC_2H_3O_2 \rightleftarrows NH_4^+ + C_2H_3O_2^-. \tag{12}$$

Since we cannot introduce hydroxyl ion or carbonate ion into a solution without simultaneously adding some cation, we may also (following a proposal of Bjerrum) include under the name of base saltlike substances such as sodium hydroxide or carbonate which are the most direct method of adding the negatively charged bases, hydroxyl ion and carbonate ion, to a solution. With this extension the word base includes all of the substances which have any historical claim to the name.

In terms of these definitions every acid can be derived from a base by the gain of a hydrogen ion.   An acid and a base which are related in this way are said to be conjugate or corresponding. Some conjugate acids and bases are:

Acid	Base
Hydrogen chloride, HCl	Chloride ion, Cl^-
Acetic acid, $HC_2H_3O_2$	Acetate ion, $C_2H_3O_2{}^-$
Water, H_2O	Hydroxyl ion, OH^-
Ammonium ion, $NH_4{}^+$	Ammonia, NH_3
Oxonium ion, $OH_3{}^+$	Water, H_2O
Bicarbonate ion, $HCO_3{}^-$	Carbonate ion, $CO_3{}^-$

It will be noted that a substance may be simultaneously an acid and a base. Water, for instance, is a base because it can add a hydrogen ion to form oxonium ion; it is an acid because it can lose a hydrogen ion to form hydroxyl ion.

Reactions which consist essentially in a transfer of hydrogen ions from one substance to another such as

$$NH_3 + HC_2H_3O_2 \rightleftarrows NH_4{}^+ + C_2H_3O_2{}^- \qquad (13)$$
$$NH_4{}^+ + H_2O \rightleftarrows NH_3 + OH_3{}^+ \qquad (14)$$
$$OH_3{}^+ + OH^- \rightleftarrows 2H_2O \qquad (15)$$

are frequently called *protolytic* reactions. The classification includes the reactions of *neutralization* of acids and bases and of *hydrolysis*, as well as those of ionization.

The extent to which an acid or base ionizes in a solvent depends upon the opposition in properties between solvent and solute. An acid ionizes most completely in a strongly basic solvent, a base ionizes most completely in a strongly acid solvent. Thus we find that ammonia, which ionizes to the extent of a few per cent in dilute aqueous solution, is practically completely ionized in the more acid solvents formic, acetic, or sulfuric acid. Water is a weak base (that is, it ionizes to a small extent) in formic acid, it is a strong base [practically all ionized according to Eq. (6)] in sulfuric acid. Acetic acid is a weak acid in water; it is a strong acid in liquid ammonia which is a more basic solvent than water. Hydrochloric acid, which is a strong acid in water, is a weak one in formic acid, which is a less basic solvent.

Oxidation-reduction Reactions.—Another extremely important type of reaction consists essentially in a transfer of electrons from one substance to another. Such reactions are called *oxidation-reduction reactions*. The following are simple examples

$$Cu^{++} + Zn \rightleftarrows Cu + Zn^{++} \qquad (16)$$
$$2Fe^{+++} + 2I^- \rightleftarrows 2Fe^{++} + I_2 \qquad (17)$$
$$Br_2 + S^= \rightleftarrows 2Br^- + S. \qquad (18)$$

A substance is said to be *oxidized* when it loses electrons. It is said to be *reduced* when it gains electrons. In the examples just given the zinc, the iodide ion, and the sulfide ion are said to be oxidized, and the cupric ion, the ferric ion, and the bromine are said to be reduced when the reaction takes place from left to right. An *oxidizing agent* or *oxidant* is a substance which can take electrons away from other substances. A *reductant* is a substance which can transfer electrons to other substances. Oxidants and reductants come in corresponding pairs just as acids and bases do. In the above equations cupric ion and copper form such an oxidant-reductant pair. So do ferric and ferrous ion; so also do bromine and bromide ion, zinc ion and zinc, iodine and iodide ion, sulfur and sulfide ion.

We further include as oxidation-reduction reactions many reactions involving complex ions which are more complicated than a simple electron transfer, but which may be considered to involve an electron transfer as an essential step in the reaction. It is not immediately obvious that the conversion of the negatively charged permanganate ion, MnO_4^-, to the positively charged manganous ion, Mn^{++}, should be called a reduction, that it should be said to involve the gain of electrons by the permanganate ion; but there are two very good reasons for doing so.

In the first place permanganate ion can be converted to manganous ion by reactions which involve the oxidation of something else. Typical reactions are

$$MnO_4^- + 8OH_3^+ + 5Fe^{++} \rightleftarrows Mn^{++} + 12H_2O + 5Fe^{+++} \qquad (19)$$
$$2MnO_4^- + 16OH_3^+ + 10I^- \rightleftarrows 2Mn^{++} + 24H_2O + 5I_2. \qquad (20)$$

The proof that these are the correct equations will be given later (page 133). Now the conversion of ferrous ion, Fe^{++}, to ferric ion, Fe^{+++}, or of iodide ion, I^-, to iodine, I_2, clearly requires the loss of electrons from the ferrous or iodide ion, and these electrons cannot simply disappear. They must have been taken up by the permanganate ion as a part of the process of conversion to manganous ion. Since this process involves the gain of electrons, it is properly called a reduction of the permanganate ion.

Electrolysis.—The other reason for considering these complex reactions to involve electron transfer depends upon important characteristics of the process of *electrical conduction*. Electrical conductors may be divided into two classes which possess entirely different mechanisms of conduction. One class, which includes the metals, but also graphite, Fe_3O_4, and some other nonmetallic substances, are called *metallic conductors*. With these substances conduction involves merely the flow of electrons, which are more or less free to move either within a single substance or from substance to substance of the class.

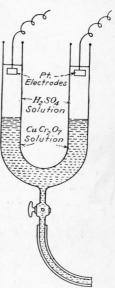

FIG. 2.

The other class of conductors are called *electrolytic conductors*. In these conduction depends upon the motion of ions, as is easily demonstrated. In the experiment shown in Fig. 2 a brown solution of cupric dichromate is placed in the lower part of a U-tube, with dilute sulfuric acid superimposed in both arms. When an electric current passes through the tube by means of platinum wires immersed in the acid, the clear blue color of cupric ion soon appears above the brown on the side where the negative current enters, and the orange color of dichromate ion appears similarly on the other side.

It appears that electrons are incapable of existing as such in an electrolytic conductor, and the ions of an electrolytic conductor cannot, of course, enter into and flow through a metallic conductor. The passage of electricity across the boundary between a metallic and an electrolytic conductor must therefore involve the attachment of electrons to, or the removal of electrons from, substances present in the solution or in the electrode. But this gain or loss of electrons is exactly what we have called reduction and oxidation.

A metallic conductor through which electric current enters or leaves an electrolytic conductor is called an *electrode,* the electrode at which electrons enter the electrolytic conductor is the *cathode*, or negative electrode, the one at which electrons leave the solution is the *anode* or positive electrode. We may now put our definitions of oxidation and of reduction into a form susceptible in every case of a direct experimental test. An oxidation is a process which can be made to take place at the anode during electrolysis; a reduction is one which may be made to take place at the cathode. Some reductions frequently observed during electrolysis are the following

$$Cu^{++} + 2e \rightarrow Cu \qquad (21)$$
$$Fe^{+++} + \ e \rightarrow Fe^{++} \qquad (22)$$
$$2OH_3^+ + 2e \rightarrow H_2 + 2H_2O. \qquad (23)$$

The letter e is used as a symbol for the electron. Some familiar electrolytic oxidations are

$$Cu \rightarrow Cu^{++} + 2e \qquad (24)$$
$$Fe^{++} \rightarrow Fe^{+++} + e \qquad (25)$$
$$4OH^- \rightarrow O_2 + 2H_2O + 4e. \qquad (26)$$

Since permanganate ion can be converted to manganous ion at a cathode during electrolysis, the process is by this criterion also a reduction.

Faraday's Laws.—It is clear that the quantity of chemical reaction which occurs at an electrode at which some single oxidation or reduction takes place must be proportional to the number of electrons, which is to say to the quantity of electricity, which traverses the boundary between electrode and solution. It is also clear that the quantity of electricity which suffices to reduce a given number of oxonium ions to hydrogen and water will suffice to reduce the same number of silver ions, Ag^+, to silver but will only reduce one-half as many cupric ions, Cu^{++}, to copper. In particular, the quantity of electricity which will reduce 107.88 g. of silver ion (which is one gram atom or 6.06×10^{23} ions) will produce 1 g. of hydrogen from oxonium ion (this is one-half a mole of H_2, hence 1 gram atom of H, or 6.06×10^{23} atoms). The same quantity of electricity will only reduce 63.57/2 or 31.79 g. of cupric ion ($\frac{1}{2}$ gram atom).

These conclusions, first observed experimentally by Faraday, and called after him *Faraday's laws of electrolysis*, have been abundantly and accurately verified. They lead to a valuable extension of the significance of the electrochemical equations we have just been using, which is analogous to a familiar dualism in the meaning of simple chemical reactions. Thus the equation

$$Na + Cl \rightarrow NaCl \tag{27}$$

means that one atom of sodium reacts with one atom of chlorine; it also means that 1 gram atom, 23.00 g. of sodium, reacts with 1 gram atom, 35.457 g., of chlorine. Similarly the equation

$$Ag^+ + e \rightarrow Ag \tag{28}$$

means that one silver ion reacts with one electron; it also means that 1 gram atom, 107.88 g., of silver ion reacts with 96,500 coulombs (6.06×10^{23} times the electron charge) of negative electricity. And the equation

$$Cu^{++} + 2e \rightarrow Cu \tag{29}$$

means that 1 gram atom, 63.57 g., of cupric ion reacts with $2 \times 96,500$ coulombs of negative electricity. Given such an equation, the weight of chemical substance reacting with any given quantity of electricity, or the quantity of electricity required to produce any given quantity of chemical change, is easily calculated.

The quantity 96,500 coulombs is called the *faraday*.

Concentration Changes during Electrolysis.—Consider the electrolysis of a silver nitrate solution between silver electrodes. For every 96,500 coulombs, 1 gram atom of silver dissolves from the anode forming silver ion, and the same amount of metal is deposited on the cathode. Imagine the solution divided into two parts, an anodic and a cathodic. If 1 gram atom of silver ion migrated from the anodic to the cathodic portion during the deposition of 1 gram atom of silver, the total flow of current through the solution would be accounted for. But the solution contains nitrate ions also, and these, too, must move and carry part of the current. (The motion of a negatively charged ion from right to left has the same effect electrically as the motion of a positively charged ion from left to right.) Therefore only part of the current can be carried by the silver ions, and more silver ion enters the anode portion of the solution from the electrode than migrates out into the cathode portion. Thus the concentration of silver ion in the neighborhood of the anode increases. Yet the solution remains electrically neutral because the migration of nitrate ions from cathode portion to anode portion leads to an exactly equivalent increase in the concentration of nitrate ion. Similarly the concentrations of both silver ion and nitrate ion decrease in the neighborhood of the cathode.

Consider also the electrolysis of a hydrochloric acid solution between electrodes of platinum or carbon (which do not themselves enter into the reaction). At the cathode, hydrogen is produced, 1 g. for every faraday, at the anode chlorine, 35.457 g. per faraday. Now it happens that oxonium ions move about five times as fast when subjected to a given electric field as do chloride ions; the oxonium ions carry therefore about five-sixths of the current. Therefore five-sixths of a mole of oxonium ion migrates into the cathode portion from the anode portion while one mole is reduced at the cathode. The net loss of oxonium ion from the cathode compartment is one-sixth of a mole per faraday; the loss of chloride ion, by migration alone, is likewise one-sixth of a mole. In the anode compartment, one mole of chloride ion is lost per faraday at the electrode, and only one-sixth of a mole migrates in from the cathode portion. The net loss of chloride ion is five-sixths of a mole; the loss of hydrogen ion, by migration alone, is also five-sixths of a mole. As a consequence of the unequal migration rates or mobilities of the oxonium and chloride ions, therefore, the concentration of hydrogen chloride decreases more rapidly in the anode portion of the solution than it does in the cathode portion. In fact these changes in concentration offer one method of measuring the relative mobilities of the different ions.

During prolonged electrolysis diffusion and other mixing processes tend to decrease the magnitude of these concentration differences; they may be very largely destroyed if desired by intense stirring of the solution.

Suggestions for Reading

Atomic structure and chemical valence: REINMUTH, *J. Chem. Education,* **5,** 1151; 1312; 1473; 1639 (1928); **6,** 341 (1929); GLASSTONE, "Recent Advances in Physical Chemistry," 2d ed., ch. I, London, 1933; LEWIS, "Valence," New York, 1923; SIDGWICK, "The Electronic Theory of

Valency," Oxford, 1927; SIDGWICK, "Annual Reports of the Progress of Chemistry for 1934," pp. 37–43, London, 1935; GETMAN and DANIELS, "Outlines of Theoretical Chemistry," chs. XXI and XXIII, New York, 1931; RODEBUSH, "Physical Chemistry," chs. XVI and XVII, New York, 1932.

Crystal structure: REINMUTH, *J. Chem. Education*, **7**, 138; 860; 1378 (1930); STILLWELL, *ibid.*, **10**, 590; 667 (1933); Sir W. H. and W. L. Bragg, "X-rays and Crystal Structure," 5th ed., London, 1925; GETMAN-DANIELS, *op. cit.*, pp. 62–80; RODEBUSH, *op. cit.*, pp. 60–74.

The nature of solutions of electrolytes: GLASSTONE, *op. cit.*, ch. IX; GETMAN-DANIELS, *op. cit.*, ch. IX.

Acids and bases: BELL, Annual Reports of the Progress of Chemistry for 1934, pp. 71–80; HALL, *J. Chem. Education*, **7**, 782 (1930); *Chem. Rev.* **8**, 191 (1931); KILPATRICK, *J. Chem. Education*, **12**, 109 (1935); DAVIDSON, *Chem. Rev.*, **8**, 175 (1931); BOND, "The Fundamentals of General Chemistry," ch. XV, New York, 1935.

Electrolysis: GETMAN-DANIELS, *op. cit.*, pp. 360–370.

Exercises

1. How many coulombs are required to liberate 1 g. of hydrogen from an aqueous solution? How many coulombs are required to deposit 1 g. of silver from a silver nitrate solution; to dissolve 1 g. of copper at a copper anode in copper sulfate solution; to produce 1 g. of chlorine at the anode in a hydrochloric acid solution; to reduce 1 g. of ferric chloride to ferrous chloride; to oxidize 1 g. of ferrous chloride to ferric chloride? How many coulombs are required to produce 1 liter of hydrogen measured at normal temperature and pressure? For each of the above cases calculate also the time required with a current of 1 ampere; the current required if the process is to be completed in 10 min.

2. Which of the following are acids, which are bases, which are oxidants, which are reductants: NH_3, CrO_4^-, $C_2H_3O_2^-$, Fe^{++}, Na.

3. In the electrolysis of a sodium hydroxide solution, the reaction

$$2H_2O + 2e \rightleftarrows H_2 + 2OH^-$$

takes place at the cathode, the reaction

$$4OH^- \rightleftarrows O_2 + 2H_2O + 4e$$

at the anode. If hydroxyl ion moves four times as fast as sodium ion in the solution what changes will take place in the total quantity of sodium hydroxide present in the anode and in the cathode portion of the solution when 1 faraday traverses the system?

CHAPTER II

THE SOLUBILITY PRODUCT PRINCIPLE

The Nature of the Equilibrium State.—The idea of a state of *equilibrium* is one of the most important concepts in chemistry, and it is especially useful in the chemistry of electrolytes. Fundamentally a system is in a state of equilibrium when no reaction is possible without the intervention of some outside agency, say by change of temperature or pressure or by the addition of new material to the system. Equilibrium represents the final, completely rundown state of a system left to itself. This does not necessarily imply that no reaction is taking place in the state of equilibrium; equilibrium may equally well result from the co-existence of two opposing and mutually cancelling reactions. In fact, this dynamic picture of the state of equilibrium leads to such useful results that it is generally accepted as representing the nature of all equilibrium states. Let us examine a simple case.

When we add chloroform, which is practically insoluble in water, to a solution of bromine in water, and then shake the mixture to bring the two liquids into intimate contact, some of the bromine will transfer from the water to the chloroform, to which it imparts its color. The mechanism of this transfer may be visualized in terms of the *kinetic theory*, which is an exceedingly successful representation of many aspects of the behavior of matter. According to this theory the molecules of gases and liquids are in a state of rapid and disordered motion, moving at random throughout the space occupied by the substance, and colliding with each other and with the walls of the container. Now a molecule of bromine in the water solution can transfer to the chloroform solution only if it collides with the interface between the two liquids, and it is clear that the frequency of such collisions must increase with increasing concentration of bromine. An exact analysis shows that the

24

frequency of collision and hence the rate, in moles per second, at which bromine transfers from water to chloroform is proportional to the concentration of the bromine in the water layer. If we represent the rate by v_1, the concentration of bromine in the water layer by c_w, we have

$$v_1 = k_1 c_w \tag{1}$$

where k_1 is a proportionality constant.

If, on the other hand, a solution of bromine in chloroform is shaken with water, the bromine is seen to transfer to the water layer. The rate of this process, v_2, must be given by an equation of exactly the same sort as Eq. (1):

$$v_2 = k_2 c_c. \tag{2}$$

c_c is the concentration of the bromine in the chloroform, and k_2 is a proportionality constant.

When a solution of bromine in water is shaken with chloroform, and the bromine transfers to the chloroform layer, the concentration of bromine in the water layer decreases. By Eq. (1) the rate of transfer v_1 also decreases. On the other hand, the concentration of bromine in the chloroform layer increases. Hence the rate v_2 at which bromine transfers back to the water layer increases. Eventually v_1 and v_2 will become equal to each other, and from then on there will be no further change in the concentrations in the two layers. Just as much bromine transfers from water to chloroform in a given time as transfers from chloroform to water. The system is in equilibrium, even though reaction has not ceased.

Since $v_1 = v_2$, we have from Eqs. (1) and (2)

$$k_1 c_w = k_2 c_c \tag{3}$$

which may be rearranged to

$$\frac{c_w}{c_c} = \frac{k_2}{k_1} = \text{a constant.} \tag{4}$$

Equation (4) is a condition which must be fulfilled if bromine is to be distributed in a state of equilibrium between water and chloroform. It means that when the concentration of bromine is increased in the one phase, its concentration must increase in exactly the same ratio in the other phase if equilibrium is to be maintained. Generalizing this result, we have the *distribution law:* Whenever a substance is distributed at equilibrium between two *phases* or physical states, the ratio of its concentrations in the two phases is a constant. [At constant temperature, the constant of Eq. (4) is a function of temperature.]

The Solubility of a Pure Solid.—If we bring a solid substance in contact with a liquid in which it dissolves, it may be supposed to dissolve at a constant rate, because the concentration of the substance in the pure solid is a constant. As soon as some of the substance composing the solid has entered the liquid phase, the reverse process will also take place, and will increase in rate as the concentration of dissolved substance increases until the rate at which solid is formed from the solution is just equal to the rate at which solid dissolves. There will then be equilibrium between solid and solution. A solution which is in equilibrium with a solid is said to be saturated with it, and the concentration of a saturated solution is called the solubility of the solid.

Pseudo-equilibrium: Supersaturation.—As a system approaches the state of equilibrium, its rate of progress toward it decreases. It is therefore entirely possible that the rate should become too small to be detected before the true state of equilibrium is attained. Consequently the only way in which we can be certain that we have a state of equilibrium is to approach it from opposite directions. Thus the solution obtained by shaking a solvent with a solute at constant temperature can certainly never attain a concentration greater than the equilibrium solubility, and a supersaturated solution from which the excess solute crystallizes can never become unsaturated. If, therefore, the same concentration is reached by dissolving more solute in an unsaturated solution and by allowing excess solute to crystallize from a supersaturated solution, this concentration is the true solubility.

A particular kind of false equilibrium, the *supersaturated* solution, is the source of much trouble in analytical chemistry. Supersaturated solutions, solutions which contain more than the equilibrium concentration of the solute, are often surprisingly stable. It is true that they do not usually persist in the presence of the solute. Thus the addition of the tiniest microscopic particle of solid sodium acetate to a very concentrated supersaturated solution of sodium acetate produces a crystallization of the excess which sets the whole solution to a solid.

Crystallization from a supersaturated solution can be initiated not only by the solid with respect to which the solution is supersaturated but by any other solid which is miscible with this. Thus $KAl(SO_4)_2(H_2O)_{12}$ and $KCr(SO_4)_2(H_2O)_{12}$ are isomorphous, form mixed crystals, and really dissolve the one in the other. The addition of chromium alum is quite as effective as the addition of aluminum alum in initiating crystallization from a supersaturated solution of aluminum alum. It is likewise true that since all gases are miscible with each other, one gas is as good as another in assisting the evolution of a gas from a supersaturated solution, or even in assisting the evolution of vapor from a solution.

This method of relieving supersaturation is impossible in analytical precipitations, where the expected substance must not be added because its appearance decides the test. It is a matter of experience that crystallization from a supersaturated solution is most easily initiated on a surface, best on a clean surface, and it is traditional and also effective to rub the walls of the containing vessel with a smooth, fire-polished stirring rod in order to assist precipitation when supersaturation is suspected. With moderately soluble crystalline substances, like sodium antimonate or magnesium ammonium phosphate, rows of tiny crystals will usually form on the invisible traces of the rod, giving an appearance as if it had made scratches. A piece of soft rubber is quite as effective as the hard stirring rod and the result evidently depends upon the removal of the invisible but ever present contamination of the surface with adsorbed material.

Gelatinous Precipitates.—What has been said of supersaturation applies only to definitely crystalline precipitates. Gelatinous, apparently amorphous precipitates like aluminum hydroxide are always extremely insoluble. It is very probable that their gelatinous nature is due to the fact that their insolubility leads to enormous degrees of supersaturation and to a rate of precipitation so great that it leaves no time for the building up of crystals (but many apparently amorphous substances have been shown by X-ray investigation to consist of extremely minute crystals). It is well established that a high degree of supersaturation tends to produce gelatinous precipitates.

Gelatinous precipitates have other distinctive, and, from the analytical point of view, unpleasant properties. Although insoluble in the ordinary sense, they are particularly prone to form colloidal solutions when brought in contact with solutions of the proper electrolyte content. They also have great capacities for occluding foreign material from solution (see page 42), and are therefore quite indefinite in composition.

The properties of gelatinous precipitates change with time. Aluminum hydroxide, freshly precipitated by the addition of ammonia to aluminum chloride solution, dissolves quickly and easily in dilute hydrochloric acid; if the same precipitate, suspended in water, is heated to the boiling point of the water for 15 min. and then cooled, it is found to dissolve in dilute hydrochloric acid only very slowly. The change is probably due to an increase in size of the particles, since freshly precipitated aluminum hydroxide gives no evidence of crystalline properties even on investigation by X-rays, while the aged material is seen by the same method to consist of extremely small crystals. In the similar case of the stannic acids, of which two quite different forms have long been supposed to be different substances, X-ray investigation has shown that the more soluble α-stannic acid contains smaller crystalline particles than the less soluble β-stannic acid, but that the crystals in both cases are SnO_2.

The Solubility Product Principle.—It has been found in general that the solubility in water of a nonelectrolyte is not greatly affected by the addition of small amounts of electrolytes. On the other hand, it is found that the solubility of a strong electrolyte is profoundly affected by the presence of even small concentrations of a second electrolyte which has an ion in common with the first.

Silver acetate serves as a convenient example because its solubility is of a suitable magnitude to make the demonstration easy. If a small amount of a concentrated solution of the very soluble sodium acetate is added to a saturated solution of the moderately soluble silver acetate, some of the dissolved silver acetate can be seen to crystallize from the solution. The addition of a concentrated solution of silver nitrate likewise causes precipitation of dissolved silver acetate. The addition of sodium nitrate solution, on the other hand, produces no visible effect. It will be noted here that the decrease in solubility is so great that precipitation takes place in spite of the addition of more water with the silver nitrate or sodium acetate. To generalize, the solubility of silver acetate is greatly decreased by the presence of any highly ionized acetate, that is of acetate ion, or by the presence of any highly ionized silver salt, that is by silver ion, and by such salts only. Similar results are obtained with other difficultly soluble salts.

These experiments may be examined from another point of view. In the original saturated solution of silver acetate in water the silver ion concentration, in moles per liter, was equal to the acetate ion concentration. The addition of sodium acetate solution increased the acetate ion concentration greatly. The resultant precipitation leaves the solution saturated, but with unequal concentrations of silver ion and acetate ion, the former smaller, the latter larger than the values present in the original solution. It is found that the decrease in the silver ion concentration is proportional to the increase in the acetate ion concentration. This result is given mathematical formulation in the solubility product principle, which may be stated for silver acetate in the equation

$$[Ag^+][C_2H_3O_2^-] = \text{a constant} \qquad (5)$$

for saturated solutions at a constant temperature. In this equation the symbol $[Ag^+]$ means the concentration of silver ion in moles per liter. It is a number, not a thing like Ag^+.

A similar equation holds for saturated solutions of any salt which, like silver acetate, contains one cation for each anion. Thus, in saturated solutions of barium sulfate

$$[Ba^{++}][SO_4^=] = \text{a constant.} \qquad (6)$$

In the case of silver sulfate, Ag_2SO_4, which contains two silver ions for every sulfate ion, it is found that the decrease in the sulfate ion concentration produced by an increase in the silver ion concentration is proportional to the square of that increase.

That is, the sulfate ion concentration decreases to one-fourth when the silver ion concentration is doubled. The mathematical formulation for this is

$$[Ag^+]^2[SO_4^=] = K. \tag{7}$$

Similarly, it is found that the criteria of saturation for Ag_3PO_4 and $Ca_3(PO_4)_2$ are

$$[Ag^+]^3[PO_4^\equiv] = K \tag{8}$$

and

$$[Ca^{++}]^3[PO_4^\equiv]^2 = K \tag{9}$$

respectively. In general the *solubility product principle* may be expressed as follows:

In saturated solutions of a difficultly soluble salt, the product of the concentrations of its ions, each concentration raised to a power equal to the number of ions of that kind per molecule of the salt, is at constant temperature a constant.

The Mechanism of Solution and Crystallization of Salts.—The simple picture which we have given for the solution and crystallization of a pure solid is obviously inadequate in the case of a salt. Here there are at least two kinds of molecular species shifting back and forth from solid to solution, yet the solution and crystallization of the one cannot be completely independent of the other because of the constant proportion in which they must exist in the crystal.

The surface of a crystal of calcium carbonate in contact with its saturated solution must be thought of as a chessboard of calcium and carbonate ions, from which ions of both kinds are constantly leaving, and to which ions of each kind are attaching themselves, calcium over carbonate, carbonate over calcium. The surface tends to be flat, but there are at any instant both humps and hollows. Figure 3 may be considered a snapshot; a picture taken at some other time would probably have a different configuration. If now calcium chloride is added to the saturated solution the resulting increase in calcium ion concentration will increase the rate of deposition of calcium ions on the surface, and transform the situation to something like Fig. 4. There are now many more favorable places on the surface of the crystal for the deposition of carbonate ion; consequently, the rate at which carbonate ions deposit on the crystal also increases. The net effect is that both calcium and carbonate ions are thrown out of the solution by an increase in the concentration of the calcium ion only, and that a new state of equilibrium results in which there is more calcium ion but less carbonate ion in the solution.

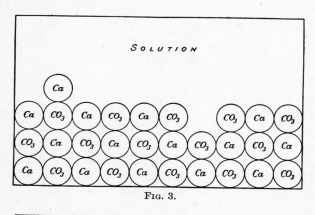

Fig. 3.

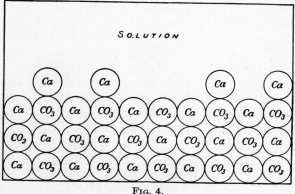

Fig. 4.

It is even possible to give a mathematical derivation of the solubility product equation in terms of this picture. Let x be the fraction of the surface of a crystal of calcium carbonate covered with calcium ions, then $1 - x$ is the fraction covered with carbonate ions. The rate, v_1, at which calcium ions go into solution should be proportional to x, which is to say, equal to a constant times x.

$$v_1 = k_1 x. \tag{10}$$

The rate at which calcium ions deposit upon the surface should be proportional to the concentration of calcium ions in the solution, and also to the number of available places on the surface, that is, to $1 - x$.

$$v_2 = k_2(1 - x)[\text{Ca}^{++}]. \tag{11}$$

At equilibrium the rates of solution and deposition must be equal, hence

$$v_1 = v_2 \tag{12}$$

and

$$k_1 x = k_2(1 - x)[\text{Ca}^{++}]. \tag{13}$$

Similar reasoning applied to the carbonate ions leads to the equation

$$k_3(1 - x) = k_4 x[\text{CO}_3^=]. \tag{14}$$

These two equations may be multiplied together, which eliminates the unknown quantity x, and a simple rearrangement gives

$$[\text{Ca}^{++}][\text{CO}_3^=] = \frac{k_1 k_3}{k_2 k_4}. \tag{15}$$

Since the k's are constant, the fraction on the right-hand side of this equation is a constant, and the equation is the solubility product equation.

Calculation of Solubility Product.—The solubility product of an electrolyte may be calculated if the concentrations of all of the ions of the substance in a saturated solution can be determined. For fairly soluble salts the usual method is to determine the solubility in water, by weighing the amount of material in a known volume of saturated solution, by analyzing the saturated solution in some other way, or by determining the conductivity of a saturated solution. Another method in which the concentration of one ion is determined in the presence of a large known concentration of the other ion is mentioned on page 167.

The relation between solubility in water and solubility product depends upon the valence type of the electrolyte. For silver chloride, a *uni-univalent* electrolyte, every mole of silver chloride dissolved means 1 mole of silver ion and 1 mole of chloride ion in the solution, provided the salt is a strong electrolyte and there is no hydrolysis or other complicating reaction. The solubility s is equal to the concentration of either ion.

$$s = [Ag^+] = [Cl^-]. \tag{16}$$

For any saturated solution

$$[Ag^+][Cl^-] = K. \tag{17}$$

These two equations are independent, the second holds for any saturated solution, even when excess of some other silver salt or chloride is present, the first only for a saturated solution in water or in a solution of a salt with no ion in common with silver chloride.

The solubility product constant K is then equal to the square of the solubility.

$$K = s^2. \tag{18}$$

The same equation holds for a *bi-bivalent* salt like $BaSO_4$.

With silver sulfate, a *uni-bivalent* salt, each mole dissolved means 1 mole of sulfate ion, but 2 moles of silver ion

$$[SO_4^=] = s, \tag{19}$$
$$[Ag^+] = 2s. \tag{20}$$

Further for any saturated solution

$$[Ag^+]^2[SO_4^=] = K; \tag{21}$$

hence,

$$(2s)^2 \cdot s = K \tag{22}$$

and

$$K = 4s^3. \tag{23}$$

The corresponding equations for salts of other valence types are easily derived.

If we wish to calculate the solubility product constant from measurements of the solubility in the presence of some salt with an ion in common, the problem is slightly different. Suppose we measure the solubility of silver acetate in a solution of silver nitrate whose concentration is c moles per liter. Let the solubility be s moles per liter of silver acetate. Then the concentration of acetate ion is s moles per liter, because each mole of silver acetate dissolved produces one mole of acetate ion. But the concentration of silver ion is $s + c$ moles per liter, c moles per liter from the silver nitrate, s moles per liter from the silver acetate. Multiplying, we have for the solubility product constant K

$$K = s(s + c). \tag{24}$$

If s is very much smaller than c, no serious error would be made if we use c instead of $s + c$, in which case the equation reduces to

$$K = sc. \tag{25}$$

This approximation would be amply precise for any problem involving analytical precipitates in the presence of a salt with an ion in common when the concentration of the latter is in the range of $0.01\ M$ or greater.

Clearly these equations may be used also to calculate the solubility if the solubility product constant is known. We can, for instance, predict the solubility of a salt in the presence of another salt with a common ion by measuring its solubility in water, and calculating the solubility product constant. This by no means exhausts the list of useful and interesting things we can do with a knowledge of the solubility product constant of a difficultly soluble salt.

First, we can calculate the concentration of one ion required to produce a precipitate with a given concentration of the other ion. Suppose we take a value of $0.0001\ M$ as the minimum concentration of silver ion which must give a precipitate if a test for silver ion is to be considered sufficiently sensitive (this is a reasonable figure because it is an attainable one and because the amount of precipitate obtained from a still smaller amount of silver ion would probably be invisible even if all of the silver precipitated). Can we get a test of this sensitivity by precipitating silver chloride? The solubility product constant of AgCl is 1.8×10^{-10}; therefore the product $[Ag^+][Cl^-]$ must be equal to this value if the solution is to be just saturated; if the product is greater than this a precipitate will appear. Substituting the value 0.0001 for $[Ag^+]$ in the equation

$$[Ag^+][Cl^-] = 1.8 \times 10^{-10} \tag{26}$$

and solving, we obtain

$$[Cl^-] = 1.8 \times 10^{-6}. \tag{27}$$

This is the value the chloride ion concentration must have if a solution is to contain 0.0001 M silver ion and be just saturated with silver chloride. If the chloride ion concentration is larger than this, the solution will be supersaturated and a precipitate will appear. Since we can easily obtain chloride ion concentrations larger than this, our query is answered affirmatively. Can we also get a test for silver ion of this sensitivity by precipitating silver sulfate? From Eq. (21) and the value of the solubility product constant from Table I we have

$$[Ag^+]^2[SO_4^=] = 7 \times 10^{-5}. \tag{28}$$

Substituting $[Ag^+] = 0.0001$ and solving, we obtain

$$[SO_4^=] = 7000. \tag{29}$$

This is an impossibly large figure and it follows that we cannot obtain a large enough concentration of sulfate ion to bring a solution containing 0.0001 M silver ion even to the saturation point, much less to precipitate silver sulfate from it.

Second, we may calculate the concentration of one ion left in a saturated solution after a salt has been precipitated. Suppose for instance that we precipitate silver chloride from a solution and add an excess of chloride so that the solution filtered from the precipitate contains 0.1 M chloride ion. If we are to make tests for other ions on this filtrate, tests with which silver ion would interfere, it is extremely important to know whether the concentration of silver ion left in the solution is large enough to interfere. Substituting $[Cl^-] = 0.1$ in Eq. (26), which must be satisfied since the solution is saturated, we find

$$[Ag^+] = 1.8 \times 10^{-9}. \tag{30}$$

Certainly this amount, which is not much more than a billionth

of a mole per liter of silver ion, will not interfere with other tests
on the solution.   It should be emphasized that this figure is
much more significant for the actual conditions of analysis than
the solubility in water.   The silver ion concentration of a saturated solution of AgCl in water is by Eq. 16 equal to the s of
Eq. 18.   Substituting the value of K, we find this silver ion
concentration to be 1.4×10^{-5} a value nearly 10,000 times
greater than the concentration of silver ion in the saturated
solution when the chloride ion concentration is 0.1 M.   If we
substitute $[SO_4^=] = 0.1$ in Eq. (28) and solve for $[Ag^+]$, we find
that the silver ion concentration remaining in a saturated solution of Ag_2SO_4 whose sulfate ion concentration is 0.1 M is 0.027
M.   The precipitation of silver sulfate therefore would not be a
satisfactory method of removing silver ion from a solution pre-
paratory to other tests.

In so far as they relate to solubilities (but not with respect
to ion concentrations), the calculations we have made in
this section may be in error with salts of very weak acids or
bases because of hydrolysis (see Chap. IV).   In both respects
they are somewhat in error because of the phenomenon called
the salt effect.

The Salt Effect on Solubilities.—Like many other principles of
great scientific and practical value (the perfect gas law, for
instance), the solubility product principle is of only approximate
validity.   If it were exact, the value of the *solubility product*,
which is the product of the concentrations of the ions in saturated solution, would be unaffected by the presence of other salts;
actually it increases with increasing total ion concentration of
the solution.   This increase is called a *salt effect*.

For a given electrical type the salt effect is approximately the
same for different ions.   Figure 5 shows the way in which the
solubility product $[Tl^+]$ $[Cl^-]$ of thallous chloride varies with
the total salt concentration when potassium chloride, thallous
nitrate, and potassium nitrate are added.

The effect is greater the greater the charge upon the ions
concerned.   The solubility product of calcium sulfate is increased
much more by the addition of magnesium sulfate than is that of
thallous chloride by the addition of potassium chloride.   This
may easily be seen from the curves of Fig. 5.

Addition of a salt with no ion in common to the saturated solution of a difficultly soluble salt increases the solubility of that salt, as shown by Fig. 6, which reproduces the effect upon the solubility of thallous chloride of potassium nitrate. Addition of a salt with an ion in common has two opposing effects.

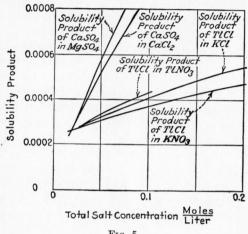

Fig. 5.

The solubility of thallous chloride in a potassium chloride solution is equal to the thallous ion concentration of the saturated solution, and this is given by the equation

$$[Tl^+][Cl^-] = K \text{ or } [Tl^+] = \frac{K}{[Cl^-]}. \qquad (31)$$

The addition of potassium chloride to a saturated solution of thallous chloride will increase the concentration of chloride ion, and tend to decrease the solubility; but like all salts potassium chloride will increase the value of K, and tend to increase the solubility. Figure 6 shows the way in which the actual solubility of thallous chloride varies upon addition of potassium chloride. The effect of the increase in $[Cl^-]$ is much greater than the effect of the increase in K, and the decrease in solubility is nearly, but not quite, as great as that predicted by the solubility product equation. In accordance with the larger charges on the ions, magnesium sulfate increases the K for calcium sulfate much more than is the case when the ions concerned are singly

charged, and the decrease in solubility of calcium sulfate produced
by magnesium sulfate is much less than that predicted by the
solubility product principle.   This also is shown in Fig. 6.

There are two reasons for believing that the salt effect is due
to the electrical forces between the ions.   First, the effect depends
primarily upon the charges and the total number of the ions
present, and only to a secondary extent upon what may be called
specific chemical properties.   Second, a theory developed by
Debye and Hückel shows that there is reason in electrical theory

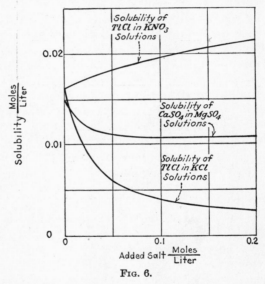

Fig. 6.

to expect such an effect, and that it should depend upon concentration and charge in much the same way as actually happens.

The Application to Analytical Chemistry.—The main conclusion
from this work is that the solubility product is a constant only
for constant environment, and that the concentration of electrical
charges is a major factor in determining the environment.   The
solubility product is practically a constant for very dilute solutions in which the environment does not differ appreciably
from that which prevails in pure water.   Even more important
for the analytical chemist it remains practically constant where-
ever the total ion concentration is not greatly varied.   For

example, the solubility product of calcium sulfate is considerably increased by the presence of much potassium nitrate in the solution. But the solubility product principle may be used with even greater precision to predict the effect of the addition of sodium or magnesium sulfate to this solution than would be the case were the potassium nitrate absent. The ion concentration of the solution is already so large that the addition of the sodium or magnesium sulfate exerts a smaller effect upon the value of the solubility product. This is exactly the situation with which the analytical chemist is confronted. The solutions with which he works usually contain, for one reason or another, a considerable electrolyte concentration, and his problem is to predict the effect of the addition of a salt with an ion in common upon the solubility of a given salt. For this purpose the solubility product principle is admirably adapted.

Another limitation upon the solubility product principle is not a matter for concern to the analytical chemist, whose precipitates must be difficultly soluble: This is that the solubility product principle has not even qualitative validity, and is entirely useless for predicting effects upon the solubility of very soluble salts. This may be easily understood. Silver chloride has a solubility of 10^{-5} moles per liter. The addition of 10^{-4} moles per liter of potassium chloride would increase the chloride ion concentration 10 times, but this small addition of salt would have only a negligible effect upon the value of the solubility product. Consequently, the prediction of the solubility product equation that the solubility should be decreased to one-tenth would be exactly true. If the solubility of a salt is large, however, say one molar, a 10 M concentration of a salt with a common ion would be necessary to increase ten times the concentration of that common ion; but such a large salt concentration would cause an enormous change in the environment, so much so that the solubility of the original salt might increase rather than decrease.

Some Solubility Product Constants.—Table I contains the values of the solubility product constants for a number of important salts. Most of the values given in Part A apply to solutions whose total ion concentration is that furnished by the saturating salt itself. Under the usual conditions of analytical chemistry somewhat higher values will prevail because of the salt effect. Part *B* contains estimates of the values for the sulfides for which any values can be given. Cadmium sulfide occludes chloride, sulfate, and other ions so extensively that a solubility

TABLE I.—SOLUBILITY PRODUCT CONSTANTS
A. Relatively Accurate Values

Salt	Temperature, °C.	Constant
AgBr..............	25	5×10^{-13}
AgC$_2$H$_3$O$_2$..........	16	3×10^{-3}
AgCl..............	25	1.8×10^{-10}
AgCN..............	25	7×10^{-15}
Ag$_2$CO$_3$..........	25	8.2×10^{-12}
Ag$_2$CrO$_4$..........	25	3.3×10^{-12}
AgI..............	25	1.0×10^{-16}
Ag$_2$O*..............	25	1.9×10^{-8}
AgSCN............	25	1.2×10^{-12}
Ag$_2$SO$_4$..............	20	7×10^{-5}
BaCO$_3$..............	25	8×10^{-9}
BaCrO$_4$............	20	2.2×10^{-10}
BaSO$_4$..............	25	1.1×10^{-10}
CaCO$_3$..............	25	4.8×10^{-9}
CaC$_2$O$_4$..............	20	2.0×10^{-9}
CaF$_2$..............	25	5×10^{-11}
CaSO$_4$..............	20	2.3×10^{-4}
Hg$_2$Cl$_2$†..........	25	1.2×10^{-18}
Hg$_2$Br$_2$†..........	25	5.5×10^{-23}
Hg$_2$I$_2$†..............	25	5.0×10^{-29}
Hg$_2$SO$_4$†..........	25	4.7×10^{-7}
Hg$_2$CrO$_4$†..........	25	2.0×10^{-9}
MgCO$_3$(H$_2$O)$_3$......	25	1×10^{-5}
Mg(OH)$_2$..........	25	5×10^{-12}
PbCO$_3$..............	18	3.3×10^{-14}
PbCrO$_4$............	18	1.8×10^{-14}
PbHPO$_4$..........	25	1.3×10^{-10}
Pb$_3$(PO$_4$)$_2$..........	25	8×10^{-43}
PbSO$_4$..............	18	1.0×10^{-8}
SrCO$_3$..............	25	1.6×10^{-9}
SrCrO$_4$............	20	3.6×10^{-5}
SrSO$_4$..............	25	2.8×10^{-7}
TlCl..............	25.7	2.2×10^{-4}

* The solubility product equation for Ag$_2$O is $[Ag^+][OH^-] = K$.

† The equations for mercurous salts are based upon the formula Hg$_2^{++}$ for mercurous ion, *e.g.*, $[Hg_2^{++}][Cl^-]^2 = K$, $[Hg_2^{++}][SO_4^-] = K$.

TABLE I.—SOLUBILITY PRODUCT CONSTANTS.—(*Continued*)
B. *Approximate Values*
All at Room Temperature

Salt	Constant
Ag_2S.............	10^{-49}
CuS.............	10^{-44}
FeS.............	10^{-19}
HgS.............	10^{-49}
MnS.............	10^{-15}
PbS.............	10^{-28}

product for CdS is of no value. Zinc, nickel, and cobalt sulfides precipitate and dissolve so slowly that only false equilibria are obtained. No solubility product constant can be determined, since the solubility product equation refers to a state of equilibrium (see page 26).

Simple Separations.—It is sometimes possible to find an anion which gives salts of widely different solubility with two cations which it is desired to separate. The solubility of many lead salts is much the same as that of the corresponding barium salts. If only the chromates, carbonates, or sulfates were considered, the separation of lead and barium ions would seem very difficult; but there is one great difference in the properties of the ions, lead sulfide is extremely insoluble and barium sulfide is very soluble. A separation requires merely the addition to the solution of a sufficient concentration of sulfide ion to precipitate the lead as sulfide and a filtration.

If lead ion is present, the filtrate from the precipitation is a saturated solution of lead sulfide. The separation is obviously more complete the smaller the concentration of lead ion in this solution. Since

$$[Pb^{++}][S^=] = K \text{ or } [Pb^{++}] = \frac{K}{[S^=]}, \tag{32}$$

this means that the separation is the more complete the larger the concentration of sulfide ion. Since, moreover, the precipitation represents also a test for lead ion, it is desirable that a precipitate result with a small concentration of lead ion in order that the test may be delicate. The concentration of lead ion required to produce a precipitate of lead sulfide is determined by the same equation, which means that the test is more delicate the greater the concentration of sulfide ion. From both points of view a large excess of the precipitating ion is desirable, and there is indeed no danger of the sulfide ion concentration becoming large enough to precipitate barium sulfide. But there are two reasons for setting a rather low limit to the excess of a reagent to be used in a precipitation. First, the salt effect makes all salts more soluble with increasing salt concentration, something which must be particularly considered with salts of higher valence type. Second, complex ions often form (see Chap. V).

Moreover, a salt may be so insoluble, as lead sulfide indeed is, that the utmost delicacy or completeness is unnecessary. It requires no very large concentration of sulfide ion to precipitate lead ion so completely that the filtrate can safely be tested for barium ion without fear that lead chromate or sulfate will precipitate. As a matter of fact the slightly ionized hydrogen sulfide instead of the highly ionized alkali sulfide gives a sufficiently good separation.

Occlusion.—Analytical separations are, unfortunately, never quite so satisfactory as might appear from this simple discussion because of the existence of *occlusion*.

If cadmium sulfide is precipitated from a solution containing barium ion, the precipitate, no matter how carefully it be washed, will contain barium. This may be shown by dissolving in hydrochloric acid and adding sulfuric acid when a precipitate of barium sulfate results. Cadmium sulfide carries down or *occludes* barium sulfide, although the latter is a very soluble substance.

The serious nature of this phenomenon for analytical chemistry will easily be seen. The solubility of barium sulfide is relied upon for the separation of lead ion from barium ion and the characterization of lead ion. But in the presence of cadmium ion, barium sulfide becomes, so to speak, insoluble to an extent which depends upon the quantity of cadmium present. If cadmium and lead are separated from barium by the precipitation of the sulfides, and the lead is separated from cadmium and tested for by precipitation of lead sulfate with sulfuric acid, the appearance of a white precipitate does not prove the presence of lead. Some further "confirmatory test" is therefore necessary.

The phenomenon is of almost universal occurrence, and is entirely specific. It is impossible to predict just what materials will be seriously occluded by a given precipitate, although it is probably most common where the precipitate and the occluded substance are most similar, that is, when the separation is otherwise most difficult. It is by far most serious with gelatinous precipitates, although it does occur to a significant extent with crystalline precipitates also.

The amount occluded depends upon the concentration in solution of the occluded material, so that in the less pronounced cases some of this remains in the solution even when only little of it is present. This makes many separations possible for the rough estimations of quantity which satisfy the demands of qualitative analysis, but unsatisfactory for more precise quantitative analysis. Sulfide precipitation, so useful in qualitative analysis, is rarely used in more precise quantitative analysis. Some assistance may be obtained by the method of double precipitation. If cadmium sulfide carries down barium, the precipitate will nevertheless have a smaller ratio of barium to cadmium than the original solution. It may then be dissolved and reprecipitated to obtain a more complete separation.

The mechanism of the phenomenon may be looked upon somewhat as follows: If the forces which hold together a particle of cadmium sulfide are essentially the electrical attractions between the positive cadmium ions and the negative sulfide ions, the surface of such a particle should attract to itself and hold at least temporarily ions of all kinds from solution, the cations being held over the sulfide ions, the anions over the cadmium ions. What happens then depends upon how like the foreign ion is in charge, size, and shape to the normal one. If a barium ion is sufficiently like a cadmium ion, growth may proceed around and over the barium ion before it escapes, and the final cadmium sulfide particle will contain barium sulfide in *solid solution*.

If the ions are unlike, growth of the particle stops at the points covered by foreign ions until these leave the surface, for they are constantly going into solution as well as depositing upon the surface. But the surface of the particle will, on the average, be contaminated by every ionic species in solution to a greater or less extent. If the surface is large relative to the volume, that is, if the substance is very finely divided, the amount of such contamination by *adsorption* may be very great. Occlusion should be greatest with the gelatinous precipitates which do indeed cause the greatest difficulties in this respect.

Separation by Change of Solvent.—The separation of strontium and calcium ions by the precipitation of strontium chromate is an example of a common situation in which a considerable difference exists in the solubilities of the salts of two metals with a given anion, but where the less soluble one, in this case strontium chromate, is too soluble to make a satisfactory analytical separation possible. Nearly all inorganic salts are much less soluble in alcohol or even in mixtures of alcohol and water than in water (see page 9). The effect of the addition of alcohol to an aqueous solution is to shift the whole scale of solubilities downward.

In this case it is possible by the addition of the correct proportion of alcohol to decrease the solubilities of both strontium and calcium chromates to such an extent that strontium chromate may now be precipitated even when only little strontium ion is present, and that calcium chromate will not precipitate even when much calcium ion is present.

The method is one which is often useful, but it must always be used with care. Too much alcohol may precipitate not only calcium chromate but even the potassium chromate used as a reagent to furnish chromate ion.

Suggestions for Reading

Salt effects: Kilpatrick, *J. Chem. Education*, **9**, 840 (1932).
Calculations: Engelder, "Calculations of Qualitative Analysis," ch. VI, New York, 1933.

Exercises

1. Calculate the solubility in water in moles per liter and in grams per liter of each of the silver salts listed in Table I. Neglect hydrolysis and the salt effect.
2. Calculate the solubilities of the same salts in 0.01 M silver nitrate solution.
3. Which is the more soluble in water, CaC_2O_4 or CaF_2? Which would give the more complete removal of calcium ion from a solution?

4. The solubility of BaF_2 is reported to be 7.5×10^{-3} moles per liter. Calculate the solubility product constant.

5. Assuming that calcium phosphate is completely ionized and not hydrolyzed, what relation should exist between its solubility product constant and its solubility in water?

6. Sodium antimonate is not very insoluble but is nevertheless the most satisfactory precipitate for the detection of sodium ion. How would you account for the fact that the test is considerably less sensitive in the presence of large concentrations of either potassium or ammonium ion?

7. Calculate: the solubility in water of $Mg(OH)_2$; the solubility of $Mg(OH)_2$ in 0.1 M $MgCl_2$ solution; the hydroxyl ion concentration necessary to precipitate $Mg(OH)_2$ from a solution containing 0.001 M magnesium ion.

8. If the solubility of PbI_2 in water is 0.0015 mole per liter, what is the solubility product constant? What is the iodide ion concentration necessary to produce a precipitate in a 0.1 M lead nitrate solution?

CHAPTER III

WEAK ELECTROLYTES: THE LAW OF CHEMICAL EQUILIBRIUM

Strong and Weak Electrolytes.—There are some acids whose hydrogen ions are so loosely bound that they transfer them almost completely to water molecules in dilute aqueous solution. Thus in a dilute solution of hydrogen chloride in water the reaction

$$HCl + H_2O \rightleftarrows OH_3^+ + Cl^- \tag{1}$$

proceeds so completely toward the right that the concentration of HCl is negligible. As a consequence a 0.1 M solution contains practically 0.1 M chloride ion and possesses the properties of chloride ion to the same extent as 0.1 M solutions of sodium or potassium chloride do. It also contains 0.1 M oxonium ion and possesses the properties of that ion to the same extent as do 0.1 M solutions of other acids of this sort. But it does not have to any detectable extent the properties of molecular HCl. For instance the vapor pressure of HCl from the solution is too small to be measured, a fact which we may verify in a rough fashion by noting that the solution is odorless.

Such acids are called *strong acids*. Some common examples are HCl, HBr, HI, HNO$_3$, HClO$_4$, H$_2$SO$_4$ (but only with respect to the first ionization, $H_2SO_4 + H_2O \rightleftarrows OH_3^+ + HSO_4^-$; the acid HSO$_4^-$ is far from strong), H$_3$Fe(CN)$_6$, and the organic sulfonic acids such as C$_6$H$_5$SO$_3$H.

Many other acids are *weak*, which is to say that the ionization reaction is incomplete. Thus with acetic acid the reaction

$$HC_2H_3O_2 + H_2O \rightleftarrows OH_3^+ + C_2H_3O_2^- \tag{2}$$

consumes only a small fraction of the total amount of acetic acid. A 0.1 M solution contains, as we shall see, only a little over a thousandth of a mole per liter of acetate and oxonium ions. But

46

it does contain nearly 99 per cent of the original acetic acid in the form of unreacted molecules. Furthermore the proportion of the molecular acetic acid which reacts to form the ions varies with the concentration of acid present and with the presence of other acetates and of acids.

As a consequence the behavior of weak acids is very different from that of true salts and of strong acids. Some of these differences can be observed in very simple experiments. Thus acetic acid lacks the property possessed by salts containing acetate ion of precipitating silver acetate upon addition of silver nitrate. And a given concentration of acetic acid converts the indicator methyl orange much less completely from yellow to red than does the same concentration of hydrochloric acid. Further certain difficultly soluble salts, such as lead sulfide and barium chromate which are easily dissolved by dilute hydrochloric acid, are not visibly affected by dilute acetic acid. Both the indicator reaction and the solution of the salts are, in ways which we shall later discuss in detail, characteristic reactions of oxonium ion in aqueous solution. Similar reactions which require a somewhat smaller concentration of oxonium ion can indeed be produced by acetic acid. Thus both acetic and hydrochloric acids turn litmus from blue to red, and both dissolve strontium chromate.

Another important class of weak electrolytes are the weak bases. Ammonia reacts with water according to a reaction

$$NH_3 + H_2O \rightleftarrows NH_4^+ + OH^- \tag{3}$$

which happens to take place under comparable concentration conditions to very nearly the same extent as the ionization of acetic acid. Its solutions contain very much smaller concentrations of hydroxyl ion than do solutions of equivalent concentration of the alkali and alkaline earth hydroxides. The latter [NaOH, KOH, Ca(OH)$_2$, etc.], although they are essentially saltlike substances, are generally called bases, in fact strong bases. Certainly they do offer the simplest method we have of obtaining a highly basic aqueous solution, for they introduce into the solution a high concentration of hydroxyl ion, and this is the most basic substance we can have in any appreciable concentration in an aqueous solution. Any substance more basic than hydroxyl ion in the sense of having a greater affinity for hydrogen ion than it does must necessarily abstract hydrogen ions from water to form hydroxyl ion. Thus amide ion, NH_2^-, in the form of sodium amide for instance, reacts practically completely with water according to the equation

$$NH_2^- + H_2O \rightleftarrows NH_3 + OH^-. \tag{4}$$

In the same way oxonium ion is the most acidic substance which can exist in aqueous solution in any considerable concentration.

Besides the acids and bases there are a number of metallic compounds which are weak electrolytes in aqueous solution. Lead acetate, mercuric cyanide, and the halides of mercuric mercury, stannic tin, cadmium, arsenic, antimony, gold, and platinum are frequently encountered examples of substances of this sort. They are sometimes called salts, but they lack the most characteristic properties of salts. Some chemists call them *pseudosalts*. It is very probable that they do not ionize by a simple dissociation, but rather that they react with the solvent in much the same way that acids do producing, however, a hydrated metallic ion, instead of a hydrated hydrogen ion (oxonium ion)

$$HgCl_2 + 4H_2O \rightleftarrows Hg(H_2O)_4^{++} + 2Cl^-. \tag{5}$$

It is a characteristic property of these pseudosalts to react with further molecules of the anion to form complex ions as

$$HgCl_2 + 2Cl^- \rightleftarrows HgCl_4^= \tag{6}$$
$$Hg(CN)_2 + 2CN^- \rightleftarrows Hg(CN)_4^= \tag{7}$$
$$PtCl_4 + 2Cl^- \rightleftarrows PtCl_6^=. \tag{8}$$

The Mechanism of Chemical Reaction.—The ionization of acetic acid or of ammonia is incomplete because it comes to a state of equilibrium. This is demonstrated by the fact that the same relative concentrations of acetic acid, water, oxonium ion, and acetate ion are obtained by allowing acetate and oxonium ions to react (for instance by mixing sodium acetate and hydrochloric acid) as are obtained by allowing acetic acid and water to react (see page 26). We may visualize the way in which such an equilibrium is established and maintained very satisfactorily in the following way: The molecules of two substances present in a gas or in a dilute solution can react only when they collide with each other, and it is obvious that they must collide the more frequently the greater the number of molecules of each kind present in a given volume, which is to say the greater the concentrations of the reacting substances. The more frequent collisions which occur with increased concentrations of the reactants should produce an increased rate of reaction, and in fact experiment shows that the rate of a chemical reaction is always approximately proportional and in certain favorable cases is very exactly proportional to the product of the concentrations of the reacting substances. In the case of the reaction of acetic acid with water to give acetate and oxonium ions [Eq. (2)], this would mean that v_1, the rate of reaction in moles per liter per second is given by the equation

$$v_1 = k_1[HC_2H_3O_2][H_2O] \tag{9}$$

where the proportionality constant k_1 is called the *reaction rate constant*. Actually the rate of this reaction and of the other simple ionization reactions with which we shall be concerned in this text is much too great to permit measurement. (This is not true, however, for the reactions of certain very weak acids and bases which are important steps in acid or base catalyzed reactions.) Nevertheless the validity of Eq. (9) is placed beyond doubt by the universal validity of corresponding equations for reactions whose rate is measurable.

The Law of Chemical Equilibrium.—In exactly the same way the rate, v_2, of the reaction of acetate and oxonium ions to form acetic acid and water must be proportional to the product of the concentrations of the reactants

$$v_2 = k_2[OH_3^+][C_2H_3O_2^-]. \tag{10}$$

If now the concentrations of acetic acid, water, oxonium ion, and acetate ion in a solution are such that $v_1 = v_2$, acetic acid and water will be formed from acetate and oxonium ions at exactly the same rate at which they are consumed by reaction with each other, and there will be no change as time goes on in their concentrations. Neither will the concentrations of oxonium and acetate ion change, and the system will therefore be in a state of equilibrium. In the state of equilibrium we have from Eqs. (9) and (10), since $v_1 = v_2$

$$k_1[HC_2H_3O_2][H_2O] = k_2[OH_3^+][C_2H_3O_2^-]. \qquad (11)$$

This rearranges to

$$\frac{[OH_3^+][C_2H_3O_2^-]}{[HC_2H_3O_2][H_2O]} = \frac{k_1}{k_2} \qquad (12)$$

and if we put the ratio k_1/k_2 of the two rate constants equal to a new constant K', we obtain

$$\frac{[OH_3^+][C_2H_3O_2^-]}{[HC_2H_3O_2][H_2O]} = K'. \qquad (13)$$

The constant K' is called an *equilibrium constant*, and the equation is a statement of the *law of chemical equilibrium* for the ionization of acetic acid.

This is a general equation. It can be somewhat simplified for the case where the reaction takes place in a dilute aqueous solution, because the concentration of water has very nearly the same value in all such solutions. Thus the concentration of water in pure water at 25°C. is 997 g. per liter and $997/18.02 = 55.35\ M$. A 0.1 M solution of acetic acid has a density of 0.998 and contains 6.003 g. per liter of acetic acid. The concentration of water is $998 - 6 = 992$ g. per liter and $992/18.02 = 55.1\ M$. Even a 1 M solution has a water concentration which is only 5 per cent less than that in pure water. If therefore we put Eq. (13) in the form

$$\frac{[OH_3^+][C_2H_3O_2^-]}{[HC_2H_3O_2]} = K'[H_2O] \qquad (14)$$

the quantity $K'[H_2O]$ will be for all practical purposes a constant with the value $55.35K'$, which we may represent by a new constant K. The equilibrium equation for the ionization thus takes the form

$$\frac{[OH_3^+][C_2H_3O_2^-]}{[HC_2H_3O_2]} = K \qquad (15)$$

in which it is usually written. The constant K is called the *ionization constant*.

In spite of appearances this equation is not significantly less accurate than Eq. (13) because the quantity K', like the solubility product constants we have studied previously, is only an approximate constant. When we add a solute to water, especially if it be an electrolyte, the value of K' is likely to change by an amount much greater than the few per cent which is the maximum change to be expected in the concentration of water.

Similarly the equilibrium in the ionization of ammonia [Eq. (3)] is determined by the equation

$$\frac{[NH_4^+][OH^-]}{[NH_3]} = K. \tag{16}$$

When an acid contains two ionizable hydrogen atoms, the law of chemical equilibrium may be applied separately to the two steps of the ionization. Thus to the reactions

$$H_2S + H_2O \rightleftarrows OH_3^+ + HS^- \tag{17}$$

and

$$HS^- + H_2O \rightleftarrows OH_3^+ + S^= \tag{18}$$

there correspond the equilibrium equations

$$\frac{[OH_3^+][HS^-]}{[H_2S]} = K_1 \tag{19}$$

and

$$\frac{[OH_3^+][S^=]}{[HS^-]} = K_2. \tag{20}$$

It has been found that the primary ionization constant, K_1, of a polybasic acid is always considerably larger than the secondary constant, K_2. In cases like that of phosphoric acid where there is a third ionization, the tertiary constant is also much smaller than the secondary one.

If Eqs. (19) and (20) are multiplied together a new equation

$$\frac{[OH_3^+]^2[S^=]}{[H_2S]} = K_1K_2 = \text{a constant} \tag{21}$$

is obtained, which must be true if the equations from which it was derived are true. It will be noted that the concentration of HS^- has been canceled out (it is sometimes difficult to realize that the symbol $[HS^-]$ must represent the total concentration of HS^- in an equilibrium equation. There is no conceivable way to distinguish between HS^- ions derived from the first ionization and those derived from the second). Now, Eq. (21) represents a relation between the concentrations of the substances which take part in the reversible reaction

$$H_2S + 2H_2O \rightleftarrows 2OH_3^+ + S^=. \tag{22}$$

It is therefore a statement of the law of chemical equilibrium for that reaction. This argument may be generalized with the following conclusion: Whenever two molecules of a substance are produced or consumed in a chemical reaction, the concentration of that substance is squared in the equation which represents the application of the law of chemical equilibrium to the reaction: or more generally, the concentration is raised to a power in the equilibrium equation which is equal to the number of molecules of the substance involved in the chemical equation.

The law of chemical equilibrium is an especially important tool in dealing with the reactions of electrolytes, because in a very large proportion of these reactions the rate of reaction is so great that it suffices for many purposes to know what the state of equilibrium is. The intermediate states leading to equilibrium are so transient that they are relatively unimportant.

Some Simple Applications.—The most important applications of the equilibrium law depend upon the corollary that the addition of one of the ions of a weak electrolyte to its solution results in a decreased concentration of the other ion. Suppose we have a solution of acetic acid in water. The concentrations of acetate and oxonium ions will be equal to each other, and these ions will be reacting at a rate which is just balanced by the reaction of acetic acid and water. If now hydrochloric acid is added the concentration of oxonium ion becomes much larger, oxonium ions and acetate ions collide more frequently, and consequently react more frequently. The unchanged rate of ionization no longer suffices to balance the increased rate of the reverse reaction, consequently the concentrations of oxonium and acetate ions decrease, and the concentration of acetic acid increases until these changes in concentration lead to rates of forward and reverse reaction which are again equal to each other. In the new state of equilibrium thus attained the equation

$$\frac{[OH_3{}^+][C_2H_3O_2{}^-]}{[HC_2H_3O_2]} = K \tag{15}$$

is again satisfied, but it is satisfied by values of $[OH_3{}^+]$ and $[HC_2H_3O_2]$ which are greater and by a value of $[C_2H_3O_2{}^-]$ which is smaller than the values which these same concentrations possessed before the addition of the hydrochloric acid.

In the same way the addition of an acid to a solution of hydrogen sulfide must decrease the concentration of sulfide ion and thus render more difficult the precipitation of a sulfide from the solution. Such effects are easily observed. If we add hydrogen sulfide to a solution of a zinc salt, a precipitate of zinc sulfide is obtained, because the ionization of the hydrogen sulfide produces enough sulfide ion to satisfy the solubility product condition for precipitation. But if we first add hydrochloric acid to the zinc salt solution no precipitate is obtained. The increased oxonium ion concentration has required a decrease in the concentration of sulfide ion to a point where the product $[Zn^{++}][S^=]$ is no longer greater than the solubility product constant.

The addition of an acetate to a solution of acetic acid must likewise disturb the equilibrium and lead to a new state of equilibrium in which the concentration of oxonium ion is smaller, but the concentrations of acetate ion and acetic acid are larger than they were previously. This effect is also easily illustrated. If we add a little acetic acid to a solution of a ferrous salt and then pass in hydrogen sulfide, no precipitate appears. If we now add sodium or ammonium acetate, a black precipitate of ferrous sulfide is formed. Here the concentration of the oxonium ion furnished by the acetic acid (a much stronger acid than hydrogen sulfide) is sufficient to keep the sulfide ion concentration at a level too low to permit precipitation. The added acetate ion decreases the concentration of the oxonium ion, the hydrogen sulfide ionizes to a greater extent, and the sulfide ion concentration rises to the point where precipitation becomes possible.

As a matter of fact, the addition of acetate ion or of any other base to a solution must always result in a decrease in the concentration of oxonium ion. This is just as true when it is added to a solution containing some other acid than acetic and especially when it is added to a solution of a strong acid. When a solution of an acetate is mixed with a solution of a strong acid, the acetate ion from the one solution will react with the oxonium ion from the other, and there will at first be no reverse reaction because there is no acetic acid. The state of equilibrium will be reached only when the concentrations of the ions have decreased and the concentration of acetic acid has increased sufficiently to make the rates of forward and reverse reactions equal. This will be the case when the concentrations satisfy Eq. (15). This effect is also easily shown by sulfide precipitation reactions. Addition of hydrogen sulfide to a solution of a zinc salt containing a little hydrochloric acid produces no precipitate. If now sodium acetate is added zinc sulfide precipitates. The acetate ion has reacted with the oxonium ion, and the decreased concentration of the latter permits a greater concentration of the sulfide ion to be formed by the ionization of the hydrogen sulfide.

In the same way the equilibrium equation [Eq. (16)] for the ionization of ammonia requires that the addition of an ammonium salt to a solution should result in a decreased hydroxyl ion concentration. This effect is important in the precipitation of hydroxides. If moderately concentrated solutions of a magnesium salt and of ammonia are mixed, the product $[Mg^{++}][OH^-]^2$ exceeds the solubility product constant and $Mg(OH)_2$ precipitates. If, however, an ammonium salt is added to one or the other or both of the solutions before they are mixed, no precipitate is formed. This is because the same concentration of ammonia gives rise to a much smaller concentration of hydroxyl ion in the presence of the large concentration of ammonium ion.

The Limitations of the Law of Chemical Equilibrium.—We have seen that this law can be expected to be true only if the rates of the opposing reactions are proportional to the concentrations of the reactants, and that this requirement will be satisfied only if the frequency of collisions between the reacting molecules is proportional to the product of their concentrations. An analysis by mathematical methods shows that exact proportionality can be expected only if there are no forces of attraction or repulsion between the molecules. It also shows that a gaseous substance or mixture in which there are no intermolecular forces must behave exactly in accordance with the laws of Boyle and Charles, and with their combination, the perfect gas law,

$$PV = RT \tag{23}$$

where P, V, and T represent respectively pressure, volume, and temperature, and R is a constant. There are no perfect gases, but the behavior of gases when not too concentrated may be described and predicted with sufficient accuracy for most practical purposes by this law.

As might be expected from the fact that the assumptions used in the derivations are the same, there is an intimate connection between the validity of the perfect gas law and the law of chemical equilibrium. Deviations from one may be used to estimate the extent of deviations from the other, and either deviation may be used to estimate the intensity of the intermolecular forces.

Like the perfect gas law, the law of chemical equilibrium is a sufficiently exact approximation for gases at low pressures to have great usefulness. It has notably been verified for the reactions $2HI \leftrightarrows H_2 + I_2$, and $2SO_2 + O_2 \leftrightarrows 2SO_3$ at pressures in the neighborhood of 1 atmosphere. But it is necessary to make considerable corrections to both laws if they are to be applied to gases at several atmospheres pressure. Thus the equilibrium constant in the reaction

$$3H_2 + N_2 \leftrightarrows 2NH_3 \tag{24}$$

changes from 0.00516 at 10 atmospheres to 0.01493 at 1,000 atmospheres, the temperature being 475°C.

Especially great difficulties may be expected in the application of the law of chemical equilibrium to an ionization reaction. The reacting molecules are here packed in closely with water molecules, instead of moving about freely in empty space; and the electrical forces between the ions are of large magnitude even when the ions are widely separated. Nevertheless, experiment shows that the application has sufficient validity to be extremely useful. We shall consider the results of conductivity measurements, and shall test the law by seeing to what extent the quantity

$$\frac{[OH_3^+][C_2H_3O_2^-]}{[HC_2H_3O_2]}$$

approximates a true constant.

The Results of Conductivity Measurements.—Conductivity, which varies inversely as resistance, is defined as the reciprocal of resistance, and the unit is the reciprocal ohm. The specific resistance of a portion of matter is the resistance, measured between opposite faces, of a cube of 1 cm. edge. The specific conductivity, symbol κ, is the reciprocal of the specific resistance. The dilution, symbol v, is the volume in cubic centimeters which contains 1 gram-equivalent of the solute. The equivalent conductivity of a solution, symbol λ, is the product of specific conductivity by dilution.

$$\lambda = \kappa v. = \frac{\kappa}{c}, \quad c = \frac{\kappa}{\lambda} \tag{25}$$

A physical picture of the meaning of equivalent conductivity seems desirable because of the great importance of the concept. The specific conductivity of a solution is the conductivity of 1 cc. But 1 cc. of a normal solution contains 0.001 equivalent of solute, while 1 cc. of a 0.1 N solution contains but 0.0001 equivalent. A comparison of specific conductivities means then a comparison of the ability to carry current of two different amounts of solute.

An imaginary system may be pictured which contains 1 gram-equivalent of solute, together with enough solvent to give the desired concentration, between electrodes 1 cm. apart and great enough in area so that the necessary volume may be contained between them. The area of the electrodes would be 1000 sq. cm. in the case of a normal, 10,000 sq. cm. in the case of a 0.1 N solution; in general, the area in square centimeters would equal the dilution in cubic centimeters per equivalent. In such a conductivity cell there would always be 1 gram-equivalent of solute between the electrodes, and the distance across which the ions must transport the electricity would always be the same, namely, 1 cm. The conductivity, therefore, would be a measure of the ability to carry current of a constant quantity of solute.

It would be most inconvenient to construct such a cell and quite futile because the conductivity can be so easily calculated from the specific conductivity of the solution. Since the area of this imaginary cell is equal to the dilution, and the path of the current, 1 cm., is the same as that for which the specific conductivity is measured, the conductivity of the imaginary cell is equal to the specific conductivity times the dilution, and this product is the equivalent conductivity. This, therefore, is the conductivity such a cell would have, and really represents the conductivity of 1 gram-equivalent of the solute.

In Tables II and III are given the conductivities at various concentrations of hydrochloric acid, a typical strong electrolyte,

TABLE II.—THE CONDUCTIVITY OF HCl SOLUTIONS AT 25°C.[1]

Concentration, equivalents per liter	Specific conductivity	Equivalent conductivity
0.2	0.07608	380.4
0.1	0.03904	390.4
0.05	0.01992	398.4
0.02	0.008134	406.7
0.01	0.004116	411.6
0.005	0.002077	415.3
0.002	0.0008372	418.6
0.001	0.0004204	420.4

[1] BRAY and HUNT, *J. Am. Chem. Soc.*, **33**, 787 (1911); PARKER, *ibid.*, **45**, 2017 (1923).

TABLE III.—THE EQUIVALENT CONDUCTIVITY AND IONIZATION CONSTANT OF ACETIC ACID AT 25°C.[1]

Concentration, equivalents per liter	Equivalent conductivity, λ	Ionization constant, K
0.2	3.650	1.821×10^{-5}
0.1	5.200	1.846×10^{-5}
0.05	7.356	1.849×10^{-5}
0.02	11.563	1.840×10^{-5}
0.0098421	16.367	1.832×10^{-5}
0.00102831	48.133	1.797×10^{-5}
0.00011135	127.71	1.778×10^{-5}

[1] MacINNES and SHEDLOVSKY, *J. Am. Chem. Soc.*, **54**, 1429 (1932).

and of acetic acid, a typical weak electrolyte, all at 25°C. The same values are plotted against the dilution in Figs. 7 and 8. With both substances the conductivity increases with dilution, but in quite different ways in the two cases. With acetic acid the conductivity is relatively small, but increases rapidly with dilution even in the most dilute solutions in which measurements

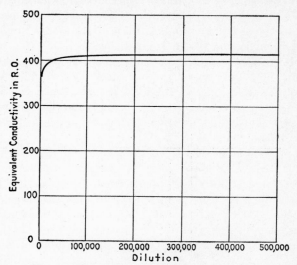

FIG. 7.—The conductivity of hydrochloric acid.

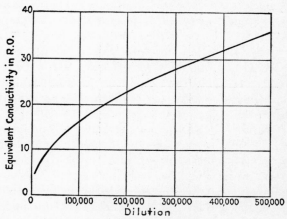

FIG. 8.—The conductivity of acetic acid.

can be made. (The conductivity due to the water itself and to conducting impurities, such as carbon dioxide, sets an experimental limit to the investigation of very dilute solutions.) With hydrochloric acid the conductivity is relatively large, but the change of conductivity with dilution is small, and rapidly becomes smaller as the dilution increases. The conductivity approaches a limit as the solution becomes more dilute and is not far from that limit in ordinary dilute solutions. Thus the limit for hydrochloric acid at 25°C. is estimated as 424.0 reciprocal ohms. This limit is usually called the conductivity at infinite dilution, and is represented by λ_∞. Its value is estimated from the curve obtained when conductivity is plotted against dilution, or better when it is plotted against concentration or some function of concentration.

It is well established that practically all this variation of the equivalent conductivity of HCl and of other strong acids and true salts is the result of electrical forces acting between oppositely charged ions. The negative ions hold back on the positive ones, the positive ions hold back on the negative ones, and the effect is the greater the nearer together the ions are, which is to say, the more concentrated the solution is. Being electrical, the magnitude of this effect depends principally upon the charge on the ions involved. As a result we find that the strong univalent acids, the true uni-univalent salts (those whose positive and negative ions both carry a single charge), and the alkali hydroxides all have equivalent conductivities in a 0.1 M solution whose value lies between 85 and 90 per cent of the conductivity at infinite dilution; whereas the same value for uni-bivalent salts like K_2SO_4 is always in the neighborhood of 73 per cent, and the value for bi-bivalent salts like $MgSO_4$ is about 40 per cent.

Like other properties of strong electrolytes, conductivities are additive. That is to say, the equivalent conductivity of a hydrochloric acid solution is the sum of the conductivity of 1 mole of oxonium ion plus the conductivity of 1 mole of chloride ion. The conductivity of the chloride ion in hydrochloric acid is the same as its conductivity in a solution of potassium chloride or other uni-univalent salt of the same concentration; and the conductivity of the oxonium ion in the hydrochloric acid is the same as the conductivity of oxonium ion in a solution of the same concentration of any other strong acid.

The sum of the conductivities of hydrochloric acid and potassium nitrate is the sum of the four ion conductivities, oxonium, potassium, chloride, and nitrate:

$$\lambda_{HCl} + \lambda_{KNO_3} = \lambda_{OH_3+} + \lambda_{K+} + \lambda_{Cl-} + \lambda_{NO_3-}. \qquad (26)$$

If now the conductivity of potassium chloride, which is the sum of the conductivities of potassium and chloride ions, is subtracted, there remains

$$\lambda_{HCl} + \lambda_{KNO_3} - \lambda_{KCl} = \lambda_{OH_3+} + \lambda_{NO_3-}. \qquad (27)$$

If the principle of additivity holds, this should be the conductivity of nitric acid. The principle of additivity can then be verified in the form

$$\lambda_{HNO_3} = \lambda_{HCl} + \lambda_{KNO_3} - \lambda_{KCl}. \qquad (28)$$

For 0.1 N solutions the actual equivalent conductivities at 25°C. are for HCl, 390.4, for KNO$_3$, 120.3, and for KCl, 129.0. The calculated value for HNO$_3$, from these figures is 381.7, the actually observed value is 385.0. For 0.002 N solutions the values are for HCl, 418.6, for KNO$_3$, 140.7, for KCl 146.4. The calculated value for HNO$_3$ is 412.9, the observed value is 413.7.

The principle of additivity works out satisfactorily; better, the more dilute the solution. The deviations are considerably greater than the experimental error, but are small compared with the actual values of the conductivities. If these deviations indicate association into molecules, they indicate that the extent of such association is small.

A similar computation for acetic acid leads to quite different results. The values for the equivalent conductivities in 0.1 N solution at 25°C. are for HCl, 390.4, for sodium acetate 72.9, for sodium chloride 106.8. If acetic acid were a strong electrolyte, its conductivity in 0.1 N solution should be 356.5, whereas the observed value is 5.20 reciprocal ohms. This is in agreement with the other evidence that 1 gram-equivalent of acetic acid gives rise to much less than 1 gram-equivalent each of oxonium and acetate ions. Obviously the relation between these figures,

356.5 and 5.20, must have an important bearing on the problem of calculating the degree of ionization of acetic acid.

This relation is, however, complicated by the fact that the value 356.5 was calculated from the conductivities of the other electrolytes in 0.1 M solution. It represents therefore the conductivity which 1 mole of acetic acid would have, if it were a strong electrolyte, when its concentration is 0.1; and because of the interionic forces this value is less than the conductivity which 1 mole each of oxonium and acetate ions would have in a solution whose ion concentration is that which prevails in the dilute acetic acid solution. Because the ion concentration of a dilute acetic acid solution is very small, we shall not, however, go far wrong if we use the conductivity which 1 mole of completely ionized acetic acid would have in infinitely dilute solution (calculated from the conductivities at infinite dilution of hydrochloric acid, sodium chloride, and sodium acetate), which is 390.6 r.o.

If, then, the actual conductivity of 1 mole of acetic acid in a 0.1 M solution is 5.200 r.o., and its conductivity would be 390.6 r.o. if it were completely ionized, the fraction of the acetic acid ionized must be 5.200/390.6 = 0.01331. In general the degree of ionization or fraction ionized, which is usually represented by the symbol α, is given by the equation

$$\alpha = \frac{\lambda}{\lambda_\infty}. \tag{29}$$

The concentration of oxonium ion is the total concentration of acetic acid times the fraction ionized, or $0.1 \times 0.01331 = 0.001331$. The concentration of acetate ion is the same. The concentration of molecular acetic acid is the total concentration of acid times the fraction which is not ionized, $0.1(1 - 0.01331) = 0.09867$. The ionization constant K is given by

$$K = \frac{[OH_3^+][C_2H_3O_2^-]}{[HC_2H_3O_2]} = \frac{0.001331 \times 0.001331}{0.09867} = 1.795 \times 10^{-5}.$$

(The value given in Table III was calculated by a more accurate method which considers the decrease in conductivity due to the interionic forces. The difference is not large.) When a similar calculation is made for other concentrations of acetic acid, the results shown in Table III are obtained. Clearly the quantity K shows a satisfactory degree of constancy, and it may be concluded that within the range studied the law of chemical equilibrium does apply reasonably well to the ionization of acetic acid. Other weak electrolytes have been found to behave in much the same way.

The Salt Effect.—It will be noted, however, that the values of K in Table III do increase somewhat with increasing concentration of acetic acid. The effect, although small, is well outside the experimental error and is observed with all weak electrolytes. Like the deviations from constancy of the solubility product, this variation of the ionization constant depends primarily upon the total ion concentration, which is, of course, small in dilute solutions of the weakly ionized acetic acid. Other methods of determining ionization constants which are more suitable than conductivity for the case where a salt is present as well as the weak acid or base show that this increase in ionization constant with increasing ion concentration, which is called a *salt effect*, may easily amount to 75 per cent in a 0.1 M salt solution. (At still higher salt concentrations the constant decreases again.)

It appears from these results and from the observations on the salt effect on the solubility product (see page 36) that the presence of ions in a solution favors the formation of more ions in that solution, whether by the dissolving of a difficultly soluble salt or by the ionization of a weak electrolyte. The same thing is also true when the formation of the new ions depends upon the dissociation of a complex ion into simpler ions, a fact which makes possible a striking demonstration of a salt effect. The complex ion $Fe(SCN)_6^{\equiv}$ has an intense red color. It is to some extent dissociated in dilute solution into colorless Fe^{+++} and SCN^- ions. Upon addition of hydrochloric or nitric acid, of sodium, potassium, or ammonium nitrate, chloride, or sulfate, of barium chloride, or indeed of practically any electrolyte, the extent of the dissociation increases and the color of the solution lightens.

Although both solubility product and ionization constants increase with increasing total ion concentration, both are as exactly fixed in solutions of large but practically unvarying total ion concentration as they are in extremely dilute solutions. Of course the values of the constants differ for each value of total ion concentration. Because the analytical chemist works under conditions of large but only slightly varying ion concentration (see page 38), he may use both laws without hesitation.

As might be expected from the close relation which exists between the equations for reaction rate and equilibrium, there is a salt effect upon reaction rates also. This is especially large when both reactants are ions. As was only rather recently discovered by Brönsted, an increase in electrolyte concentration decreases the rate of a reaction between oppositely charged ions, but increases the rate of a reaction between like charged ions; the magnitude of the effect being greater the greater the product of the charges on the ions reacting.

Activity Coefficients.—It has been found that both solubility product and equilibrium expressions may be made exact if each concentration is multiplied by an *activity coefficient*, for which the symbol f is generally used. These activity coefficients vary with changing concentration of solute and especially with changing concentration of electrolyte. They are to a first approximation, especially in dilute solutions, determined by the electrical charge on the substance to which they refer and by what is called the *ionic strength* of the solution.

The ionic strength of a solution is calculated as follows: the concentration of each ion is multiplied by the square of its charge, the numbers thus obtained are added together, and the sum is divided by two. The ionic strength of a 0.1 M solution of KCl is 0.1, that of a 0.1 M solution of $MgSO_4$ is 0.4. It is a quantity which gives expression to the fact that the effect of one ion upon the properties of another increases rapidly with increase in the charge on the first ion. The value of the activity coefficient of any solute in aqueous solution is by definition equal to 1 when a very small amount of the substance is dissolved in an extremely large amount of pure water. The values for electrically neutral substances are not very much affected by changes in ionic strength up to 0.1, the values for ionic substances decrease, the rate of decrease being the more rapid the greater the charge on the ion. In a solution of 0.1 ionic strength, the value of f for a singly charged ion is about 0.7 to 0.8; for a doubly charged ion it is about 0.3, and for a triply charged ion about 0.2. These values may be obtained from the study of equilibria which involve the ions concerned, and especially from the solubility of salts. Thus the equation

$$[Ag^+][C_2H_3O_2^-]f_{Ag^+}f_{C_2H_3O_2^-} = K$$

or

$$[Ag^+][C_2H_3O_2^-] = \frac{K}{f_{Ag^+}f_{C_2H_3O_2^-}} \tag{30}$$

is the exact expression of the solubility product equation applied to silver acetate. Therefore the fact that the value of the product $[Ag^+][C_2H_3O_2^-]$ in a saturated solution of silver acetate in a 0.119 M sodium acetate solution is 1.15 times greater than it is in a saturated solution in water tells us that the product $f_{Ag^+}f_{C_2H_3O_2^-}$ is $1/1.15 = 0.87$ times as great in the first solution which has an ionic strength of 0.147 as it is in the second whose ionic strength is 0.060.

The chief utility of these activity coefficients is the fact that a value derived from a study of one equilibrium can be applied to another equilibrium or to a reaction rate in the same medium. Thus an activity coefficient value for acetate ion in a certain medium, derived from a study of the solubility of silver acetate, may be used to predict salt effects upon the ionization of acetic acid.

The product of the concentration and the activity coefficient of a substance is called its *activity*.

The Table of Ionization Constants.—The ionization constants of a number of important weak electrolytes are given in Table IV. The values here given are those prevailing in solutions of very low ion concentration. They depend upon conductivity measurements on solutions of slightly ionized substances, or, in the case of the more highly ionized substances, they are values corrected for the salt effect and for the variation of mobility with ion concentration.

Some Calculations of Ion Concentrations.—The utility of an ionization constant resides in the possibility of calculating from it the concentrations of the ions of the electrolyte concerned in various solutions. For the purposes of such calculations we

TABLE IV.—IONIZATION CONSTANTS

Reaction	Temperature, °C.	Constant	
$H_3AsO_3 + H_2O \rightleftarrows OH_3^+ + H_2AsO_3^-$...	25	6	$\times 10^{-10}$
$H_3AsO_4 + H_2O \rightleftarrows OH_3^+ + H_2AsO_4^-$...	25	5	$\times 10^{-3}$
$H_2AsO_4^- + H_2O \rightleftarrows OH_3^+ + HAsO_4^-$...	25	4	$\times 10^{-5}$
$HAsO_4^- + H_2O \rightleftarrows OH_3^+ + AsO_4^=$.....	25	6	$\times 10^{-10}$
$H_3BO_3 + H_2O \rightleftarrows OH_3^+ + H_2BO_3^-$.....	25	5.8	$\times 10^{-10}$
$CO_2 + 2H_2O \rightleftarrows OH_3^+ + HCO_3^-$.......	25	4.4	$\times 10^{-7}$
$HCO_3^- + H_2O \rightleftarrows OH_3^+ + CO_3^=$.......	25	5.6	$\times 10^{-11}$
$HCN + H_2O \rightleftarrows OH_3^+ + CN^-$.........	25	7.2	$\times 10^{-10}$
$H_3PO_4 + H_2O \rightleftarrows OH_3^+ + H_2PO_4^-$.....	25	7.5	$\times 10^{-3}$
$H_2PO_4^- + H_2O \rightleftarrows OH_3^+ + HPO_4^=$.....	25	6.2	$\times 10^{-8}$
$HPO_4^= + H_2O \rightleftarrows OH_3^+ + PO_4^=$.......	25	5	$\times 10^{-13}$
$HNO_2 + H_2O \rightleftarrows OH_3^+ + NO_2^-$.......	18	4.5	$\times 10^{-4}$
$HSO_4^- + H_2O \rightleftarrows OH_3^+ + SO_4^=$.......	25	1.20	$\times 10^{-2}$
$H_2S + H_2O \rightleftarrows OH_3^+ + HS^-$..........	18	9	$\times 10^{-8}$
$HS^- + H_2O \rightleftarrows OH_3^+ + S^=$............	18	1	$\times 10^{-15}$
$SO_2 + 2H_2O \rightleftarrows OH_3^+ + HSO_3^-$........	25	1.2	$\times 10^{-2}$
$HSO_3^- + H_2O \rightleftarrows OH_3^+ + SO_3^=$........	25	5	$\times 10^{-6}$
$HC_2H_3O_2 + H_2O \rightleftarrows OH_3^+ + C_2H_3O_2^-$..	25	1.75	$\times 10^{-5}$
$NH_3 + H_2O \rightleftarrows NH_4^+ + OH^-$.........	25	1.8	$\times 10^{-5}$
$2H_2O \rightleftarrows OH_3^+ + OH^-$................	25	1	$\times 10^{-14}$
$2H_2O \rightleftarrows OH_3^+ + OH^-$................	100	5	$\times 10^{-13}$

shall represent the measured or *stoichiometric* concentration of acetic acid in a solution by c_a. The actual concentration of the substance $HC_2H_3O_2$ is smaller than this because of the ionization; the stoichiometric concentration is the number of moles used to make up 1 liter of the solution. Let α be the fraction of the acetic acid which is ionized. Then

$$[OH_3^+] = [C_2H_3O_2^-] = c_a\alpha \tag{31}$$

and

$$[HC_2H_3O_2] = c_a(1 - \alpha). \tag{32}$$

Substituting in the equilibrium equation (15), we have

$$\frac{c_a\alpha \cdot c_a\alpha}{c_a(1 - \alpha)} = K \tag{33}$$

which simplifies to

$$\frac{c_a\alpha^2}{1 - \alpha} = K. \tag{34}$$

To obtain the degree of ionization of any weak acid whose constant is known we need only substitute the constant and the value of c_a in this equation and solve for α. The concentration of the ions produced from the acid may then be obtained by multiplying this value of α by c_a.

Equation (34) may be considerably simplified in case the extent of ionization is not large, for $1 - \alpha$ will not then differ materially from 1. If, therefore, we write 1 instead of $1 - \alpha$, we may solve explicitly for α obtaining

$$\alpha = \sqrt{\frac{K}{c_a}}. \tag{35}$$

As a specific example we shall calculate the concentrations of oxonium and acetate ions in a 0.1 M acetic acid solution. c_a is 0.1, and from the table we find K to be 1.75×10^{-5}. Substitution in Eq. (35) gives

$$\alpha = \sqrt{\frac{1.75 \times 10^{-5}}{0.1}} = \sqrt{1.75 \times 10^{-4}} = 0.013$$

and

$$[OH_3{}^+] = [C_2H_3O_2{}^-] = c_a\alpha = 0.0013.$$

It must be emphasized that these formulae apply only to solutions of acetic acid in the absence of any other source of acetate or oxonium ion. Only then is it true that

$$[C_2H_3O_2{}^-] = [OH_3{}^+] = c_a\alpha.$$

Suppose we have a solution containing c_a moles per liter of acetic acid and c_s moles per liter of sodium acetate. Let α again equal the degree of ionization of the acid. Then

$$[OH_3{}^+] = c_a\alpha \tag{36}$$
$$[C_2H_3O_2{}^-] = c_s + c_a\alpha \tag{37}$$
$$[HC_2H_3O_2] = c_a(1 - \alpha) \tag{38}$$
$$\frac{c_a\alpha(c_s + c_a\alpha)}{c_a(1 - \alpha)} = K \tag{39}$$

from which α may be calculated. Within a satisfactory degree of precision for most purposes, however, we may note that the true concentration of acetic acid will be very nearly c_a because the proportion ionized is very small, much smaller than in the absence of the salt. Also the amount of acetate ion produced by the ionization of the acid is so small compared with that due to the salt that the error involved in setting the concentration of acetate ion equal to c_s is negligible. Making these substitutions in Eq. (15), we obtain

$$\frac{[OH_3^+]c_s}{c_a} = K \qquad (40)$$

or

$$[OH_3^+] = K \frac{c_a}{c_s}. \qquad (41)$$

This may also be derived by suitable approximations from the exact equation (39).

To take some specific cases, the oxonium ion concentration of a solution containing 0.1 *M* acetic acid and 0.1 *M* sodium acetate is 1.8×10^{-5}. In fact, it is generally true that the oxonium ion concentration of an equimolecular mixture of a weak acid and the conjugate base (acetate ion) is equal to the ionization constant of the acid. The oxonium ion concentration of a solution containing 0.01 *M* acetic acid and 0.1 *M* sodium acetate is one-tenth as great, namely, 1.8×10^{-6}.

In the same way the acetate ion concentration of a solution containing acetic acid and a strong acid can be calculated from the equation

$$[C_2H_3O_2^-] = K \frac{c_a}{c_H} \qquad (42)$$

where c_a equals the concentration of acetic acid and c_H equals the concentration of strong acid. In this way we calculate that the concentration of acetate ion in a solution containing 0.1 *M* acetic acid and 0.1 *M* hydrochloric acid is 1.8×10^{-5}. It will be noted that these figures agree with our previous qualitative conclusions (page 52). The presence of 0.1 *M* sodium acetate decreases the oxonium ion concentration of 0.1 *M* acetic acid from 1.3×10^{-3} to 1.8×10^{-5}; the presence of 0.1 *M* hydrochloric acid in 0.1 *M* acetic acid decreases the acetate ion concentration from 1.3×10^{-3} to 1.8×10^{-5}.

It is not difficult to calculate the concentration of oxonium ion which results when an acetate and a strong acid are mixed. Suppose equal volumes of 0.2 M hydrochloric acid and 0.2 M sodium acetate are mixed. If no reaction took place, the concentrations of oxonium and acetate ions would each be 0.1 M because of the doubling of the volume. But reaction must take place (see page 54), and the state of equilibrium attained by this reaction will be one in which the concentrations of oxonium and acetate ions are equal, because their initial concentrations were equal and they are consumed by the reaction in equivalent amounts. The state of equilibrium will therefore be identical (except for the salt effect of the sodium and nitrate ions) with that which results from the ionization of 0.1 M acetic acid. We have already calculated the concentrations present in this system.

A little consideration will show that the concentrations of oxonium and acetate ions and of acetic acid present in a solution containing 0.2 M sodium acetate and 0.1 M hydrochloric acid will be identical, except for a small salt effect, with those present in a solution containing 0.1 M sodium acetate and 0.1 M acetic acid.

The results of these various calculations are summarized in Table V.

TABLE V.—SOME CONCENTRATION CALCULATIONS

Solution	$[OH_3^+]$	$[C_2H_3O_2^-]$	$[HC_2H_3O_2]$
0.1 M acetic acid...............	0.0013	0.0013	0.0987
0.1 M sodium acetate (p. 89)...	1.4×10^{-9}	0.1	7.3×10^{-6}
0.1 M acetic acid- 0.1 M sodium acetate........	1.8×10^{-5}	0.1	0.1
0.1 M acetic acid- 0.1 M hydrochloric acid......	0.1	1.8×10^{-5}	0.1
0.1 M sodium acetate- 0.1 M hydrochloric acid......	0.0013	0.0013	0.0987
0.2 M sodium acetate- 0.1 M hydrochloric acid......	1.8×10^{-5}	0.1	0.1

Buffer Solutions.—Solutions containing a weak acid and a highly ionized salt of that acid, or a weak base and a highly ionized salt of that base are called "buffer solutions" on account of their very important property of being weakly acid or alkaline (or even neutral) and yet of resisting change in the concentration of oxonium or hydroxyl ion.

It has been shown that a solution containing 0.1 mole per liter each of acetic acid and sodium acetate has the small oxonium ion concentration of 0.000018 M. A 0.000018 M hydrochloric acid solution would have the same oxonium ion concentration as this acetic acid-sodium acetate solution, but there would be an important difference in the properties of the solutions.

The addition of 0.000018 mole per liter of sodium hydroxide to the hydrochloric acid solution would neutralize it, and reduce the oxonium ion concentration to 10^{-7} M. The same amount of sodium hydroxide added to the acetic acid-sodium acetate buffer solution would have only a negligible effect upon the acidity, because the oxonium ions removed by combination with hydroxyl ions would be largely replaced by further ionization of acetic acid. It would require nearly 0.1 mole per liter of sodium hydroxide to neutralize the buffer solution, which is therefore said to possess reserve acidity. Similarly, a small amount of acid would multiply by many times the oxonium ion concentration of the hydrochloric acid solution, but would have only a small effect upon the acidity of the buffer solution, because a large proportion of the added oxonium ions would disappear by combination with the large concentration of acetate ions present. The solution possesses also reserve alkalinity.

The buffer solution maintains its oxonium ion concentration practically unchanged even with considerable additions of acid or alkali, the dilute hydrochloric acid could not be exposed to the air without increasing in acidity by dissolving carbon dioxide, nor kept in closed glass bottles without becoming alkaline by dissolving the glass. A solution of ammonia and ammonium chloride is also a buffer solution. It is only slightly alkaline, yet resists the effect of added acid or alkali.

Buffer solutions have important applications in all fields of chemistry, and are used in many important analytical separations.

The Separation of Barium and Strontium Ions.—It is now possible to discuss intelligently the separation of barium and strontium ions, a very thoroughly worked-out example of what may be called separation by adjustment of acidity. The difficulty is that corresponding barium and strontium salts have solubilities which do not differ very widely, and even when, as with the chromates, there is considerable difference in solubility, both salts are comparatively insoluble so that it becomes a problem to precipitate one without the other.

The separation may be considered satisfactory if a precipitate is obtained with 0.0001 M barium ion, if 0.1 M strontium ion gives no precipitate, and if barium is precipitated so completely, even when its concentration is 0.1 M, that the filtrate does not give a false indication of the presence of strontium ion.

In order to precipitate barium chromate from any solution it is necessary that the product of the concentrations of the barium and chromate ions be greater than the solubility product constant, which is 2.2×10^{-10}. If this is to occur when the barium ion concentration is as little as 0.0001, it is necessary that the chromate ion concentration be so large that

$$0.0001 \times [CrO_4^=] > 2.2 \times 10^{-10} \qquad \text{or} \qquad [CrO_4^=] > 2.2 \times 10^{-6}.$$

In order that strontium chromate shall not precipitate from a solution when the strontium ion concentration is as large as 0.1 M it is necessary that the chromate ion concentration be so small that

$$0.1 \times [CrO_4^=] < 3.6 \times 10^{-5} \qquad \text{or} \qquad [CrO_4^=] < 3.6 \times 10^{-4}$$

since 3.6×10^{-5} is the solubility product constant of strontium chromate.

The separation is possible only if the chromate ion concentration is kept between the limits of 3.6×10^{-4} and 2.2×10^{-6}. If the chromate ion concentration is above the upper limit, strontium may precipitate in the barium test; if the chromate ion concentration is below the lower limit, the test for barium ion will not be sufficiently delicate.

But this small concentration of chromate ion is insufficient to precipitate more than a trace of barium chromate unless some provision is made to furnish new chromate ion to take the place of that removed by precipitation. Fortunately the second ionization of chromic acid is that of a weak acid, which means that the addition of potassium chromate to an acid solution results in the removal of much of the chromate ion by the reaction

$$OH_3^+ + CrO_4^- \rightleftarrows HCrO_4^- + H_2O. \tag{43}$$

The further reaction

$$2HCrO_4^- \rightleftarrows Cr_2O_7^- + H_2O \tag{44}$$

which is believed to take place to a large extent has only the same effect as a decreased ionization of $HCrO_4^-$, since the water concentration is constant. If now the oxonium ion concentration is kept at the proper figure, a large amount of potassium chromate can be added to the solution, sufficient chromate will be available to combine with all the barium ion present, but the actual concentration of chromate ion will be so small that strontium chromate will not precipitate even with large concentrations of strontium ion.

The oxonium ion concentration required is quite small, and must therefore be stabilized and maintained by a buffer solution. Bray, who worked out this separation, found that 0.48 *M* acetic acid and 1.2 *M* ammonium acetate gave the proper oxonium ion concentration. Neglecting the salt effect this may be calculated

$$[OH_3^+] = 0.000018\frac{[HC_2H_3O_2]}{[C_2H_3O_2^-]} = 0.000018\frac{0.48}{1.2} = 0.000008.$$

The Solubility of Salts in Acids.—The words soluble and insoluble should be used with caution. One is tempted by the results of a test-tube experiment to say that barium chromate is insoluble in acetic acid, but soluble in hydrochloric acid, and that strontium chromate is soluble in both. This gives altogether too simple a picture of the separation treated in this section. Barium and strontium chromates are, of course, somewhat soluble in water, and they are both more soluble in dilute acetic acid than in water, because the reaction of Eq. (43) removes some of the chromate ion and necessitates increased concentration of the barium or strontium ion to maintain saturation. Although the proportionate increase in solubility will be essentially the same with both salts, the solubility of the strontium chromate has become large enough to be analytically significant, while the increased solubility of the barium chromate is still too small to be easily detected.

Salts of weak acids are always more soluble in acid solutions, no matter how weakly acid, than in water, but some salts of weak acids are so insoluble that even the greatly increased solubility in strongly acid solutions is analytically negligible. This is in particular true of many sulfides, which dissolve to only a minute extent in acid solutions in spite of the fact that hydrogen sulfide is an extremely weak acid. Salts of strong acids are no more soluble in acids than in water except as a result of the salt effect.

A salt is very soluble in another salt only when some weak electrolyte is formed. Lead sulfate is easily soluble in ammonium acetate, because the combination of lead ions and acetate ions to form the weakly ionized lead acetate makes the solution unsaturated. Less soluble lead salts like the chromate and sulfide remain practically insoluble in ammonium acetate because they were originally so insoluble that the increased solubility in the acetate solution is still negligible.

Solubility Product for Hydrogen Sulfide.—The solubility of a nonelectrolyte in an aqueous solution at a given pressure and temperature is very slightly affected by the composition of the solution, provided it remains dilute. Of course, the solubility of a given solute is different in different solvents, and the addition of anything to water makes it, to some extent, a different solvent. There is, for example, a salting-out effect by which the solubility of a nonelectrolyte decreases as the total ion concentration increases, but this is of comparatively little influence at low concentrations, and for dilute solutions is almost entirely determined by the total salt concentration. One may say that the solubility remains practically constant if the total salt concentration does not vary greatly, a conclusion similar to that arrived at with respect to the law of chemical equilibrium and the solubility product principle.

This result may be taken over to the case of the true solubility of a weak electrolyte, the concentration of the un-ionized molecules in its saturated solution. The total solubility in water of hydrogen sulfide at 25°C. and 760 mm. total pressure is almost exactly 0.1 M. Since it is so weakly ionized nearly all of the dissolved hydrogen sulfide remains as molecules, and the concentration of molecular hydrogen sulfide in a saturated aqueous solution of not too great salt concentration may be taken as 0.1 M under these conditions of temperature and pressure. A dilute solution of sodium hydroxide might be saturated with hydrogen sulfide, much more than 0.1 mole per liter would dissolve, because it reacts with the alkali; but the concentration of hydrogen sulfide in the saturated solution would be 0.1 M.

Since the standard method of using hydrogen sulfide as a reagent consists in saturating the solution with the gas, the conditions prevailing in the saturated solution are particularly important, and the equations which apply may be materially simplified.

The application of the law of chemical equilibrium to the primary ionization of hydrogen sulfide gives at 25°C.,

$$\frac{[OH_3^+][HS^-]}{[H_2S]} = 9 \times 10^{-8} \text{ or } [OH_3^+][HS^-] = 9 \times 10^{-8}[H_2S]. \quad (45)$$

But since the concentration of hydrogen sulfide is constant and equal to 0.1 mole per liter for saturated solutions at room temperature and 1 atmosphere, it follows that under these conditions

$$[OH_3^+][HS^-] = 9 \times 10^{-9}. \quad (46)$$

This is a solubility product equation for hydrogen sulfide; the solubility product principle thus applies to weak electrolytes as well as to strong ones. It is generally used when working with saturated solutions because it gives an equation with two variables instead of three, and is simpler.

Similarly, from the equation (see page 51)

$$\frac{[OH_3^+]^2[S^=]}{[H_2S]} = 1 \times 10^{-22} \quad (47)$$

it follows that

$$[OH_3^+]^2[S^=] = 1 \times 10^{-23}. \quad (48)$$

This amounts to the very simple statement that the sulfide ion concentration of a saturated solution of hydrogen sulfide is inversely proportional to the square of the oxonium ion concentration. It means that increasing the oxonium ion concentration twice decreases the sulfide ion concentration four times; that increasing the oxonium ion concentration 10 times decreases the sulfide ion concentration 100 times. The following values of the sulfide ion concentration at 25°C. in solutions saturated with hydrogen sulfide at 1 atmosphere total pressure are useful.

The secondary ionization of hydrogen sulfide is so much less extensive than the primary that the concentrations of oxonium and hydrosulfide (HS$^-$) ions may be taken as practically equal to each other in a saturated solution in water or in a solution of another electrolyte which does not furnish or react with oxonium or sulfide ions. The number of hydrosulfide ions lost by the secondary ionization

$$HS^- + H_2O \rightleftarrows OH_3^+ + S^= \qquad (49)$$

and the number of oxonium ions gained by it are insignificant in comparison with the concentrations of the ions formed by the first ionization.

If

$$[OH_3^+] = [HS^-] \qquad (50)$$

and

$$[OH_3^+][HS^-] = 9 \times 10^{-9} \qquad (51)$$

then

$$[OH_3^+] = [HS^-] = \sqrt{9 \times 10^{-9}} = 9.5 \times 10^{-5}. \qquad (52)$$

In the equation for the secondary ionization

$$\frac{[OH_3^+][S^=]}{[HS^-]} = 1 \times 10^{-15} \qquad (53)$$

substitution of the relation $[OH_3^+] = [HS^-]$, which holds for saturated solutions in water, gives

$$[S^=] = 1 \times 10^{-15}. \qquad (54)$$

The calculation for solutions containing other acids is simpler. The sulfide ion concentration of a saturated solution of hydrogen sulfide at 25°C. and 1 atmosphere total pressure in a 0.1 *M* hydrochloric acid solution follows immediately from the equation

$$[OH_3^+]^2[S^=] = 1 \times 10^{-23}. \qquad (55)$$

The oxonium ions produced by ionization of the hydrogen sulfide will be negligible in amount compared with those from the hydrochloric acid, and the oxonium ion concentration of the solution may be taken as that due to the hydrochloric acid alone; that is, 0.1 mole per liter. Substitution gives

$$(0.1)^2[S^=] = 1 \times 10^{-23} \quad \text{and} \quad [S^=] = 1 \times 10^{-21}. \quad (56)$$

It should be noted that these solubility product constants are more dependent upon temperature than are most ionization constants, because of the marked dependence of the solubility upon temperature.

The Solubilities of the Metallic Sulfides.—The relative solubilities of the metallic sulfides may be estimated from the oxonium ion concentrations necessary to prevent their precipitation, the comparison being made with equal concentrations of the metallic ions. The order is:

The sulfides of the alkalis, of the alkaline earths, of aluminum and chromium cannot be precipitated from aqueous solutions under any known conditions.

Manganous sulfide can only be precipitated from definitely alkaline solution. For the other metallic ions there will be given the conditions necessary to prevent the precipitation of the sulfide when a 0.1 M solution of the metallic ion is saturated with hydrogen sulfide at room temperature and 1 atmosphere total pressure.

Ferrous, cobaltous, and nickelous sulfides precipitate in an acetic acid-acetate buffer (and, of course, in alkaline solutions or in acid solutions which are less acid than the acetate buffer), but dilute acetic acid to which no acetate has been added is sufficiently acid to prevent the precipitation.

Zinc sulfide precipitates in a dilute acetic acid solution free of acetates, but 0.2 M hydrochloric acid prevents the precipitation.

Cadmium sulfide precipitates quantitatively in 0.3 M hydrochloric acid, but not at all in 3 M hydrochloric acid. Hydrochloric acid has about the same effect upon the precipitation of lead, tin, and bismuth sulfides. Because of the formation of chloride complex ions hydrochloric acid is much more effective in preventing the precipitation of cadmium and lead sulfides than is for instance nitric acid. It is not at all unlikely that similar effects appear with others of the heavy metal ions.

Cupric sulfide precipitates in 3 M hydrochloric acid, but not in 12 M acid. Of the same order of solubility are the antimony sulfides.

Mercuric and arsenic sulfides can be precipitated from 12 M hydrochloric acid.

Two very important group separations of qualitative analysis are based upon these differences in solubility and upon the control of the sulfide ion concentration. Silver, mercury, lead, copper, cadmium, arsenic, antimony, and tin are separated from zinc, cobalt, nickel, iron, manganese, aluminum, chromium, and the alkaline earths and alkalis by precipitating the first group as sulfides in 0.3 M hydrochloric or nitric acid. Zinc, nickel, cobalt, iron, and manganese are separated from the alkaline earths and alkalis, by precipitating the sulfides of the former in alkaline solution.

In addition, arsenic and mercury can be separated from antimony and tin by sulfide precipitation in hot 12 M hydrochloric acid. Antimony can be separated from tin by sulfide precipitation in 2.2 M hydrochloric acid at 100°C.

A Separation Based upon Slow Reaction.—A separation of unusual type is based upon the slow rate of solution of cobalt and nickel sulfides. If a solution of nickel or cobalt salt which has been made slightly alkaline with ammonia is divided into two portions, and the same two reagents, hydrogen sulfide and hydrochloric acid, are added to each portion but in the reverse order, the results will be quite different in the two cases. When the hydrogen sulfide is added first, the precipitate formed remains when the hydrochloric acid is added; but when the acid is added first, hydrogen sulfide produces no precipitate. Such a result can only mean that the reactions are slow and that one or the other solution has not reached equilibrium. Actually the precipitate will dissolve in the hydrochloric acid if sufficient time is allowed. Cobalt and nickel ions may be separated, though not perfectly, from zinc, iron, and manganese ions by precipitating the sulfides, dissolving out the zinc, iron, and manganese with dilute hydrochloric acid, and filtering before large amounts of cobalt or nickel sulfide have dissolved.

It is to be expected that sulfides which dissolve slowly should also precipitate slowly, and it is true that the precipitation of nickel sulfide in acid solutions is slow, so slow that its catalysis by the glass of the container leads to the frequent formation of a mirror of nickel sulfide, when the precipitation is made in an acetate buffer. The precipitation of zinc sulfide in acid solutions is likewise slow, and in moderately strong hydrochloric acid solutions a precipitate may appear only after some hours.

Slow reactions in ionic reactions are commoner than is generally appreciated. They are very common among reactions which involve the more stable complex compounds, for instance, in a great many reactions involving platinum and cobaltic compounds, the formation and decomposition of ferricyanide ion (see page 123), the electrodeposition of copper from a cyanide solution, and most oxidation-reduction reactions involving the ions of oxygen acids (see page 138). They also appear in many reactions of hydrolysis, as with ferric, chromic, and bismuth salts; in the reactions of passive metals, as iron, nickel, and chromium; and in the precipitation of magnesium oxalate and lithium phosphate (which precipitate when a solution is boiled and do not redissolve on cooling).

Ammonium Ion: Salts of a Volatile Base.—The separation of ammonium ion from the other alkali ions rests upon a difference in volatility rather than upon one in solubility. Two methods are possible.

The mixture of salts may be evaporated to dryness and heated until the ammonium salts have evaporated, which can easily be done without much loss of the other alkalis. This is the most satisfactory method of removing ammonium compounds before testing for the other alkalis, but makes the recovery and detection of the ammonium ion difficult. This removal is important because the solubilities of ammonium salts are very near those of the corresponding potassium salts, and potassium can only be tested for by precipitation if the ammonium ion has previously been removed by means of this difference in volatility, and because the sodium antimonate test usually used for sodium ion suffers in sensitiveness by the presence of ammonium salts, or indeed of potassium salts.

If excess sodium hydroxide is added to a solution containing ammonium ion reaction of hydroxyl and ammonium ions takes place to a large extent. When the solution is warmed, the ammonia evaporates displacing equilibrium so that the ammonium ion may be completely removed. The ammonia may be redissolved in water and tested for either by the reactions of the hydroxyl ion which it there produces or by some other property.

Ammonium ion plays a very special part in schemes of analysis. The other alkali ions can only be tested for in solutions from which all other metallic ions have been removed. When in the process of this removal it becomes necessary to make the solution alkaline, ammonia is used; when it becomes necessary to add a salt, ammonium salts are used. This is because ammonium salts, thus added, can be removed by volatilization, and because ammonium ion is the only cation which can be detected by a single direct test. (This direct test does assume that compounds of hydrazine and of volatile organic bases are absent.)

Suggestions for Reading

General: GETMAN-DANIELS, *op. cit.*, chs. XII, XV, XVI; RODEBUSH, *op. cit.*, chs. IX, X.

Calculations: ENGELDER, *op. cit.*, ch. V.

Salt effects: KILPATRICK, *J. Chem. Education*, **9**, 840 (1932).

Exercises

1. The resistance of a rectangular cell containing 0.1 N NaCl at 25°C. is 11.70 ohms. The distance between the electrodes which form the opposite faces of the cell is 0.5 cm., the area of the electrodes is 4 sq. cm. Calculate the equivalent conductivity of 0.1 N NaCl at this temperature.

2. At 18°C. the conductivity at infinite dilution of KCl is 130.10 r. o., of NaF 90.15, of NaCl 108.99. What is the conductivity at infinite dilution of KF?

3. At 18°C. the specific resistance of 0.1 M solution of acetic acid is 2140 ohms. The conductivity at infinite dilution of acetic acid at this temperature is 347 reciprocal ohms. Calculate the ionization constant of acetic acid at this temperature.

4. What is the oxonium ion concentration of a solution containing 0.1 M acetic acid, and 0.01 M sodium acetate? Of a solution containing 0.01 M acetic acid, and 0.1 M sodium acetate? Of one containing 0.01 molar acetic acid, and 0.01 molar sodium acetate?

5. What is the sulfide ion concentration of 0.3 M solution of hydrochloric acid saturated with hydrogen sulfide at room temperature and atmospheric pressure?

6. Could a separation of lead and barium ions be based upon the difference in solubility of the respective sulfates? Could barium and calcium ions be separated by sulfate precipitation?

7. Calculate the limits between which the sulfide ion concentration must lie in order that 0.0001 M lead ion shall give a precipitate of lead sulfide and 0.025 M ferrous ion shall give no precipitate. Between what limits must the oxonium ion concentration lie if this separation is to be made by saturating the solution with hydrogen sulfide?

8. What mathematical relation must exist between the concentration of Pb^{++} and the concentration of OH_3^+ in a solution from which PbS has been precipitated by saturation with H_2S under the usual conditions of temperature and pressure?

9. Would you use a buffer solution to obtain an oxonium ion concentration of 0.1 M?

10. In this chapter the solubility product principle has been derived from the law of chemical equilibrium for the weak electrolyte H_2S. Why can it not be derived for a strong electrolyte in the same way?

11. The specific resistance of a 0.01 N solution of lactic acid is 2540 ohms. The conductivity at infinite dilution is 360 r. o. Calculate the ionization constant.

12. The specific resistance of a 0.04 M solution of ammonia is 4400 ohms. The conductivity at infinite dilution is 271 r. o. What is the ionization constant of ammonia?

13. Calculate the oxonium ion concentration of 0.1 M solutions of each of the following, boric acid, nitrous acid, phosphoric acid. Calculate the oxonium ion concentration of solutions containing each of these acids at 0.1 M concentration plus the corresponding sodium salt, likewise at 0.1 M concentration.

14. Calculate the hydroxyl ion concentration of a 0.1 M solution of ammonia; of a solution containing 0.01 M ammonia and 0.01 M ammonium chloride.

15. Calculate the concentrations of oxonium ion, bisulfite ion, and sulfite ion in a 0.1 M solution of sulfur dioxide; in a 0.1 M solution of sodium bisulfite.

CHAPTER IV

THE IONIZATION OF WATER: ACIDITY AND BASICITY: HYDROLYSIS

The Ionization Equilibrium of Water.—A solvent like water, which is itself both an acid and a base, must necessarily enter into protolytic reactions with every other acid and base which may be present. A state of equilibrium for the solution as a whole can exist only if the conditions for equilibrium in all these possible reactions are satisfied. We have previously considered two reaction types, one in which the base water reacts with an electrically neutral acid like acetic acid

$$HC_2H_3O_2 + H_2O \rightleftarrows OH_3^+ + C_2H_3O_2^- \tag{1}$$

and one in which the acid water reacts with an electrically neutral base like ammonia.

$$NH_3 + H_2O \rightleftarrows NH_4^+ + OH^-. \tag{2}$$

We shall next consider the ionization of water, which consists in the transfer of a hydrogen ion from one water molecule to another

$$2H_2O \rightleftarrows OH_3^+ + OH^-. \tag{3}$$

In applying the law of chemical equilibrium, we may include the constant concentration of water in the equilibrium constant just as we did on page 50 and thus obtain the equation

$$[OH_3^+][OH^-] = K_w \tag{4}$$

instead of one involving the square of the water concentration in the denominator which we should have to use if the water concentration were not for all practical purposes constant.

The extent of this reaction and the value of the constant may be determined, although with some difficulty, from measurements of the conductivity of pure water. The difficulty resides in the preparation of really pure water and in obtaining any assurance that it is sufficiently free from impurities of carbon dioxide, ammonia, and other electrolytes. Fortunately, the same value for the constant is obtained by several indirect methods, one of which, that depending upon hydrolysis, we shall discuss shortly, as from the conductivity measurement.

The Water Constant.—The value of the constant for the ionization of water thus obtained is 1×10^{-14} at 25°C. The constant is much more dependent upon temperature than most ionization constants; it increases with rising temperature and reaches a value of 5×10^{-13} at 100°C. Like all other constants for reactions which involve the formation of ions in solution, its value increases considerably with increasing ionic strength.

Oxonium and Hydroxyl Ion Concentrations: pH.—Because of the equilibrium relationship [Eq. (4)] the concentration of oxonium ion in an aqueous solution cannot be zero; a zero value of oxonium ion concentration would require an infinite, that is to say, an impossibly large, concentration of hydroxyl ion. For the same reason no aqueous solution can be free from hydroxyl ions. Furthermore, for any given oxonium ion concentration there is at a given temperature and ionic strength one, and only one, hydroxyl ion concentration possible; if either oxonium ion concentration or hydroxyl ion concentration is fixed, the other is also; if one is known the other may be calculated from the equilibrium equation. For dilute aqueous solutions the whole set of properties which are called acidity, alkalinity, neutrality may be taken as functions of either oxonium ion or hydroxyl ion concentration, but there would be an unnecessary complication if we were to use oxonium ion concentration in acid solutions and then shift suddenly to hydroxyl ion concentration in alkaline solutions to describe what is really the same thing. It is the usual convention to state the oxonium ion concentration of a solution whether it is acid or alkaline.

When we are working with aqueous solutions, it is convenient to call a neutral solution one which possesses equal concentrations of oxonium and hydroxyl ions. Pure water is therefore neutral. In a neutral solution of low ionic strength

$$\text{at 25°C., } [OH_3^+] = [OH^-] = \sqrt{K_w} = 1 \times 10^{-7} \qquad (5)$$
$$\text{at 100°C., } [OH_3^+] = [OH^-] = 7 \times 10^{-7}. \qquad (6)$$

Similarly, when we are talking about dilute aqueous solutions, we call a solution acid when its oxonium ion concentration is greater than its hydroxyl ion concentration, and we call it alkaline when its hydroxyl ion concentration is greater than its oxonium ion concentration. At 25°C. an acid solution in water is one whose oxonium ion concentration is greater than 1×10^{-7}; an alkaline solution one whose oxonium ion concentration is less than this value.

Acidity and alkalinity of aqueous solutions are frequently stated in terms of the value of the pH, the negative logarithm of the oxonium ion concentration. That is, if the oxonium ion concentration is 0.1 or 1×10^{-1}, the pH is 1, if the oxonium ion concentration is 10^{-7} (the solution is neutral), the pH is 7. If the oxonium ion concentration is 2×10^{-3}, the pH is $3 - \log 2$, or 2.7.

The Measure of Acidity and Basicity.—Oxonium and hydroxyl ions as criteria of acidity and basicity are, however, limited to dilute aqueous solutions. More fundamentally we must recognize that a strongly acid solution is one which has a very great tendency to transfer hydrogen ions to dissolved bases; a weakly acid solution is one which has little tendency to do this. Similarly, a strongly basic solution is one which has a great tendency to take hydrogen ions from dissolved acids. If therefore we wish to compare the acidity of a solution in some other medium with that of an aqueous solution, we shall have to determine the extent to which some base whose strength is known in water ionizes in the other solution. If we represent the base by the symbol B and the cation or acid produced by its ionization by BH^+, then the measure of acidity becomes the ionization ratio $[BH^+]/[B]$. In this way it has been determined that the acidity of pure sulfuric acid is nearly 10^{11} times greater than that of an aqueous solution with an oxonium ion concentration of 1 mole per liter.

This scale of acidity becomes proportional to the oxonium ion concentration in dilute aqueous solutions, and may be made identical with the oxonium ion concentration by suitable choice of the proportionality constant. This is so because there must be equilibrium between the base B and the oxonium ion according to the equations

$$B + OH_3^+ \rightleftarrows BH^+ + H_2O \tag{7}$$

and

$$\frac{[BH^+]}{[B][OH_3{}^+]} = K \quad \text{or} \quad \frac{[BH^+]}{[B]} = K[OH_3{}^+]. \quad (8)$$

Indicators.—A direct and frequently a satisfactory method of determining the acidity or basicity of solutions both in the region of dilute aqueous solutions and in other systems depends upon the use of indicators. An indicator consists of a conjugate acid-base system in which the acid has a different color from the base. (The reason for this difference in color has been a matter of considerable interest to the organic chemist; for the use of these substances as indicators the fact that there is a difference in color is sufficient.) Thus, in the case of methyl orange, the acid is red and the base is yellow; the strength of the acid is such that practically all of the substance will be in the acid form at pH's less than 3 and practically all will be in the form of the base when the pH is greater than 4.5. When a little of the indicator is added to a solution whose acidity lies between these limits, the shade of color produced is characteristic of the acidity. It is thus possible to determine the acidity of a solution by comparison of the color exhibited by the indicator in the unknown solution with that which it shows in solutions of known acidity.

Phenolphthalein, another common indicator, has a colorless neutral acid which loses one hydrogen ion to form a likewise colorless singly charged anion, but loses a second hydrogen ion to form a doubly charged anion with an intense red color. The constant for the second ionization is so small that the concentration of the red form is too small to be detected at pH's below 8. Practically all of the substance is converted to the red form at pH's above 10. Between these limits, therefore, the intensity of the red color produced when a small amount of phenolphthalein is added to a solution, is a measure of the alkalinity of the solution. Indicators are known which may be used for the determination of acidity and basicity in any range from strongly alkaline aqueous solutions to pure sulfuric acid.

We have previously used methyl orange to show that a dilute aqueous solution of acetic acid contains less oxonium ion than a solution of the same concentration of hydrochloric acid (page 47).

Some further experiments will illustrate the way in which indicators follow changes in acidity. Thus methyl orange added to a dilute solution of acetic acid is largely converted to the red acid form; when sodium acetate is added, the color reverts to the yellow form because of the decreased acidity produced by the acetate ion. Phenolphthalein turns intensely red when added to a dilute solution of ammonia; when an ammonium salt is added, the intensity of the color decreases because of the decreased hydroxyl ion concentration.

Hydrolysis.—This name is given to several types of reaction of very great importance, all of which involve positively charged acids, negatively charged bases, or both. Three commonly encountered types are the following:

$$C_2H_3O_2^- + H_2O \rightleftarrows HC_2H_3O_2 + OH^- \tag{9}$$
$$NH_4^+ + H_2O \rightleftarrows NH_3 + OH_3^+ \tag{10}$$
$$NH_4^+ + C_2H_3O_2^- \rightleftarrows NH_3 + HC_2H_3O_2. \tag{11}$$

The first of these occurs in any solution of a salt formed by the neutralization of a strong base (NaOH) by a weak acid ($HC_2H_3O_2$); the second in a solution of a salt formed from a strong acid (HCl) and a weak base (NH_3); the third in the solution of a salt formed from a weak acid ($HC_2H_3O_2$) and a weak base (NH_3). That such reactions as 9, 10, and 11 actually do take place is very easily shown. Potassium cyanide, sodium sulfide, sodium carbonate, and other salts of weak acids with strong bases react alkaline with indicators, produce precipitates of the hydroxide in solutions of salts of aluminum and ferric iron, and have to a pronounced extent the properties of hydroxyl ion. A precipitate of aluminum hydroxide can result only if the product $[Al^{+++}][OH^-]^3$ becomes greater than the solubility product constant; that is, the precipitate forms only if the concentration of hydroxyl ion in the solution is increased over the value which it had before the addition of the carbonate, cyanide, or other hydrolyzed salt. But potassium cyanide or sodium carbonate does not contain hydroxyl ion or even its elements, and the hydroxyl ion can only have been derived from water by a reaction of hydrolysis. As other evidence we may note that a potassium cyanide solution has an easily detected vapor pressure of HCN, and that a solution of ammonium sulfide has large vapor pressures of both NH_3 and H_2S. In fact, no solid product is obtained when a solution of the latter salt is evaporated because the ammonia and hydrogen sulfide produced by the hydrolysis evaporate, and further hydrolysis then takes place until finally the salt has disappeared before the water has.

The Relation between Hydrolysis Constant and Ionization Constant.—Application of the law of chemical equilibrium to the hydrolysis of potassium cyanide

$$CN^- + H_2O \rightleftarrows HCN + OH^- \tag{12}$$

gives the equation

$$\frac{[HCN][OH^-]}{[CN^-]} = K_{hyd} \tag{13}$$

in which K_{hyd} is the *hydrolysis constant*. Besides this equilibrium the solution must, however, be in equilibrium with respect to the ionization of the HCN formed by the hydrolysis, and any aqueous solution must be in equilibrium with respect to the ionization of water. Therefore the concentrations of the various components of the solution must satisfy the equations

$$\frac{[OH_3^+][CN^-]}{[HCN]} = K_{HCN} \tag{14}$$

and

$$[OH_3^+][OH^-] = K_w. \tag{15}$$

If, now, we divide Eq. (15) by Eq. (14), the concentration of oxonium ion cancels out and we obtain the equation

$$\frac{[HCN][OH^-]}{[CN^-]} = \frac{K_w}{K_{HCN}}. \tag{16}$$

Comparing this with Eq. (13), we see that the hydrolysis constant must equal the ratio of the ionization constants of water and of HCN

$$K_{hyd} = \frac{K_w}{K_{HCN}} \tag{17}$$

because both quantities are equal to the ratio $[HCN][OH^-]/[CN^-]$.

A number of interesting calculations may be made with Eq. (16). Let us limit ourselves first to the case that potassium cyanide is dissolved in water, because in that case the concentrations of HCN and of OH^- are equal. They are formed in equal amounts by the hydrolysis, there is no other important source of either, and neither is consumed by a further reaction. (If we used ammonium cyanide, the ammonium ion would react with the hydroxyl ion.) As in the ionization calculations, let c be the total or stoichiometric concentration of cyanide and α the fraction of the cyanide which has undergone the hydrolysis reaction. Then

$$[HCN] = [OH^-] = c\alpha \tag{18}$$
$$[CN^-] = c(1 - \alpha) \tag{19}$$

and substituting in Eq. (16),

$$\frac{c\alpha^2}{1 - \alpha} = \frac{K_w}{K_{HCN}}. \tag{20}$$

One of the most reliable methods for the determination of the important water constant, K_w, utilizes this equation. Suppose we determine the extent of hydrolysis of the sodium or potassium salt of some acid whose ionization constant has been measured. This is possible in several ways. We may determine the concentration of hydroxyl ions formed by the hydrolysis by the use of an indicator or in one of several other available methods; or we may determine the concentration of molecular acid formed, for instance, by measuring its vapor pressure from solution if it is volatile as hydrocyanic acid is. Substituting the values of c, K_{HCN}, and α in Eq. (20), we may calculate K_w.

Or we may calculate the ionization constant of a weak acid by measuring the extent of hydrolysis of one of its salts with a strong base. Substituting the known values of c, K_w, and α, we calculate the ionization constant. This method of determining ionization constants is frequently used with very weak acids and is especially useful for measuring the secondary and tertiary constants of polybasic acids.

Finally we may calculate the extent of hydrolysis, the concentration of the products of hydrolysis, and the pH of a solution of a salt of this type if the ionization constant of the weak acid formed in the hydrolysis is known. For the purpose of this calculation it is frequently sufficiently accurate to use an approximation formula derived, as in the similar case of the ionization formula (page 66), by neglecting α compared to 1. This gives

$$\alpha = \sqrt{\frac{K_w}{cK_a}} \qquad (21)$$

an equation valid when the hydrolysis is not too extensive.

In the case of a 0.1 M solution of potassium cyanide $c = 0.1$, $K_w = 1 \times 10^{-14}$, $K_a = 7 \times 10^{-10}$. The substitution gives $\alpha = 0.012$. This is sufficiently small compared with unity to justify the approximation involved in Eq. (21). By Eq. (18)

$$[OH^-] = [HCN] = 0.1 \times 0.012 = 0.0012.$$

Further

$$[OH_3^+] = \frac{K_w}{[OH^-]} = \frac{1 \times 10^{-14}}{1.2 \times 10^{-3}} = 0.8 \times 10^{-11}.$$

Taking the negative logarithm of this we find pH $= 11.1$.

Equation (20) permits some general deductions. The extent of hydrolysis of a salt is greater the weaker the acid formed in the hydrolysis, varying inversely as the square root of the ionization constant. Similarly the hydrolysis varies directly as the square root of the ionization constant of water, and since this increases 50 times when the temperature is raised from 25 to 100°C., this temperature rise increases the hydrolysis 7 times. Finally, the fraction hydrolyzed varies inversely as the square root of the concentration of the salt. The concentration of the products of the hydrolysis which is equal to $\sqrt{cK_w/K_a}$ increases with increasing salt concentration, but only proportional to the square root of that concentration. Thus a hundred-fold increase in the concentration of potassium cyanide would result in only a tenfold increase in the concentration of hydroxyl ion.

The extent of hydrolysis of a salt may be considerably decreased by the addition of one of the products of the hydrolysis. Thus a solution containing 0.1 M potassium cyanide and 0.1 M hydrocyanic acid has a concentration of HCN which differs only slightly from 0.1 and a concentration of CN$^-$ which is likewise practically 0.1 M. Substitution in Eq. (16) gives $[OH^-] = 1.4 \times 10^{-5}$. This solution therefore has a hydroxyl ion concentration nearly 100 times smaller than one containing potassium cyanide alone.

Hydrolysis When the Base Is Weak and the Acid Strong.—In this case, of which ammonium chloride is an example, the hydrolysis produces an acid solution, the reaction being that shown in Eq. (10). The equilibrium equation for the hydrolysis is

$$\frac{[OH_3^+][NH_3]}{[NH_4^+]} = \frac{K_w}{K_{NH_3}}. \tag{22}$$

As an approximation when the degree of hydrolysis is small

$$\alpha = \sqrt{\frac{K_w}{cK_{NH_3}}}. \tag{23}$$

From this equation it may be calculated that the oxonium ion concentration of 0.1 M NH$_4$Cl is 7.5×10^{-6}. This is 75 times as large as that of pure water.

Hydrolysis When Both Acid and Base Are Weak.—In case both acid and base are weak, the hydrolysis must be greatly increased. For if an ammonium salt of a strong acid be supposed to have come to a state of equilibrium with a certain concentration of oxonium ion formed, the addition of acetate ion will be seen to necessitate further progress of the reaction by removing some of the oxonium ion. The total reaction for the hydrolysis of ammonium acetate is that given by Eq. (11), and combination of the equations

$$\frac{[NH_4^+][OH^-]}{[NH_3]} = K_{NH_3} \tag{24}$$

$$\frac{[OH_3^+][C_2H_3O_2^-]}{[HC_2H_3O_2]} = K_{HC_2H_3O_2} \tag{25}$$

and

$$[OH_3^+][OH^-] = K_w \tag{26}$$

all of which must be satisfied at equilibrium gives

$$\frac{[NH_3][HC_2H_3O_2]}{[NH_4^+][C_2H_3O_2^-]} = \frac{K_w}{K_{NH_3}K_{HC_2H_3O_2}}. \tag{27}$$

One interesting conclusion is that in this case the extent of the hydrolysis is independent of the concentration of the salt. For if all of the concentrations in the above equation were halved by the addition of water, the fraction would still have the same value, and no reaction would be necessary since the system would still be in equilibrium.

Calculation shows that ammonium acetate is 0.56 per cent hydrolyzed, whereas 0.1 M ammonium chloride or sodium acetate is only 0.0075 per cent hydrolyzed. Similarly 0.1 M KCN is 1.2 per cent hydrolyzed, but a salt of HCN with an equally weak base would be 99.3 per cent hydrolyzed.

The acidity or alkalinity of salts of this type may be predicted by a simple rule. If acid and base have equal ionization constants, as happens to be the case with ammonium acetate, the solution is neutral. For the ammonium ions react with hydroxyl ions to just the same extent that the acetate ions react with oxonium ions. If the base is the stronger electrolyte, the solution is alkaline. This is true of ammonium cyanide, ammonium carbonate, ammonium sulfide, which all react decidedly alkaline. If the acid is stronger the solution reacts acid.

Salts of Polybasic Acids.—The more complex-appearing case of a salt of a polybasic acid turns out fairly simply. For of the two successive reactions which might occur in a sodium carbonate solution

$$CO_3^= + H_2O \rightleftarrows HCO_3^- + OH^- \tag{28}$$
$$HCO_3^- \rightleftarrows CO_2 + OH^- \tag{29}$$

the first must far outweigh the second, for the ionization constant

$$K_2 = \frac{[OH_3^+][CO_3^=]}{[HCO_3^-]} \tag{30}$$

which determines the first reaction is much smaller than

$$K_1 = \frac{[OH_3^+][HCO_3^-]}{[CO_2]} \tag{31}$$

which determines the second. Furthermore, the second reaction takes place in a solution which contains the hydroxyl ions produced in the first step. The second reaction is therefore negligible, and the hydrolysis may be calculated by the formula used for a monobasic acid, the constant for the acid being the secondary ionization constant of carbonic acid. A 0.1 M sodium carbonate solution will have a hydroxyl ion concentration of 0.004 M, and be 4 per cent hydrolyzed.

The bicarbonate ion of a solution of $NaHCO_3$ can undergo two possible reactions:

$$HCO_3^- + H_2O \rightleftarrows OH_3^+ + CO_3^= \tag{32}$$
$$HCO_3^- \rightleftarrows OH^- + CO_2 \tag{33}$$

the first tending to make the solution acid, the second, to make it alkaline. With this salt the second is more important, and sodium bicarbonate solutions are distinctly alkaline—how alkaline may be calculated from the same formula, using this time the primary ionization constant of carbonic acid. This gives $[OH^-] = 5 \times 10^{-5}$, per cent hydrolyzed = 0.05 per cent.

On Reaction Mechanisms.—It is possible to suppose that the hydrolysis of cyanide ion consists in the direct transfer of hydrogen ion from a water molecule to a cyanide ion expressed in Eq. (12). But it is also entirely possible to suppose that it takes place in two successive steps, in the first of which water ionizes by Eq. (3)

$$2H_2O \rightleftarrows OH_3^+ + OH^- \tag{3}$$

while in the second cyanide ion reacts with the oxonium ion produced by that ionization

$$OH_3^+ + CN^- \rightleftarrows HCN + H_2O. \tag{34}$$

The removal of oxonium ion leads to a further ionization of water, and this leads to further reaction of oxonium and cyanide ions. The total effect is the same by the two-step process as by the one-step process. In both cases one water molecule and one cyanide ion react, in both cases one molecule of hydrocyanic acid and one hydroxyl ion are formed. In the two-step process oxonium ion is produced in the first step, but it is consumed in the second. If we treat our reaction equations according to the rules for algebraic equations, they take account of this situation very satisfactorily. Thus the addition of Eqs. (3) and (34) gives

$$2H_2O + OH_3^+ + CN^- \rightleftarrows OH_3^+ + OH^- + HCN + H_2O \tag{35}$$

and cancellation of the oxonium ion and the one molecule of water which appear on both sides gives Eq. (12)

$$H_2O + CN^- \rightleftarrows HCN + OH^-. \tag{12}$$

The law of chemical equilibrium gives no assistance in mechanism problems. The development leading to Eqs. (16) and (17) on page 85 might seem to favor the two-step process because the equilibrium equation for the hydrolysis reaction is derived from the equations for the reactions under consideration as possible steps, but the appearance is misleading. The argument involved in that development utilized the fact that the solution must be in equilibrium with respect to the reactions expressed by Eqs. (3) and (34); in no way was it assumed that these were steps in the hydrolysis.

Only when the reaction rates can be measured is it possible to decide between such alternative mechanisms. As we have seen (page 49) the rate of a reaction is proportional to the product of the concentrations of the reactants; it is independent of the concentrations of the substances produced in the reaction. This method has been used to settle a question about the reactions of carbon dioxide. It has been usually supposed that carbon dioxide dissolves in water to form carbonic acid

$$CO_2 + H_2O \rightleftarrows H_2CO_3 \tag{36}$$

that this ionizes

$$H_2CO_3 + H_2O \rightleftarrows OH_3^+ + HCO_3^- \tag{37}$$

and that the oxonium ion reacts with hydroxyl ion if the solution is alkaline

$$OH_3^+ + OH^- \rightleftarrows 2H_2O. \tag{38}$$

Adding Eqs. (36), (37), and (38), we obtain

$$CO_2 + OH^- \rightleftarrows HCO_3^- \tag{39}$$

which is the total reaction occurring when carbon dioxide dissolves in a moderately alkaline solution. Obviously this reaction might take place directly instead of through the three steps, in fact, we know from reaction-rate studies that it does go directly. The rate of the reaction is slow enough to permit measurement, and it has been found that it is proportional to the product of the concentrations of hydroxyl ion and of carbon dioxide. This is obviously in agreement with a one-step reaction, whereas the rate of the three-step reaction must be independent of the hydroxyl ion concentration.   The latter conclusion follows from the fact that reaction (38) is extremely rapid; therefore the slow reaction which determined the rate of the whole series of reactions would have to be (36) or (37); but these reactions do not consume hydroxyl ion; hence their rates should be independent of its concentration.

Although the hydrolysis of cyanide ion is too rapid to permit measurement, this is not true of all protolytic reactions.   In fact, the typical acid catalyzed reaction seems to consist of two or more steps of which the first is a simple transfer of a hydrogen ion from an acid to a molecule of sucrose or ethyl acetate or the like.   In the further steps of the reaction the cation produced in the first step reacts further producing among other products the original acid.   The acid therefore is not consumed; it is merely temporarily used and then regenerated.   Because the first step is slow compared with the later ones, the rate at which the whole series of reactions takes place is the rate of the first step, which is a simple protolytic reaction, the transfer of a hydrogen ion from an acid to a base.   The brilliant recent work of Brönsted and Pedersen in Denmark has shown from the study of such reactions that the rate of the reaction between a base and an acid is proportional to the concentration of the acid; that, when several acids are present, the base reacts simultaneously with all of them; and that the rate of reaction is greater the stronger the acid.

It seems therefore probable that the hydrolysis of cyanide ion takes place by both of the mechanisms we have discussed.   The one-step process [Eq. (12)] is a protolytic reaction between the base cyanide ion and the acid water; the two-step process depends upon the reaction of the base cyanide ion with the acid oxonium ion [Eq. (34)].   If the concentration of oxonium ion were equal to that of water, the reaction would undoubtedly go overwhelmingly by the two-step route, because oxonium ion is a much stronger acid than water.   But the water concentration is so much larger than the oxonium ion concentration that the one-step reaction probably takes place at a rate comparable to that of the two-step one.

On Writing Chemical-reaction Equations.—One of the most fundamental and necessary things we wish to know about any chemical reaction is its equation. If we know the equation, we can easily calculate the proportions by weight in which the various reactants enter into the reaction and in which the various reaction products are formed. We can also calculate the proportions by volume for gaseous reactions. Fortunately the problem of writing the equation for any reaction has a unique solution; given a set of reactants and products, there is only one chemically possible equation, only one proportion in which reaction can take place. By a chemically possible equation or a *balanced equation* we mean one which does not violate the fundamental chemical law of the conservation of the elements; one which does not represent an atom of oxygen or some other substance or an electric charge appearing from nowhere or vanishing into nothingness.

When a reaction is complicated, it is usually a great help in deriving its equation to imagine a series of steps by means of which the reaction might proceed. These steps are so chosen as to be simpler reactions for which it is easy to write equations. The equations for these steps are then combined algebraically to form an equation which involves only the actual reactants and products. If the equations for the steps were balanced, their combination will be balanced also; and since there is only one balanced equation involving a given set of reactants and products, the equation thus obtained for the reaction is necessarily the correct one.

This method of writing equations is a valuable expedient, one which is especially useful in writing complicated oxidation-reduction reactions, but it does have some psychological dangers. It is very difficult to avoid the attribution of some reality to a series of reaction steps which one has used in writing the equation for a reaction, but it is very important to do so. It is always possible to write more than one series of steps which would lead to the actual reaction, and the choice which we make between these possibilities depends partly upon mere chance, partly upon simplicity. Only by reaction-rate measurements if at all can we decide what the actual steps are by which a reaction proceeds.

In the case of the hydrolysis of cyanide ion we have considered two routes for the reaction and have concluded that it takes place to some extent by both routes. If, however, we had any difficulty in writing the equation for the reaction, the simplest way to derive it would be to suppose that a hydrogen ion dissociated from water, and that this then combined with cyanide ion.   The steps are

$$H_2O \rightleftarrows H^+ + OH^- \tag{40}$$

and

$$H^+ + CN^- \rightleftarrows HCN \tag{41}$$

and their combination by addition gives the correct equation for the hydrolysis [Eq. (12)].   These steps represent an imaginary and improbable route for the reaction, but writing equations for them is the easiest way to write a correct equation for it.

On the Form of Chemical-reaction Equations.—There are certain conventions about the final form of a chemical equation to which it is useful to adhere.   In the first place, we do not in general write in our equations the formulae of substances which are necessarily present but which do not actually enter into the reaction.   Thus we write the equation for the reaction of a strong acid and a strong base

$$OH_3^+ + OH^- \rightleftarrows 2H_2O \tag{42}$$

and not, for instance,

$$OH_3^+ + Cl^- + Na^+ + OH^- \rightleftarrows 2H_2O + Na^+ + Cl^-. \tag{43}$$

The first equation is obviously a much more general one, and it represents all that happens in the second one, because in the latter the sodium and chloride ions are present before the reaction takes place, and are still present in the same amount after it is over.

Secondly, when we have a decidedly weak electrolyte which may enter into reaction through its ions, we write the reaction in terms of the molecular substance rather than in terms of the ion.   Thus we write the equation for the reaction of acetic acid with sodium hydroxide in the form

$$HC_2H_3O_2 + OH^- \rightleftarrows C_2H_3O_2^- + H_2O \tag{44}$$

and not in the form

$$OH_3^+ + OH^- \rightleftarrows 2H_2O. \tag{45}$$

We write the equation for the precipitation of magnesium hydroxide with ammonia as

$$Mg^{++} + 2NH_3 + 2H_2O \rightleftarrows Mg(OH)_2 + 2NH_4^+ \qquad (46)$$

and not as

$$Mg^{++} + 2OH^- \rightleftarrows Mg(OH)_2. \qquad (47)$$

This convention has the advantage that the equation indicates that certain reaction products should tend to decrease the extent of the reaction. Thus Eq. (46) immediately suggests that ammonium salts should have a solvent action on magnesium hydroxide, as they do. This conclusion can, of course, be derived from Eq. (47) and a knowledge of the fact that ammonia is a weak base, but it is certainly not so obvious in this case.

Hydrolysis and the Precipitation of Salts.—The importance of hydrolysis in analytical chemistry is twofold: in the precipitation of salts, and in the precipitation of hydroxides. In the first case hydrolysis is a factor working against success. Because most salts are highly ionized, neutralization of a weak acid increases the concentration of the anion of the acid. But the existence of hydrolysis, which is incomplete neutralization, means that the addition of one equivalent of base to a solution of a weak acid will not give the maximum concentration of the anion, and the maximum tendency to precipitate a difficultly soluble salt. With most salts of strong bases this is not very serious. If potassium cyanide is 1.3 per cent hydrolyzed, only 1.3 per cent of the available cyanide ion is lost through hydrolysis. A 0.1 M sodium carbonate solution loses by hydrolysis only 4 per cent of its carbonate ion. In the case of sulfides the effect is much greater. A 0.1 M sodium sulfide solution has a sulfide ion concentration of only 0.001 M, the solution is 99 per cent hydrolyzed. A greater sulfide ion concentration may nevertheless be obtained if sodium hydroxide is added to the sodium sulfide solution. For in the equation

$$\frac{[OH^-][HS^-]}{[S^=]} = K = \frac{K_{H_2O}}{K_{HS^-}} \qquad (48)$$

an increase in the hydroxyl ion concentration necessitates a decrease in the concentration of SH^- and an increase in the concentration of $S^=$ by the reaction

$$SH^- + OH^- \leftrightarrows S^= + H_2O. \qquad (49)$$

This method of increasing the sulfide ion concentration becomes important in certain cases of sulfide complex formation (see page 124).

But the ammonium salts of weak acids are much more hydrolyzed than are the sodium salts, and their solutions contain therefore smaller concentrations of the anion. While 0.1 *M* sodium carbonate solution contains 0.096 *M* carbonate ion, ammonium carbonate solution of the same concentration contains only 0.024 *M* carbonate ion.

If the solubility product constant of magnesium carbonate is 1×10^{-5}, it may be calculated from these figures for the carbonate ion concentrations that 0.1 *M* sodium carbonate will give a precipitate with 1×10^{-4} *M* magnesium ion, whereas 0.1 *M* ammonium carbonate would require 4×10^{-4} *M* magnesium ion. Since the precipitation of the carbonate is of no importance as a means of detecting magnesium ion, and is desirable only as a means of removing magnesium ion in order that the filtrate can be tested for sodium ion without interference, the ammonium salt must nevertheless be used. This becomes possible, as was shown by Bray, if the carbonate ion concentration is increased by the addition of a large excess of ammonia, which holds back on the hydrolysis reaction

$$CO_3^= + NH_4^+ \rightleftarrows HCO_3^- + NH_3 \qquad (50)$$

and if the solubility product constant is decreased by the addition of alcohol (see page 44).

The precipitation of magnesium ammonium phosphate offers a somewhat similar problem. Phosphate ion is the ion of a very weak acid ($HPO_4^=$), and an alkaline solution is necessary if a large concentration of phosphate ion is to be obtained. But the precipitation of magnesium ammonium phosphate depends upon the ion product

$$[Mg^{++}][NH_4^+][PO_4^=]. \qquad (51)$$

A high concentration of ammonium ion and a strongly alkaline solution are incompatible because of the reaction

$$NH_4^+ + OH^- \rightleftarrows NH_3 + H_2O \qquad (52)$$

and some sort of compromise is necessary. If the solution contains an ammonium salt the ammonium ion concentration will be large, and if ammonia is added, the solution will be as alkaline as any solution containing a large concentration of ammonium ion can be. Under these conditions the precipitation is satisfactory.

If the ammonium salt is omitted and the solution is made alkaline with ammonia, the ammonium ion concentration will be small, because ammonia is not highly ionized; and the hydroxyl ion concentration will be larger than in the presence of ammonium salt (see page 54). The precipitate formed under these conditions is $Mg_3(PO_4)_2$ instead of $MgNH_4PO_4$. This is a disadvantage because $Mg_3(PO_4)_2$ is gelatinous and similar in appearance to $Ca_3(PO_4)_2$ and the other alkaline-earth phosphates. The formation of the crystalline $MgNH_4PO_4$ is evidence that the removal of the other alkaline-earth ions, which is a necessary prerequisite for the performance of the magnesium test, has been sufficiently complete. From the point of view of quantitative analysis the crystalline precipitate is to be preferred also because it is more definite in composition and less prone to occlusion than is the gelatinous one.

Whenever magnesium ammonium phosphate is to be precipitated a high concentration of ammonium ion is desirable because the precipitate is an ammonium salt. When the precipitation is made as a test for magnesium ion, this is the only function of the addition of ammonium salt. No precipitate can form unless magnesium ion is present and if a precipitate does form it will be either $MgNH_4PO_4$ or $Mg_3(PO_4)_2$. When the same precipitate or the similar magnesium ammonium arsenate is used as a test for phosphate or arsenate, there is an additional function of the ammonium salt. The solution contains a high concentration of magnesium ion added as a reagent, and there is the possibility that magnesium hydroxide may precipitate. The presence of ammonium salt prevents this because it is impossible to get a concentration of hydroxyl ion large enough to precipitate magnesium hydroxide in a solution which contains much ammonium ion.

The general method of precipitating salts of weak acids is to make the solution alkaline if the precipitate does not appear in acid or neutral solution. This method fails however in many cases because the hydroxide of the metal precipitates instead of the desired salt.

Hydrolysis and the Precipitation of Hydroxides.—The precipitation of hydroxides by salts is especially important in the case of the hydroxides of aluminum, chromium, and ferric iron. The principle is simple. Aluminum hydroxide can precipitate only if the product

$$[Al^{+++}][OH^-]^3$$

exceeds a certain value. Given a solution of an aluminum salt the only way to precipitate the hydroxide is to increase the concentration of hydroxyl ion. Such reagents as ammonium sulfide or sodium carbonate are alkaline, do increase the hydroxyl ion concentration, and do precipitate aluminum hydroxide instead of the sulfide or carbonate, which are incapable of existence in the presence of water. The reactions are

$$2Al^{+++} + 3S^= + 6H_2O \rightleftarrows 2Al(OH)_3 + 3H_2S \qquad (53)$$
$$2Al^{+++} + 3CO_3^= + 3H_2O \rightleftarrows 2Al(OH)_3 + 3CO_2. \qquad (54)$$

These relatively complex equations furnish useful examples of the general methods of writing equations which we have recently discussed. We may suppose that the reaction proceeds by the liberation of hydroxyl ion by hydrolysis of the sulfide. This hydrolysis itself may be thought of as proceeding by the steps

$$S^= + H_2O \rightleftarrows HS^- + OH^- \qquad (55)$$

and

$$HS^- + H_2O \rightleftarrows H_2S + OH^-. \qquad (56)$$

Addition of these gives

$$S^= + 2H_2O \rightleftarrows H_2S + 2OH^-. \qquad (57)$$

We may then suppose that the hydroxyl ion thus formed reacts with aluminum ion

$$Al^{+++} + 3OH^- \rightleftarrows Al(OH)_3. \qquad (58)$$

To combine Eqs. (57) and (58), we note that since one aluminum ion reacts with three hydroxyl ions, we shall have to have some multiple of three hydroxyl ions produced by the sulfide hydrolysis. The smallest possible value is 6, and to obtain 6 hydroxyl ions by the reaction of Eq. (57), we require that 3 sulfide ions and 6 water molecules react, and that 3 molecules of hydrogen sulfide be formed. That is, we must multiply Eq. (57) by 3 term by term. The 6 hydroxyl ions suffice for the reaction of 2 aluminum ions and produce 2 molecules of aluminum hydroxide. The equations thus become

$$3S^= + 6H_2O \rightleftarrows 3H_2S + 6OH^- \tag{59}$$

and

$$2Al^{+++} + 6OH^- \rightleftarrows 2Al(OH)_3. \tag{60}$$

Adding and canceling the 6 hydroxyl ions which appear on both sides of the resulting equation, we obtain Eq. (53). We may note that we could equally well have used the steps

$$Al^{+++} + 3H_2O \rightleftarrows Al(OH)_3 + 3H^+ \tag{61}$$

and

$$S^= + 2H^+ \rightleftarrows H_2S. \tag{62}$$

Obvious steps to use in writing Eq. (54) are

$$CO_3^= + H_2O \rightleftarrows CO_2 + 2OH^- \tag{63}$$

and Eq. (58).

The Basic-acetate Precipitation.—It is not even necessary in order to precipitate aluminum hydroxide that the hydroxyl ion concentration increase sufficiently to make the solution alkaline, for the addition of sodium or ammonium acetate to a solution of an aluminum salt causes a quantitative precipitation of the aluminum when the solution is boiled. Under these conditions the hydroxide occludes acetate ion so largely that the precipitate is usually called aluminum basic acetate, but the phenomenon differs only in degree and not in kind from the occlusion of every anion in the solution which takes place with this precipitate. The reaction is

$$Al^{+++} + 3C_2H_3O_2^- + 3H_2O \rightleftarrows Al(OH)_3 + 3HC_2H_3O_2 \tag{64}$$

and a test with litmus shows that the solution in which the precipitate is suspended is appreciably acid. Ferric ion gives a similar reaction, but the other familiar trivalent ion, chromic ion, does not.   If then aluminum hydroxide can precipitate in a solution whose hydroxyl ion concentration is less than that of water, why does it not precipitate to some extent when aluminum chloride is dissolved in water?   The solution of aluminum chloride is acid to litmus, therefore some hydrolysis has taken place. One product of this hydrolysis is oxonium ion, but the other is not aluminum hydroxide, and the reaction is not so simple as

$$Al^{+++} + 6H_2O \rightleftarrows Al(OH)_3 + 3OH_3^+. \qquad (65)$$

The solution of this problem involves the nature of colloidal solutions, and will be discussed in a later chapter (page 128).

Some Separations by Hydroxide Precipitation.—The hydroxides of aluminum, chromium, and ferric iron are materially less soluble than those of nickel, cobalt, manganese, zinc, and of magnesium and the other alkaline earths.   There is, however, no real correlation between valence and solubility, for the bivalent stannous hydroxide is as insoluble as any of the trivalent hydroxides, and the trivalent lanthanum hydroxide is as soluble as any of the bivalent hydroxides except those of the alkaline earths.

A most important separation based upon these differences is that in which aluminum, chromic, and ferric ions are separated from the alkaline earths.   This may be done by adding ammonia in the presence of an ammonium salt.   The ammonium salt furnishes a high concentration of ammonium ion, which decreases the ionization of the ammonia and keeps the hydroxyl ion concentration at a low value.   Such a hydroxyl ion concentration is sufficient to precipitate quantitatively the hydroxides of aluminum, chromium, and ferric iron, but it is insufficient to exceed the solubility product constant of magnesium hydroxide or of the other more soluble alkaline-earth hydroxides.   It should be noted that magnesium hydroxide can be precipitated from a moderately concentrated solution by the addition of ammonia if the ammonium ion concentration of the solution is small.

The separation fails, however, when the solution contains ions like phosphate or oxalate which form difficultly soluble salts with the alkaline earths.   Although calcium or magnesium hydroxides do not precipitate in the slightly alkaline solution used to precipitate ferric or aluminum hydroxides, the phosphates or oxalates of these metals do precipitate if these anions are present in the solution. Oxalate ion may be removed by oxidation or ignition, but this cannot be done with phosphate. In the presence of phosphate ion, the amphoteric properties of aluminum hydroxide, and the possibility of oxidizing chromic salts to chromates are relied upon to separate aluminum and chromium from the alkaline earths, but iron must be separated in acid solution by the basic-acetate precipitation.

Suggestions for Reading

General: GETMAN-DANIELS, *op. cit.*, pp. 410–418; CLARK, "The Determination of Hydrogen Ions," chs. I–IX, Baltimore, 1928.

Acidity: KILPATRICK, *J. Chem. Education*, **9**, 1010; 1227 (1930); HAMMETT, *Chem. Rev.* **16**, 67 (1935); GLASSTONE, *op. cit.*, ch. X; also the other references cited in ch. I.

Reaction kinetics: GETMAN-DANIELS, *op. cit.*, ch. IV.

Reaction mechanisms: BRAY, *Chem. Rev.*, **10**, 161 (1932).

Calculations: ENGELDER, *op. cit.*, ch. VIII.

Exercises

1. What is the pH of each of the solutions referred to in problems 4, 13, 14, and 15, of Chap. III?

2. Calculate the oxonium ion concentration and the pH of 0.1 M solutions of each of the following salts: $NaNO_2$, NH_4Cl, Na_2HPO_4.

3. What is the concentration of HCN in a solution containing 0.1 M KCN and 0.1 M KOH?

4. Letting α be the fraction hydrolyzed, derive from Eq. (27) an equation analogous to Eq. (21) for the case of ammonium acetate.

5. What happens to the oxonium ion concentration of a solution of sodium acetate when the solution is raised from 25 to 100°C.?

6. What is the sulfide ion concentration of a solution containing 0.1 M Na_2S and 0.1 M NaOH?

7. Explain why solutions of NaH_2PO_4 are weakly acid, solutions of Na_2HPO_4 weakly alkaline, and solutions of Na_3PO_4 strongly alkaline.

8. When potassium thiocyanate is added to a very dilute ferric salt solution, the pink color is considerably increased in intensity by the addition of hydrochloric or nitric acid. Explain.

9. Ammonium sulfide precipitates aluminum hydroxide from a solution of an aluminum salt. Will hydrogen sulfide do the same?

10. BiOCl dissolves in water according to the equation

$$BiOCl + H_2O \rightleftarrows Bi^{+++} + 2OH^- + Cl^-$$

Write the equation for the solubility product. Explain why BiOCl can be precipitated by the addition of NH_4Cl to a solution of $Bi(NO_3)_3$;

why HCl dissolves BiOCl; and why the precipitate forms again when the solution in HCl is diluted.

11. Name the substances present in a dilute solution of sodium carbonate and indicate whether the concentration of each is large or small.

12. Will $Mg(OH)_2$ precipitate when equal volumes of 0.1 M $MgCl_2$ and 0.1 M KCN are mixed?

13. $Mg(OH)_2$ dissolves easily in NH_4Cl solution. Write the reaction that takes place and explain.

CHAPTER V

COMPLEX COMPOUNDS

Hydration of Ions.—It is probable that metallic ions in aqueous solution are hydrated, that is to say, combined with water, in much the same way that hydrogen ion is hydrated to oxonium ion. Yet we are forced to rely upon indirect methods for the determination of the extent of the hydration. There is, of course, no method for analyzing an ion while it is in solution, and the determination of the composition of solid compounds of the ion, which is sufficient to settle most questions about the composition of ions in solution, cannot settle this one, because the process of solution may be accompanied by further hydration.

We shall illustrate the various indirect methods of estimating the extent of hydration of a metallic ion on two examples, cobaltous ion and cupric ion. Cobaltous ion as it exists in a dilute aqueous solution has a characteristic pink color. An identical pink color is possessed by those solid salts which contain 6 or more molecules of water for every cobalt ion, whereas the anhydrous salts and the hydrates with less than 6 molecules of water have different colors ($CoCl_2$ is blue, $CoSO_4$ is nearly white). Further an extremely large proportion of cobalt salts crystallize from water with 6 molecules of so-called water of crystallization. This includes the chloride, the bromide, the iodide, and the nitrate. The sulfate contains 7 molecules of water, but it is so general a rule that metallic sulfates contain one more molecule of water than other salts of the same metal that we can with some assurance assign one water molecule to the sulfate ion leaving 6 for the cobaltous ion. Finally the coordination number, the capacity for combination which a metallic ion possesses, tends to be the same for all of its compounds. Thus the cobaltous ammonia complex contains 6 ammonia molecules, $Co(NH_3)_6^{++}$, and the cobaltocyanide complex contains 6 cyanide ions, $Co(CN)_6^{\equiv}$. The cumulative effect of these various evidences makes it very probable that the formula of cobaltous ion in dilute aqueous solution is $Co(H_2O)_6^{++}$.

In the case of cupric ion the familiar blue color appears in solid salts only when they contain at least 4 molecules of water ($CuSO_4$ is white, the familiar blue vitriol contains 5 molecules of water). The coordination number of cupric ion is consistently 4. Hence it is probable that the formula of cupric ion in dilute aqueous solution is $Cu(H_2O)_4^{++}$.

In many cases the evidence is less compelling, and it is therefore an accepted convention to write the formulas of metallic ions in chemical equations as if they were anhydrous, even though they are known to be hydrated. This avoids a decision on the number of water molecules to write in the formula.

So long as we are concerned only with dilute aqueous solutions the hydration of the ions makes very little difference (if it did make a difference, the difference could be used to calculate the extent of hydration). This is because the concentration of water is practically constant in such solutions (see page 50). Suppose we have a metallic ion, whose total concentration in solution is c_M. Let $[M^{++}]$ be the concentration of the anhydrous ion, and $[M(H_2O)_6^{++}]$ the concentration of a hydrate. Then $c_M = [M^{++}] + [M(H_2O)_6^{++}]$. Consider the precipitation of a difficultly soluble salt MX. This can take place only if the solubility product principle in the form

$$[M^{++}][X^=] = K_s \tag{1}$$

is satisfied. There must be in the solution an equilibrium between hydrated and anhydrous ions which satisfies the equation

$$\frac{[M^{++}][H_2O]^6}{[M(H_2O)_6^{++}]} = K_e. \tag{2}$$

Dividing Eq. (1) by (2) and rearranging the result slightly, we have

$$[M(H_2O)_6^{++}][X^=] = \frac{K_s}{K_e}[H_2O]^6. \tag{3}$$

Adding (1) and (3), we obtain

$$\{[M^{++}] + [M(H_2O)_6^{++}]\}[X^=] = K_s + \frac{K_s}{K_e}[H_2O]^6. \tag{4}$$

The terms on the right are all constant in dilute aqueous solution; the quantity $\{[M^{++}] + [M(H_2O)_6^{++}]\}$ is equal to c_M. Equation (4) is therefore equivalent to the equation

$$c_M[X^=] = \text{a constant.} \qquad (5)$$

The fact that this equation is valid for the precipitation of anhydrous salts of hydrated ions gives no information about the state of hydration of the cation. It would be valid if all of the ion were in the anhydrous form, it would be valid with any proportion of hydrated and anhydrous ions.

The same considerations apply to all other equilibria in a dilute aqueous solution; so long as the concentration of water is practically constant, no information about hydration of ions can be gained from the application of the equilibrium law. And if we change the water concentration by any large amount, we change the nature of the medium in which the reaction takes place and this in itself changes the values of all the equilibrium constants.

The Behavior of Amphoteric Hydroxides.—If sodium hydroxide is added to a solution of a zinc salt a precipitate of $Zn(OH)_2$ appears at first, and then redissolves upon further addition of sodium hydroxide. Potassium hydroxide and other soluble highly ionized hydroxides act in the same way, but sodium or potassium chloride or sulfate do not. These facts are sufficient to prove that the solution of the precipitate is not due to the salt effect by which all solubility product constants are somewhat increased by increase in total ion concentration, that it is not dependent upon the presence of sodium ion or any other particular cation, but that it is a specific reaction of the hydroxyl ion of the strong base.

The simplest interpretation of these results is that suggested by Pfeiffer. According to this zinc ion can combine with more than 2 hydroxyl ions to form a hydroxyl complex ion, the reaction being

$$Zn^{++} + 4OH^- \rightleftarrows Zn(OH)_4^=. \qquad (6)$$

(The choice of the figure 4 for the number of hydroxyl ions in the complex ion is based upon evidence which we shall present later. See page 107.) With small concentrations of hydroxyl ion the precipitation takes place because it requires only 2 hydroxyl ions for each zinc ion; with larger concentrations the complex formation, which requires 4 hydroxyl ions is favored. The ion $Zn(OH)_4^=$ is called zincate ion, the corresponding salts are called zincates.

Zincate ion carries a negative charge and it should therefore migrate toward the anode in electrolysis. This prediction can easily be verified, but it is important to distinguish the migration from the electrode processes. Zinc metal deposits on the cathode from a zincate solution, but this is no more to be taken as evidence that zincate ion is positively charged than is the fact that permanganate ion can be reduced to manganous ion at a cathode to be considered evidence that permanganate ion has a positive charge (see pages 20 and 133). To investigate the migration, we must see what happens to the concentration of zinc in the anode and cathode portions of the solution during the electrolysis. We then find that this concentration increases in the anode portion, and that the total amount of zinc in the cathode portion (including the metal deposited on the electrode as well as that in the solution) decreases during the electrolysis. This can only be the case if the larger part of the zinc present in the solution is in the form of a negative ion.

The Equilibrium between Cation and Anion.—Application of the law of chemical equilibrium to Eq. (6) gives

$$\frac{[Zn^{++}][OH^-]^4}{[Zn(OH)_4^=]} = K_e. \qquad (7)$$

It will be seen that no solution of a zinc salt can be entirely free from zincate; the concentration of zincate ion cannot be zero unless the concentration of zinc ion or of hydroxyl ion is also zero. But the hydroxyl ion concentration cannot be zero in any aqueous solution, and the zinc ion concentration is certainly not zero in a zinc salt solution.

The presence of zinc ion in mobile equilibrium with zincate ion is demonstrated by the fact that zinc sulfide is precipitated when sodium sulfide is added to a zincate solution. There must be zinc ion sufficient to satisfy the solubility product expression

$$[Zn^{++}][S^=] = K \qquad (8)$$

otherwise the solution would be unsaturated and the precipitate would dissolve. The equation for this precipitation may be written by supposing that the process takes place by dissociation of zinc ion from the complex

$$Zn(OH)_4^= \rightleftarrows Zn^{++} + 4OH^- \tag{9}$$

(this is simply Eq. 6 written in reverse direction). The dissociation is followed by combination of zinc ions and sulfide ions

$$Zn^{++} + S^= \rightleftarrows ZnS. \tag{10}$$

Adding Eqs. (9) and (10), we have

$$Zn(OH)_4^= + S^= \rightleftarrows ZnS + 4OH^-. \tag{11}$$

It should be emphasized that we have not proven and cannot prove, except possibly by reaction-rate measurements, that the reaction really proceeds by these steps (see page 90).

The Precipitation of Amphoteric Hydroxides.—Any solution saturated with zinc hydroxide must satisfy the equation

$$[Zn^{++}][OH^-]^2 = K_b. \tag{12}$$

Any solution containing zinc compounds must satisfy Eq. (7). Dividing (12) by (7), we obtain an equation

$$\frac{[Zn(OH)_4^=]}{[OH^-]^2} = \frac{K_b}{K_e} \tag{13}$$

which must also be satisfied in any solution saturated with zinc hydroxide. According to this equation the concentration of zincate ion and hence the solubility of zinc hydroxide in a sodium hydroxide solution is proportional to the square of the hydroxyl ion concentration. When the latter is doubled, the solubility must increase 4 times. This prediction has been amply confirmed by experiment, which thus demonstrates the correctness of the formula $Zn(OH)_4^=$. If the complex ion had been $Zn(OH)_3^-$, the solubility would vary as the first power of the hydroxyl ion concentration; if it had been $Zn(OH)_5^=$, it would vary as the cube.

If we multiply Eq. (13) by the square of the equation

$$[OH_3^+][OH^-] = K_w \tag{14}$$

which holds for the ionization of water we obtain an equation

$$[OH_3{}^+]^2[Zn(OH)_4{}^=] = \frac{K_b K_w{}^2}{K_e} \qquad (15)$$

which is a solubility product expression for the precipitation reaction

$$2OH_3{}^+ + Zn(OH)_4{}^= \rightleftarrows Zn(OH)_2 + 4H_2O. \qquad (16)$$

In fact the constant quantity $K_b K_w{}^2/K_e$ is usually called the acid solubility product of the hydroxide and represented by the symbol K_a. K_b is the basic solubility product.

The total solubility of zinc hydroxide in any solution is the sum of the concentrations of zinc ion, which is given by the equation

$$[Zn^{++}] = \frac{K_b}{[OH^-]^2} \qquad (17)$$

of zincate ion, given by the equation

$$[Zn(OH)_4{}^=] = \frac{K_b}{K_e}[OH^-]^2, \qquad (18)$$

and of a possible small and constant concentration of molecular zinc hydroxide. Clearly a strongly acid solution, whose concentration of hydroxyl ion is small, can dissolve much zinc hydroxide in the form of zinc ion, and a strongly alkaline one can dissolve much in the form of zincate ion. If the constants K_b and K_b/K_e are small, solutions with an intermediate value of hydroxyl ion concentration will not be able to dissolve much hydroxide in either form. This is the case with zinc hydroxide, whose solubility is large in strongly acid or alkaline solutions, but very small in the neighborhood of the neutral point.

There is a certain concentration of hydroxyl ion for which the total solubility of the hydroxide is at a minimum, and the hydroxyl or hydrogen ion concentration at which this minimum occurs is called the "isoelectric point" of the amphoteric hydroxide, because it is the point at which the positive ionization to give zinc ion, and the negative ionization to give zincate ion are equal.

The isoelectric point is very important in the theory of amphoteric substances, and particularly so in the application to analytical chemistry, because the point of minimum solubility is the point of most complete precipitation. Thus the isoelectric point of aluminum hydroxide appears to be in a slightly alkaline solution. Its most complete precipitation therefore is obtained by the use of a slightly alkaline buffer, such as ammonia plus an ammonium salt. (In the absence of ammonium salt ammonia has considerable solvent action on aluminum hydroxide.) This is fortunate, for the buffer solution which permits quantitative precipitation of aluminum hydroxide is not sufficiently alkaline to precipitate magnesium hydroxide and other alkaline-earth hydroxides. It is by this means that aluminum ion is separated from the alkaline-earth ions.

If a solution of an aluminum salt is on the acid side of the isoelectric point, that is, if it contains chiefly aluminum ion rather than aluminate ion, aluminum hydroxide can only be precipitated by an increase in hydroxyl ion concentration. Ammonium sulfide reacts alkaline and does precipitate the hydroxide from such a solution, but the process has nothing to do with the sulfide ion, which restrains slightly rather than aids the precipitation.

An aluminate solution, on the other hand, is on the alkaline side of the isoelectric point, and hydroxide can only be precipitated by decrease in hydroxyl ion concentration. A weak acid such as hydrogen sulfide precipitates aluminum hydroxide from such a solution, so does an ammonium salt, for the ammonium ions of the salt combine with hydroxyl ions and make the solution less alkaline.

Some Alternative Interpretations.—If we remember that metallic ions are hydrated we see that Eq. (6) ought really to be written in some such form as

$$Zn(H_2O)_4^{++} + 4OH^- \rightleftarrows Zn(OH)_4^= + 4H_2O \qquad (19)$$

(the exact number of water molecules in the hydrated zinc ion being uncertain). The simplest interpretation of this reaction is to suppose that the hydroxyl ions remove hydrogen ions from the hydrated zinc ion. On this interpretation the hydrated metallic ion is an acid, in the most general sense which includes any substance that can lose hydrogen ions. Brönsted has recently obtained reaction-rate evidence that strongly supports this interpretation.

There is another interpretation of the behavior of amphoteric hydroxides which is less probable than either of those which we have previously considered, but which was invented at an earlier period in chemical thought, and appears in much of the literature for that reason. According to this interpretation zinc hydroxide does not add hydroxyl ions to form $Zn(OH)_4^=$, it rather dissociates hydrogen ions

$$Zn(OH)_2 \rightleftarrows ZnO_2^= + 2H^+. \tag{20}$$

There is no direct method of distinguishing between these interpretations. The ions $ZnO_2^=$ and $Zn(OH)_4^=$ differ only by two molecules of water and we have no way of determining the extent of hydration of an ion.

There are nevertheless two kinds of indirect evidence for the hydroxyl complex ion interpretation [Eq. (6) or (19)]. In the first place hydroxyl complexes certainly exist. Thus starting with Na_2PtCl_6, the sodium salt of the stable complex ion $PtCl_6^=$, it is possible to replace the chloride ions one by one with hydroxyl ions through the series Na_2PtCl_5OH, $Na_2PtCl_4(OH)_2$, Na_2PtCl_3-$(OH)_3$, $Na_2PtCl_2(OH)_4$, and $Na_2PtCl(OH)_5$ to $Na_2Pt(OH)_6$. In the light of the existence of this series it would be rather far-fetched to write the last of these salts as a trihydrate of Na_2PtO_3.

Since the plumbates and stannates are isomorphous with the platinates and form mixed crystals with them, it seems certain that these also should be written as salts of the hydroxyl complex ions $Pb(OH)_6^=$ and $Sn(OH)_6^=$, rather than as hydrated salts of oxy-complexes, $PbO_3^=$ and $SnO_3^=$.

Furthermore, it seems to be very generally true that the solid salts which crystallize out from these alkaline solutions of amphoteric hydroxides contain at least enough water to permit their formulation as hydroxyl complexes. Thus sodium antimonate can be written $NaSb(OH)_6$ (it has also been written $NaSbO_3.3H_2O$, and, for no very good reason, $Na_2H_2Sb_2O_7.5H_2O$).

The Amphoteric Hydroxides.—The following common hydroxides are amphoteric to an extent which is significant in aqueous solutions: $Zn(OH)_2$, $Al(OH)_3$, $Cr(OH)_3$, $Pb(OH)_2$, $Sn(OH)_2$.

The hydroxides of quadrivalent tin and of arsenic and antimony are frequently reckoned as amphoteric, and they do dissolve easily in alkalis and hence have acidic properties. It is, however, questionable whether they should be considered to have any basic properties. For these hydroxides are not, in general, soluble in acids, and dissolve only in the presence of chloride ion and certain other anions to form solutions in which the metal unquestionably exists as a complex ion (see page 125). There is no direct evidence of the existence of the ions Sn^{++++}, As^{+++}, As^{+++++}, Sb^{+++}, Sb^{+++++}, and their existence in traces is inferred mainly from the fact that sulfides can be precipitated from the acid solutions.

Other hydroxides have acidic properties in traces. The hydroxides of copper and cobalt dissolve in very concentrated sodium or potassium hydroxide solutions sufficiently to color the solution, in both cases blue. Ferric hydroxide is converted by fused, practically anhydrous sodium hydroxide to sodium ferrite, $NaFeO_2$, which is, however, quantitatively hydrolyzed by water to $Fe(OH)_3$. Chromic hydroxide may be considered to be less acidic than aluminum hydroxide, for sodium chromite solutions are hydrolyzed with quantitative precipitation of chromic hydroxide on boiling, and sodium aluminate solutions are not.

The formation of aluminate, chromite, plumbite, and stannite ions involves the addition of only one hydroxyl ion to the hydroxide, instead of two as in the case of zincate (the evidence for this depends upon the variation of the solubility of the hydroxide with hydroxyl ion concentration—see page 107). Typical equations are therefore

$$Al^{+++} + 4OH^- \rightleftarrows Al(OH)_4^- \tag{21}$$

or

$$Al(H_2O)_4^{+++} + 4OH^- \rightleftarrows Al(OH)_4^- + 4H_2O \tag{22}$$

and

$$Sn^{++} + 3OH^- \rightleftarrows Sn(OH)_3^- \tag{23}$$

or

$$Sn(H_2O)_3^{++} + 3OH^- \rightleftarrows Sn(OH)_3^- + 3H_2O. \tag{24}$$

These ions are, however, frequently formulated as oxide complexes, for instance AlO_2^- and $HSnO_2^-$.

Stannic hydroxide, or metastannic acid as it is usually called, dissolves in alkalis according to the equation

$$Sn(OH)_4 + 2OH^- \rightleftarrows Sn(OH)_6^=. \qquad (25)$$

Applications to Analytical Separations.—The amphoteric properties of aluminum and zinc hydroxides offer a valuable means of separating these ions from ferric, manganous, nickel, and cobaltous ions, whose hydroxides are not amphoteric to any significant extent. It is necessary only to add excess of sodium hydroxide and filter, when the aluminum and zinc will be in the filtrate, and the other ions in the precipitate. The presence of chromium makes for difficulty. The hydroxide is weakly acidic, and in addition, it forms insoluble chromites. When both zinc and chromium are present the zinc chromite is only incompletely dissolved by excess sodium hydroxide. If it is attempted to avoid this by oxidizing the chromite to chromate with sodium peroxide, the cobaltic hydroxide and manganese dioxide formed occlude zinc hydroxide seriously so that it is necessary either to take special precautions to minimize this occlusion or to test for zinc both in the precipitate and in the filtrate.

The Formation of Ammonia Complex Ions.—If a solution of ammonia in water is added to a solution of a nickel salt, the precipitate of $Ni(OH)_2$ formed at first dissolves upon further addition of ammonia, and the solution obtained has a blue color very different from the green of the original nickel salt. Obviously the solution of the precipitate and the formation of the blue color are related phenomena. The nickel ion has reacted with some constituent of the ammonia solution to form the blue compound, and the resultant decrease in the nickel ion concentration has decreased the value of the product $[Ni^{++}][OH^-]^2$ to a point where the solution has become unsaturated with nickel hydroxide.

It is easily shown that the reaction is not caused by the hydroxyl ion which the ammonia solution contains, and that the blue color is not that of a nickelate ion. No amount of sodium hydroxide, whose solutions contain much larger concentrations of hydroxyl ion than ammonia solutions do, is able to dissolve a perceptible quantity of nickel hydroxide. Nor is the reaction due to the ammonium ion of the ammonia solution, for the addition to a solution of a nickel salt of an ammonium salt, whose solution contains much more ammonium ion than the ammonia solution does, causes no change in the green color. It is certainly not due to water, whose concentration is not increased by the addition of ammonia solution, nor to oxonium ion, whose concentration is decreased.

The process of elimination leaves a reaction with NH_3 as the only reasonable explanation for the solution of the nickel hydroxide and the appearance of the blue color. This conclusion is confirmed by the fact that a wide variety of salts may be isolated which have the same blue color as the solution, and which contain ammonia. A typical formula is $Ni(NH_3)_6Cl_2$. According to the results of X-ray crystal-structure investigation these salts contain complex ions composed of nickel ion and ammonia. Each nickel ion is surrounded in a symmetrical fashion by six ammonia groups, and these $Ni(NH_3)_6^{++}$ ions then form a typical ionic lattice (see page 7) with the chloride ions.

By measuring the vapor pressure of ammonia from solutions containing a complex ammonia ion it is possible to estimate the concentration of uncombined ammonia. If the total ammonia concentration and the stoichiometric concentration of metal ion are known, it is then possible to calculate the quantity of combined ammonia and the number of ammonia molecules present in one molecule of the complex ion. In this way it has been found that the maximum number of ammonia molecules combined with nickel ion in aqueous solution is six. Since the green nickel ion is very probably a hexahydrate, the equation for the formation of this complex is

$$Ni(H_2O)_6^{++} + 6NH_3 \rightleftarrows Ni(NH_3)_6^{++} + 6H_2O. \qquad (26)$$

The application of the law of chemical equilibrium to these nickel-ammonia solutions demonstrates that at least two other complexes with smaller proportions of ammonia are present in nickel-ammonia solutions, and that it is only at high ammonia concentrations that practically all of the nickel is converted to $Ni(NH_3)_6^{++}$. A sample reaction equation for these lower ammoniated complexes is

$$Ni(H_2O)_6^{++} + 4NH_3 \rightleftarrows Ni(H_2O)_2(NH_3)_4^{++} + 4H_2O. \qquad (27)$$

Visual evidence of the existence of more than one complex is easily obtained because the complexes differ somewhat in color. Thus the addition of just enough ammonia to redissolve the nickel hydroxide gives a deep-blue solution, and the further addition of a large excess of ammonia produces a paler violet color.

The Ammonia Complex Ions.—In listing the more familiar ammonia complexes we give the formula of that complex stable in aqueous solution which contains the maximum number of ammonia molecules. In most cases (the NH_3 complexes derived from Ag^+ and H^+ are notable exceptions) other complexes with smaller proportions of ammonia are known to exist. In the case of Co^{+++}, Cr^{+++}, Pt^{++}, and Pt^{++++} many less highly ammoniated complexes are known (see page 126). With these provisos our list of complex ammonia ions is $Ni(NH_3)_6^{++}$, $Co(NH_3)_6^{++}$, $Co(NH_3)_6^{+++}$, $Fe(NH_3)_6^{++}$, $Cr(NH_3)_6^{+++}$, $Zn(NH_3)_4^{++}$, $Cd(NH_3)_4^{++}$, $Cu(NH_3)_3^+$, $Cu(NH_3)_4^{++}$, $Ag(NH_3)_2^+$, NH_4^+, $Pt(NH_3)_4^{++}$, $Pt(NH_3)_6^{++++}$.

The following special points are worthy of consideration. Solutions containing cobaltous ammonia ion are powerful reducing agents and react with such oxidizing agents as iodine or permanganate ion to form chiefly $Co(NH_3)_6^{+++}$. Exposed to the air they react with oxygen forming a complex mixture of cobaltic complexes containing both ammonia and peroxide ion.

Chromic hydroxide is only slowly acted on by ammonia, giving a lavender-colored solution of uncertain composition. The complex is quantitatively decomposed with precipitation of chromic hydroxide when the solution is boiled. For this reason the analytical precipitation of chromic hydroxide can only be relied upon when the solution is boiled. $Cr(NH_3)_6^{+++}$ is an extremely stable substance but is not formed by the action of aqueous ammonia on chromic salts. It may be made by oxidation of the chromous ammonia complex ion, or by the action of liquid ammonia on anhydrous $CrCl_3$.

In the case of zinc the argument used with nickel fails, because zinc hydroxide is amphoteric. The solution of zinc hydroxide in ammonia contains zincate ions, all solutions of zinc compounds contain zincate ions; and the ammonia solution contains more zincate ion than a zinc chloride solution does because the hydroxyl ion concentration is greater. The question is whether the solution of the zinc hydroxide is due primarily to the formation of zincate ion or to the formation of an ammonia complex ion.

This can most simply be decided by a migration experiment. When a current passes through a zinc-ammonia solution it is found that, allowing for the metal deposited upon the cathode, the quantity of zinc in the solution near the cathode increases, and the quantity of zinc in the solution near the anode decreases. This proves that most of the zinc in the solution is present as positively charged zinc-ammonia ion rather than as negatively charged zincate ion.

The complex ammonia ion of hydrogen ion is, of course, the familiar ammonium ion NH_4^+.

Equilibrium Relations.—Application of the law of chemical equilibrium to the reaction of Eq. (26) gives

$$\frac{[Ni(H_2O)_6^{++}][NH_3]^6}{[Ni(NH_3)_6^{++}]} = K \tag{28}$$

from which certain simple corollaries may be drawn. The complex is quantitatively decomposed by hydrogen sulfide if the excess of ammonia is not large. There is enough nickel ion to exceed the solubility product constant of nickel sulfide, and the removal of some nickel ion by precipitation causes further dissociation of the complex to replace that lost. But when several volumes of concentrated ammonia solution are added to a nickel-salt solution, the resulting solution gives no precipitate with hydrogen sulfide. This is easily understood, for increasing ammonia concentration must decrease the nickel ion concentration very rapidly, since the effect depends upon a high power of the ammonia concentration. A tenfold increase in ammonia concentration should decrease the nickel ion concentration to one millionth.

Decreasing the ammonia concentration must cause further dissociation of the complex and increase the nickel ion concentration. The most certain way to decrease the ammonia concentration of a solution is to add acid and convert the ammonia to ammonium ion, and indeed the blue color of a nickel-ammonia solution disappears and the green of nickel ion appears when acids are added to the ammoniacal solution. The reaction is

$$Ni(NH_3)_6^{++} + 6OH_3^+ \rightleftarrows Ni(H_2O)_6^{++} + 6NH_4^+. \tag{29}$$

Most complex ammonia ions in aqueous solution are decomposed by acids, but there are exceptions. For instance, cobaltic ammonia ion, $Co(NH_3)_6^{+++}$, is not decomposed by boiling with strong hydrochloric acid, and the ammonia complexes of the platinum metals and of chromic ion are similarly resistant to acids.

Hydroxide Precipitation and Ammonia Complexes.—The competition between hydroxide precipitation and complex formation has a different aspect in this case from that which it bears in the case of an amphoteric hydroxide. In the latter case it is the same constituent, the hydroxyl ion, which first precipitates, and then redissolves the hydroxide. In the case of the ammonia complexes, hydroxyl ion precipitates the hydroxide, ammonia forms the complex. But the concentrations of hydroxyl ion and of ammonia are independently variable. If a precipitate of nickel hydroxide is dissolved in ammonia, the addition of sodium hydroxide solution reprecipitates the nickel hydroxide, and completely destroys the blue color of the solution. There exists sufficient nickel ion in the complex solution to exceed the solubility product constant of nickel hydroxide when the hydroxyl ion concentration is raised from the small value it has in an ammonia solution to the large value it has in the sodium hydroxide solution.

On the other hand, the concentration of hydroxyl ion in an ammonia solution is greatly decreased by the presence of ammonium salts (see page 54). If, therefore, a large concentration of ammonium chloride or other ammonium salt is added to a nickel-salt solution, the addition of ammonia causes the formation of the blue complex ion, but no precipitate of the hydroxide appears at any time during the addition.

Zinc, cobaltous, ferrous, cadmium, and cupric ions behave in this respect like nickel ion. In the absence of ammonium salts ammonia precipitates the hydroxide at first, then dissolves it with larger amounts of ammonia. In the presence of ammonium salts, the hydroxide is not precipitated, and the complex ammonia ion forms directly.

This behavior may be compared with that of magnesium and manganese ions which form no complex ammonia ions. Ammonia in the absence of ammonium salts precipitates the hydroxides, which do not dissolve in excess. Ammonia in the presence of ammonium salts in sufficient concentration does not precipitate magnesium, manganous, or ferrous hydroxides, because the high ammonium ion concentration keeps the hydroxyl ion concentration too low to exceed the solubility products of the hydroxides. In the presence of air, however, $Fe(OH)_3$ and hydrated MnO_2 do precipitate when ammonia is added to solutions of ferrous and manganous salts, for the oxygen oxidizes the ferrous and manganous ions to the higher valences. This oxidation is extremely rapid with ferrous salts; slower with manganous salts, but rapid enough to make impossible a separation of manganous ion from aluminum, ferric, and chromic ions by this method.

Analytical Applications.—These facts have important analytical applications. In the separation of aluminum and zinc ions, it is much more satisfactory to prevent the precipitation of zinc hydroxide by having a large concentration of ammonium salt present, than it would be to precipitate a mixture of zinc and aluminum hydroxides, and then to attempt to dissolve the zinc hydroxide out of the mixture by excess of ammonia. The large concentration of ammonium salts which is always used in this separation gives incidentally the correct hydroxyl ion concentration for the optimum precipitation of aluminum hydroxide.

In practice this does not differ from the separation of aluminum, ferric, and chromic ions from the alkaline-earth ions, where the former are precipitated as hydroxides by ammonia in the presence of ammonium salts. The hydroxyl ion concentration is kept so low that magnesium hydroxide and the other more soluble alkaline-earth hydroxides do not precipitate. These are not, however, converted to ammonia complexes, as the zinc ion is, but remain in solution unprecipitated solely because the hydroxyl ion concentration is not large enough to precipitate them.

One instance in which complex ammonia ions are of crucial importance for analytical purposes is the detection of silver ion. The silver-ammonia complex ion is so stable that ammonia solution dissolves silver chloride, and indeed many other difficultly soluble silver salts. The precipitation in acid solution of a chloride, which is soluble in ammonia, and which reprecipitates when the ammonia is converted to ammonium ion by the addition of acid is a sufficient test for silver ion.

The Mercuric Amides.—There is another type of ammonia compound which can in no way be called a complex ion, which is a substitution product rather than an addition product of ammonia. A large number of amides, compounds of the type $NaNH_2$, are known, and may be considered as salts of ammonia which demonstrate the existence of acidic properties in ammonia

$$NH_3 \leftrightarrows H^+ + NH_2^-. \tag{30}$$

But ammonia is a much weaker acid than water, and these amides when soluble and highly ionized are quantitatively hydrolyzed

$$NH_2^- + H_2O \leftrightarrows OH^- + NH_3. \tag{31}$$

Such amides cannot of course form in an aqueous solution.

The mercuric amides (also those of gold) are so insoluble or so weakly ionized that their solutions contain too little amide ion for this hydrolysis to take place to a significant extent. The addition of ammonia to a solution of a mercuric salt results then in the precipitation of a difficultly soluble mixed amide. With mercuric chloride the reaction is

$$HgCl_2 + 2NH_3 \leftrightarrows HgNH_2Cl + NH_4^+ + Cl^-, \tag{32}$$

and the product, $HgNH_2Cl$, is a mixed amide chloride—a double salt.

Many of the amides are soluble and highly ionized in liquid ammonia, in which they play the same part as hydroxides do in aqueous solutions. For the amide ion, NH_2^-, which is ammonia deprived of a hydrogen ion, bears the same relation to ammonia that hydroxyl ion does to water. Franklin and Kraus have developed a whole system of chemistry founded upon ammonia, in the same way that most ordinary chemistry is founded upon water, and obtained results of far-reaching importance for chemical theory.

The Formation of Complex Cyanide Ions.—If potassium cyanide is added to silver nitrate solution, the precipitate of AgCN which forms at first dissolves in excess of the cyanide. The reaction is obtained only with soluble highly ionized cyanides. It is, therefore, not a general salt effect nor a reaction of potassium ion, but is a reaction of the cyanide ion itself. If 1 silver ion reacts with 1 cyanide ion, silver cyanide precipitates, but some other reaction between silver ion and cyanide ion must be possible. In this a soluble product is formed, and more than 1 cyanide ion must react with each silver ion because the reaction takes place when a greater cyanide ion concentration is present than that necessary to precipitate silver cyanide.

In the saturated solution of silver cyanide the equation

$$[Ag^+][CN^-] = K \tag{33}$$

is satisfied, and, although the salt effect must somewhat increase K, the concentration of silver ion must be decreased considerably by this increased cyanide ion concentration. The solution obtained contains much silver in some form of combination, but it can contain only a very minute concentration of silver ion. The silver ion concentration is too small to precipitate silver cyanide in spite of the large concentration of cyanide ion, too small to precipitate silver chloride if sodium chloride is added. That some silver ion is present is nevertheless demonstrated by the fact that ammonium sulfide precipitates the very insoluble silver sulfide.

If silver ion, carrying unit positive charge, reacts with 2 or more cyanide ions, each carrying unit negative charge, the product should be negatively charged. This conclusion has been verified by migration experiments similar to those described on page 106 which prove that the silver in these solutions is really part of a negatively charged ion. The negative nature of the complex cyanide ions is more easily shown when the ion is colored. Thus an experiment like that described on page 19 can be used to show that the yellow ferricyanide ion moves toward the anode on electrolysis.

It is possible to isolate the compound $KAg(CN)_2$ from the solution obtained by dissolving AgCN in excess of KCN. In the light of these experiments this must be considered to be a strong electrolyte existing in solution, and presumably also in the solid state as K^+ and $Ag(CN)_2^-$. The reaction which dissolves the silver cyanide is then

$$Ag^+ + 2CN^- \leftrightharpoons Ag(CN)_2^- \tag{34}$$

or
$$AgCN + CN^- \leftrightarrows Ag(CN)_2^-. \tag{35}$$

The equilibrium equation for the reaction is

$$\frac{[Ag^+][CN^-]^2}{[Ag(CN)_2^-]} = K. \tag{36}$$

The precipitation of silver cyanide with small amounts of cyanide ion and its solution in excess can be accounted for in exactly the same way as the precipitation of an amphoteric hydroxide by small amounts of hydroxyl ion and its solution in excess. The two problems are indeed identical in all essential respects.

It is interesting to note, however, that an alternative explanation may be offered for both reactions. This proposes that the cyanide precipitate is not silver cyanide, $AgCN$, but the silver salt of the silver cyanide complex ion, $AgAg(CN)_2$, which has the same composition. The condition for saturation on this hypothesis is

$$[Ag^+][Ag(CN)_2^-] = K_s \tag{37}$$

which can be combined with the equilibrium Eq. (36) giving

$$[Ag^+]^2[CN^-]^2 = K_sK_e \tag{38}$$

and taking the square root, we have

$$[Ag^+][CN^-] = \text{a constant} \tag{39}$$

the same result that is obtained on the assumption that the precipitate is $AgCN$. It was at one time rather generally supposed that both silver cyanide and silver argentocyanide existed, the first being formed by the addition of potassium cyanide to silver nitrate solution, the other by the addition of silver nitrate to potassium argentocyanide solution. X-ray analysis has shown that the two products are identical, without however deciding which formula is correct, and there is no other method for determining the molecular weight of a solid. There are indeed good reasons for supposing the saturated solution of silver cyanide to contain essentially silver ions and argentocyanide ions rather than silver ions and cyanide ions, but this proves nothing about the composition of the solid.

The formation of these complex cyanide ions is a reversible reaction. In the case of the silver compound this is demonstrated by the fact, already mentioned, that an incomplete precipitation of silver sulfide takes place when ammonium sulfide is added to a solution of the complex. This can happen only if the silver ion concentration is large enough to make the product $[Ag^+]^2[S^=]$ greater than the solubility product constant of silver sulfide. If the silver ion concentration is decreased by addition of a large excess of cyanide, the sulfide no longer precipitates. Furthermore, silver sulfide can be dissolved in potassium cyanide solution.

Silver metal can be obtained on the cathode by electrolysis of cyanide complex solutions. The process may be interpreted as a dissociation of the complex followed by reduction of the silver ion thus formed to the metal at the negative electrode, but this is not necessarily the correct mechanism (see page 90). This method of electrodeposition is of considerable technical importance because for some obscure reason a smoother, finer grained, and more coherent electroplate is usually obtained from a stable complex ion than from the simple hydrated ion. Thus electrolysis of a complex silver cyanide solution produces a smooth electroplate on the cathode, electrolysis of silver nitrate produces large, nonadherent crystals of silver.

The Complex Cyanide Ions.—The following are the more common complex cyanide ions: $Zn(CN)_4^=$, $Ni(CN)_4^=$, $Co(CN)_6^{\equiv}$, $Co(CN)_6^=$, $Fe(CN)_6^{\equiv}$, $Fe(CN)_6^=$, $Mn(CN)_6^=$, $Cd(CN)_4^=$, $Cu(CN)_3^=$, $Hg(CN)_4^=$, $Ag(CN)_2^-$, $Au(CN)_2^-$, $Au(CN)_4^-$, $Pt(CN)_4^=$.

In most cases the cyanides are difficultly soluble, and the addition of potassium cyanide to a solution of the metallic salt first produces a precipitate of the cyanide, then dissolves it in excess of cyanide to form a solution of the complex. In the case of mercuric salts, the mercuric cyanide is appreciably soluble, and does not precipitate. It is, however, very slightly ionized (see page 48).

That the cuprocyanide ion, $Cu(CN)_3^=$, is a derivative of cuprous ion may be seen simply by writing the equation

$$Cu(CN)_3^= \rightleftarrows 3CN^- + Cu^+. \tag{40}$$

That it is formed when cyanide is added to a cupric salt is due to the fact that the cupric ion oxidizes some of the cyanide, either to cyanogen or to cyanate ion (see page 142).

Some idea of the relative stability of these ions may be gained from the reaction with acids, which reduce the cyanide ion concentration by forming hydrocyanic acid. This removal of cyanide ion necessitates a more or less extensive further ionization of the complex ion. The complexes $Fe(CN)_6^{\equiv}$, $Fe(CN)_6^{\equiv}$, and $Co(CN)_6^{\equiv}$, are not significantly affected by acids, and must be considered to be extremely stable. The complexes of zinc, nickel, silver, and manganese are decomposed, either with precipitation of the cyanide, notably in the case of silver, or with complete liberation of the metallic ion. The mercuric cyanide complex is not appreciably decomposed by sulfuric acid, but is extensively decomposed by hydrochloric acid. Here the combination of mercuric ion and chloride ion to form stable mercuric chloride complexes aids the combination of hydrogen and cyanide ions to form weakly ionized hydrocyanic acid in decomposing the mercuric cyanide complex into mercuric ion and cyanide ion.

Another evidence of stability, and one of analytical importance, is the precipitation of sulfides, provided due allowance be made for the differences in solubility of the sulfides. Of the above complexes, those of manganese, cadmium, and mercury give quantitative precipitation of the sulfide, unless a very large excess of cyanide is present. In the case of mercury this testifies to the extreme insolubility of mercuric sulfide rather than to instability of the complex, which is indeed one of the most stable. The complex cyanides of zinc and silver give incomplete precipitation of the sulfide, solutions of the other complexes give no sulfide precipitation.

The ability to regulate the concentration of the cations, which the stable cyanide complexes provide, may be used for analytical separations, just as the ability to regulate the anion concentration by adjusting the acidity is of use for the same purpose. The cuprocyanide ion is so much more stable than the cadmium cyanide complex that it is possible to precipitate cadmium sulfide quantitatively in the presence of copper compounds in spite of the fact that copper sulfide is much less soluble than cadmium sulfide. The details of the reaction of cupric and cyanide ions are discussed on page 142. Similarly, manganous sulfide may be precipitated quantitatively in the presence of cyanide, while the less soluble nickel sulfide remains unprecipitated because of the stability of the nickel-cyanide complex.

With certain metallic ions potassium cyanide reacts by virtue of the alkalinity of the solution rather than because of the presence of cyanide ion. Aluminum, ferric, chromic, and bismuth solutions precipitate the hydroxide upon the addition of potassium cyanide. The other product of the reaction is the volatile and poisonous hydrogen cyanide

$$Al^{+++} + 3CN^- + 3H_2O \leftrightarrows Al(OH)_3 + 3HCN \qquad (41)$$

and cyanide should not therefore be added to solutions of salts of these ions.

The case of ferric ion seems peculiar in view of the existence of ferricyanide ion, $Fe(CN)_6^{\equiv}$, which is certainly a cyanide complex of ferric ion. This is, however, never prepared from ferric salts by the addition of cyanide, but always by the oxidation of ferrocyanide ion, which can be prepared directly from ferrous salts and potassium cyanide. When chlorine is used as an oxidizing agent the reaction is

$$2Fe(CN)_6^{\equiv} + Cl_2 \leftrightarrows 2Fe(CN)_6^{=} + 2Cl^-. \qquad (42)$$

The apparent stability of ferricyanide ion is due to sluggish reaction rather than to true stability, and ferricyanide solutions decompose slowly, giving a complex mixture of products.

Complex Sulfide Ions.—The complex sulfide ions are of great analytical importance, being universally used for the separation of the ions of arsenic, antimony, and tin, and sometimes of mercury also from the other ions whose sulfides can be precipitated in moderately acid solution. The ions whose sulfides are not dissolved except in traces by sodium or ammonium sulfide are called the copper group, those whose sulfides are dissolved are called the tin group. Taking stannic tin as an example the reaction is

$$SnS_2 + S^= \leftrightarrows SnS_3^= \qquad (43).$$

and does not differ in any material respect from the solution of silver cyanide by excess of potassium cyanide. Here too a small concentration of sulfide ion precipitates stannic sulfide, a larger concentration dissolves the precipitate. In practice, the sulfide ion concentration is controlled by adjusting the oxonium ion concentration. When it is desired to precipitate stannic sulfide, a low sulfide ion concentration is obtained by using hydrogen sulfide in acid solution; when it is desired to obtain a solution of sulfostannate, $SnS_3^=$, a high concentration of sulfide ion is obtained by using ammonium or sodium sulfide. Similarly, the addition of acid to a solution of one of these complex sulfides reverses the reaction by removing sulfide ion, and the sulfide precipitates. Too large a concentration of acid will even redissolve the precipitate again, as other sulfides are dissolved by acids.

The reaction by which the complexes are formed is represented by an equation of the type

$$As_2S_3 + 3S^= \leftrightarrows 2AsS_3^= \tag{44}$$

for As_2S_3 and Sb_2S_3, by one of the type

$$As_2S_5 + 3S^= \rightleftarrows 2AsS_4^= \tag{45}$$

for As_2S_5 and Sb_2S_5, and by the equation

$$HgS + S^= \rightleftarrows HgS_2^= \tag{46}$$

for HgS.

As_2S_3, As_2S_5, Sb_2S_3, Sb_2S_5, and SnS_2 dissolve easily in either sodium or ammonium sulfide, and require therefore no higher concentration of sulfide ion than exists in ammonium sulfide solution. Mercuric sulfide is very slightly soluble in ammonium sulfide solution, and dissolves in sodium sulfide solution largely only when the hydrolysis is decreased and the sulfide ion concentration increased by the addition of sodium hydroxide.

Stannous ion forms no sulfide complex, and stannous sulfide does not dissolve in alkaline sulfide solutions. Tin must therefore always be in the oxidized state for the separation. This can be assured by having the oxidizing agent polysulfide ion present in the sulfide solution (see page 152), or by evaporation with nitric and hydrochloric acids before the sulfide precipitation. Bismuth and cupric sulfides dissolve to a small extent in sodium sulfide plus sodium hydroxide. This is a serious disadvantage because the colors of these sulfides are so intense that even a small amount obscures the tests for antimony and tin which depend upon the characteristic color of their sulfides. Bismuth and copper sulfides together with mercuric sulfide can be precipitated from the sulfide solution by the addition of a large concentration of ammonium salt. The ammonium ion combines with hydroxyl ion, and the decrease in the hydroxyl ion concentration permits a further hydrolysis of the sulfide and causes a decrease in the sulfide ion concentration. Copper sulfide dissolves to a much greater extent in polysulfide than in simple sulfide solutions, and remains dissolved even in the presence of large concentrations of ammonium ion.

There is a close relation between these sulfide complexes and the ions of the oxygen acids. This is brought out not merely by the similarity of such formulæ as $AsS_4^=$ and $AsO_4^{\equiv}$, but by the existence of the complete series of intermediate oxy-sulfo arsenates, $AsS_3O^{\equiv}$, $AsS_2O_2^{\equiv}$, and $AsSO_3^{\equiv}$. Salts of all these ions are known, and an equilibrium mixture is formed when As_2S_5 is treated with sodium or ammonium hydroxides, in either of which it is easily soluble. Sb_2S_5, As_2S_3, and SnS_2 likewise dissolve in sodium and ammonium hydroxides, probably because of the formation of similar compounds.

Other Types of Complexes.—The only stannic, antimonic, and antimonous compounds which can exist in aqueous solution are complex ions. If the attempt is made to prepare the nitrate or sulfate only the hydroxide is obtained; hydrolysis takes place whenever a solution contains more than traces of stannic, antimonic, or antimonous ions. The most common mode of occurrence of these metals in acid solution is as the complex chloride ions, $SnCl_6^=$, $SbCl_6^-$, $SbCl_6^=$, which are quite stable, particularly if the solution contains considerable chloride ion.

Mercuric and cadmium ions form chloride complexes $HgCl_4^=$ and $CdCl_4^=$, of high stability, and it is possible to prevent the precipitation of cadmium sulfide by saturating a cadmium salt solution with sodium chloride. If cupric ion is present cupric sulfide precipitates under these conditions, and cupric and cadmium ions can thus be separated. Dilution of the filtrate from the copper sulfide decreases the chloride ion concentration and permits the precipitation of cadmium sulfide if cadmium ion is present.

Nitrite complexes are familiar because the difficultly soluble potassium cobaltinitrite is used as a test for potassium and also as a test for cobalt (see page 147). The familiar red color produced by the reaction of ferric and thiocyanate ions is due to a complex thiocyanate ion $Fe(SCN)_6^{\equiv}$. In fact, complexes are known which are derived from nearly all known anions. There are complex sulfates, carbonates, acetates, oxalates, fluorides, bromides, iodides, and so on. Perchlorate ion seems to have by far the smallest tendency toward the formation of complex ions, and is a suitable anion to use when it is desired to examine the properties of a hydrated metallic ion. Nitrate ion is also a feeble complex former.

Some Instability Constants.—The equilibrium constant for the decomposition of a complex ion is called the *instability constant* of the complex. Thus the constant in Eq. (7) is the instability constant of zincate ion and the constant in Eq. (28) is the instability constant of nickel ammonia complex ion. Table VI contains the values of some representative instability constants.

TABLE VI.—INSTABILITY CONSTANTS OF COMPLEX IONS AT 25°C.

Complex ion	K
$Zn(OH)_4^-$	3.6×10^{-16}
$Ag(NH_3)_2^+$	7×10^{-8}
NH_4^+	5.6×10^{-10}
$Hg(CN)_4^-$	4.0×10^{-42}
$Ag(CN)_2^-$	4.5×10^{-19}
$HgCl_4^-$	1.1×10^{-16}
$HgBr_4^-$	2.3×10^{-22}
HgI_4^-	5.0×10^{-31}

Werner Theory.—One of the landmarks of chemical history is the discovery in 1893 by Alfred Werner (at that time only twenty-six years old) that the capacity for combination with other atoms, molecules, or ions exhibited by a particular kind of ion tends to be a constant. This capacity for combination is called the *coordination number*. We have already met some examples. Thus, cobaltous ion combines with 6 molecules of ammonia to form $Co(NH_3)_6^{++}$, with 6 cyanide ions to form $Co(CN)_6^{\equiv}$, with 6 water molecules to form $Co(H_2O)_6^{++}$. But the principle is much better exemplified by the compounds of cobaltic and of platinic ions, where the great stability and sluggishness of reaction permit the existence of a variety of substances that can be equaled only among the compounds of carbon.

It is possible by suitable oxidation of a cobaltous ammonia solution to obtain a compound, yellow in color, and with the formula $Co(NH_3)_6Cl_3$, which behaves with respect to all its three chlorines like a true salt. It has an ionic lattice in the solid state, its conductivity in solution is that to be expected of a uni-trivalent salt, and all of its chlorine is immediately precipitated from solution by silver nitrate. Here the cobaltic ion, Co^{+++}, is obviously combined with 6 ammonia molecules; it is no more combined with the chloride ions, than sodium and chloride ions are combined in sodium chloride (see page 6). It is also possible to obtain a purple compound which contains one less ammonia molecule, and has the formula $Co(NH_3)_5Cl_3$. This, however, has approximately the same conductivity in solution as barium chloride, and only two-thirds of its chlorine is precipitated by silver nitrate. That is its behavior shows that its ions are $Co(NH_3)_5Cl^{++}$ and $2Cl^-$. The cobaltic ion is combined with 5 ammonias and 1 chloride ion, and the negative charge of the chloride ion combined with the triple positive charge of the cobaltic ion gives a net charge of $+2$. There is also a green compound, $Co(NH_3)_4Cl_3$, whose solutions have about the same conductivity as those of potassium chloride, and precipitate only one-third of their chlorine with silver nitrate. Obviously the cobaltic ion is here combined with 6 groups again, 4 ammonias and 2 chloride ions, forming $Co(NH_3)_4Cl_2^+$, and the third chlorine is a free chloride ion. Finally, there is known a compound $Co(NH_3)_3Cl_3$, which is a nonelectrolyte. Here also the cobaltic ion is combined with 6 groups, the net charge on the compound being zero.

Other compounds in which cobaltic ion exhibits a coordination number of 6 are $Co(CN)_6^{\equiv}$, $Co(NO_2)_6^{\equiv}$, $Co(NH_3)_2(NO_2)_4^-$, $Co(NH_3)_3(NO_2)_3$, $Co(NH_3)_4(NO_2)_2^+$, $Co(NH_3)_5(NO_2)^{++}$.

A similar example of constancy of coordination number is offered by the substances $Pt(NH_3)_6^{++++}$, $Pt(NH_3)_5Cl^{+++}$, $Pt(NH_3)_4Cl_2^{++}$, $Pt(NH_3)_3Cl_3^+$, $Pt(NH_3)_2Cl_4$, $Pt(NH_3)Cl_5^-$, and $PtCl_6^{\equiv}$, for whose existence and composition the same kind of evidence may be found as in the case of the cobalt compounds just cited.

There are definite principles used in the nomenclature of these compounds, which are most easily presented in the form of examples. Thus $Co(NH_3)_6^{+++}$ is hexammine cobaltic ion, $Co(NH_3)_5Cl^{++}$ is chloro pentammine cobaltic ion, $Co(NH_3)_4$-$(NO_2)_2^+$ is dinitro tetrammine cobaltic ion, $PtCl_6^=$ is hexachloroplatinate ion.

It is not always appreciated that the principle of constancy of coordination number applies as well to the nitrogen in the complex ammonia ions as it does to the metal. Ammonia may be looked upon in some ways (see page 13) as a compound of nitride ion, $N^=$, with 3 hydrogen ions, and ammonium ion is then a complex of nitride ion with 4 hydrogen ions. In the complex ammonia ions the nitride ion is combined with 3 hydrogen ions and 1 metal ion, and the coordination number is still 4. There are also substances, called polynuclear complexes, in which a nitride ion is combined with 2 hydrogen ions and 2 metal ions, thus maintaining a coordination number of 4. For instance there is a stable cobalt compound whose reactions and properties indicate that it contains the ion

$$(NH_3)_5Co\text{—}NH_2\text{—}Co(NH_3)_5^{+++++}.$$

Similarly the coordination number of oxide ion is 3. In oxonium ion it is combined with 3 hydrogen ions, in a hydrated metallic ion it is combined with 2 hydrogen ions and 1 metallic ion, in polynuclear complexes such as

$$(NH_3)_5Cr\text{—}OH\text{—}Cr(NH_3)_5^{+++++}$$

it is combined with 1 hydrogen ion and 2 metallic ions.

Colloidal Solutions.—Suppose a hydrated ferric ion, $Fe(H_2O)_6^{+++}$, loses a hydrogen ion by reaction with water (hydrolysis) or with some other base (hydroxyl ion, acetate ion, ammonia, etc.). The product $Fe(H_2O)_5OH^{++}$ has an oxygen atom in the hydroxyl group which is coordinatively unsaturated, that is it is capable of combining with some other atom or ion. It may, for instance, do this by displacing a water molecule from another hydrated ion giving

$$\begin{array}{c} H \\ | \\ (H_2O)_5Fe\text{—}O\text{—}Fe(H_2O)_5^{+++++} \end{array}$$

This ion contains two iron atoms and is nearly twice as heavy and as large as the original hydrated ferric ion. It can itself lose hydrogen ions and become linked through the hydroxyl groups thus formed to still other iron atoms. This may lead eventually to a very large aggregate carrying a relatively small average charge per iron atom because each hydrogen ion that dissociates decreases by one unit the total positive charge.

Some such process as this is what occurs when a ferric or aluminum salt hydrolyzes or when it is treated with an amount of base insufficient to produce precipitation. Such solutions do indeed contain a substance shown by its migration to be positively charged, which has all the properties to be expected of substances composed of very large molecular groupings. It diffuses very slowly, and it does not pass through collodion or parchment membranes, which are easily permeable to ordinary molecules and ions. Optically, too, the solutions act as if they contained large particles. For while they are clear when viewed by transmitted light, the path of a beam of light viewed at right angles to the direction of the beam is visible as it is not in water. Some constituent of the solutions scatters light more than do ordinary molecules and ions. Solutions with these properties are called colloidal.

In the case of ferric salts the colloidal constituent is reddish brown in color. In fact the yellowish color of a ferric nitrate solution is entirely due to the colloidal hydrolysis products, because the color disappears immediately upon addition of nitric acid which represses the hydrolysis by increasing the concentration of oxonium ion, one of the hydrolysis products. Hydrated ferric ion is itself colorless. At least part of the color of a ferric chloride solution, however, is due either to molecular ferric chloride or to a chloride complex, which has a distinct greenish yellow color. Because of this the intensity of the yellow color of a ferric chloride solution is considerably increased by the addition of hydrochloric acid, which increases the concentration of the yellow substance.

We possess less definite information about the nature of certain other colloidal substances which are often met with in analytical work. They are all electrically charged, and act as if they contain very large molecular aggregates, but the type of linkage is not so clear. So-called colloidal sulfur is formed by oxidation by atmospheric oxygen in any solution containing hydrogen sulfide. It causes much trouble in analysis because some of the sulfur is coagulated and thrown out of the solution with each new treatment, and causes small precipitates in every test made upon the solution. Ferrous sulfide colloidal solutions of an olive-green color form when solutions containing a very small concentration of ferrous ion are treated with ammonium sulfide. These colloids can usually be coagulated and gotten rid of by boiling the solution.

Almost any of the sulfides may appear as colloids if the electrolyte concentration of the solution is small. Such colloidal solutions as those of arsenic or cadmium sulfides can usually be coagulated by the addition of ammonium salts, or the formation of the colloid may be prevented by the presence of ammonium salts or of other electrolytes.

The Properties of Chromic Salts.—In the case of chromic salts some of the reactions involving the hydrated ion are slow, and this leads to interesting results. If the violet hydrated salt $Cr(H_2O)_6Cl_3$ is dissolved in water, a violet solution is obtained in which all of the chlorine appears to be in the form of free uncombined chloride ion. When the solution stands, however, its color changes to green, its conductivity decreases, and some of the chlorine is not precipitated immediately by silver nitrate. Evidently such reactions as

$$Cr(H_2O)_6{}^{+++} + Cl^- \rightleftarrows Cr(H_2O)_5Cl^{++} + H_2O$$

have taken place, and the chloroaquo compounds produced are green.

Chromic salts have some peculiar reactions in the basic-acetate procedure (see page 99). The addition of sodium acetate to a violet chromic salt gives a precipitate in the cold, whereas only a colloidal solution is obtained with ferric and aluminum salts. The green solutions, however, give no precipitate, and the precipitate formed in the violet one dissolves if the solution is boiled (heating, of course, accelerates the change from violet to green). This is exactly opposite to the behavior of ferric and aluminum salts which give no precipitate with sodium acetate in the cold but do give a precipitate on heating.

It has been found that when a solution contains ferric or aluminum ion and chromic ion, the latter seems to enter into colloidal complexes containing both metals when hydrolysis takes place. The behavior of the mixed complex is determined by the metal which is in excess. When a solution contains much more aluminum or iron than chromium, the addition of sodium acetate and boiling leads therefore to a precipitation of the chromium as well as of the other metal; when it contains more chromium than aluminum or iron neither the chromium nor the other metals can be precipitated by the basic-acetate procedure.

Suggestions for Reading

General: EPHRAIM-THORNE, "A Text-book of Inorganic Chemistry," pp. 257–292, London, 1934; SCHWARZ-BASS, "The Chemistry of the Inorganic Complex Compounds," New York, 1923; THOMAS, "Complex Salts," London, 1924; DEDE, "Komplexchemie," Berlin, 1928; WERNER-PFEIFFER, "Neuere Anschauungen auf dem Gebiete der anorganischen Chemie," Braunschweig, 1923.

The determination of instability constants: JAQUES, "Complex Ions," London, 1914; JELLINEK, "Lehrbuch der physikalischen Chemie," Bd. IV, Stuttgart, 1933.

Amides and solutions in liquid ammonia: FRANKLIN, "The Nitrogen System of Compounds," New York, 1935.

Colloids: THOMAS, "Colloid Chemistry," New York, 1934.

Exercises

1. Explain with equations for the reactions what happens when sodium sulfide solution is added to aluminum chloride solution, to sodium aluminate solution, to zinc chloride solution, to sodium zincate solution, to sodium arsenite solution. What happens when hydrogen sulfide is added to solutions of the same salts? Write equations and explain. What happens when hydrochloric acid is added to solutions of the same salts? Write equations and explain.

2. Explain with equations for the reactions what happens when sodium hydroxide is added to a zinc salt, to an aluminum salt, to a magnesium salt, to a mercuric salt; when ammonia is added to solutions of the same salts; when ammonia is added to solutions of the same salts, each containing much ammonium chloride.

3. Suggest two different ways to determine whether the nickel-ammonia complex ion is more or less stable than the nickel-cyanide complex.

4. Could a difficultly soluble metallic hydroxide be very soluble in NaOH solution and yet no more soluble in NH_3 solution than in water?

5. Calculate the concentration of silver ion in a 0.01 M solution of $Ag(NH_3)_2^+$. (The complex is so stable that we can set $[Ag(NH_3)_2^+]$ = 0.01 without appreciable error. Let $x = [Ag^+]$, then $[NH_3] = 2x$.

Substitute in the equilibrium equation for the decomposition of the complex). Calculate also the silver ion concentration of a solution containing $0.01\ M$ $Ag(NH_3)_2{}^+$ and $0.5\ M$ NH_3. Would $0.01\ M$ chloride ion produce a precipitate in either of these solutions?

6. Which of the silver halides can be precipitated by addition of $0.1\ M$ halide ion to a $0.1\ M$ solution of $Ag(CN)_2{}^-$? Which can be precipitated by the addition of $0.1\ M$ halide ion to a solution containing $0.1\ M$ $Ag(CN)_2{}^-$ and also $0.1\ M$ CN^-?

7. Tartrate ion and the ions of other organic hydroxy acids form complex ions with Al^{+++}, Fe^{+++}, and Cr^{+++} in whose solutions ammonia produces no precipitate. In what way would the presence of these anions interfere with the analysis for the cations?

8. Structural formulæ such as

$$Ca\!\!\underset{O}{\overset{O}{\diamondsuit}}\!\!C=O$$

have sometimes been proposed for inorganic salts. Why must such a formula be considered incorrect?

9. Potassium amide is highly ionized in liquid ammonia. When a solution of KNH_2 in liquid ammonia is added to one of AlI_3 in the same solvent, a white precipitate forms at first and then dissolves when more KNH_2 is added. From the solution thus obtained the substance $KAl(NH_2)_4$ can be isolated by evaporation of the NH_3. Write equations for the reactions concerned. To what reactions in aqueous solution are these analogous? When NH_4I is added to a liquid ammonia solution of $KAl(NH_2)_4$, AlI_3, KI, and NH_3 are formed. Explain.

10. Davidson, *J. Am. Chem. Soc.*, **50**: 1,890 (1928), found that zinc acetate is practically insoluble in anhydrous pure acetic acid, but dissolves upon addition of sodium acetate. Is this reaction related to any that occur in aqueous solution?

11. The usual soluble salts of titanium are derived from the ion Ti^{++++}. The hydroxide $Ti(OH)_4$ is even less soluble than the hydroxides of Al^{+++}, Fe^{+++}, and Cr^{+++}, and is not amphoteric. No sulfide can be precipitated from aqueous solution. Ti^{++++} gives no color reaction with SCN^-, but does give a yellow to red color with H_2O_2 in acid solution. How would you modify the method of analysis given on page 197 if titanium ion is to be tested for?

12. The common compounds of molybdenum are derived from molybdate ion, $MoO_4{}^-$. This resembles $CrO_4{}^-$ in many ways but gives a slow precipitation of MoS_3 when H_2S is passed into an acid solution. MoS_3 is practically insoluble in 12 n HCl, but dissolves in warm HNO_3 and in solutions of Na_2S and $(NH_4)_2S$. It is reprecipitated from the solutions in alkali sulfides by addition of acids. What further information about the properties of molybdenum do you need in order to expand the scheme of analysis for the cations to include tests for the ions of molybdenum?

CHAPTER VI

OXIDATION-REDUCTION REACTIONS

On the Writing of Oxidation-reduction Reactions.—The equation for an oxidation-reduction reaction may be written whenever the actual reactants and products are known by a procedure which we shall illustrate in terms of the reaction between permanganate and ferrous ions in acid solution. We treat the reaction as the result of two steps, the oxidation of ferrous ion to ferric ion which liberates electrons, and the reduction of permanganate ion to manganous ion which consumes electrons (see page 18). The equation for the first of these is easily written; it consists in the conversion of ferrous ion with two positive charges to ferric ion with three by the loss of an electron. If we use the symbol e for the electron the equation is therefore

$$Fe^{++} \rightleftarrows Fe^{+++} + e. \tag{1}$$

It is an important feature of this equation that it is balanced electrically as well as chemically. The electrical charge on the left consists of the two positive charges of the ferrous ion; the net charge on the right is likewise two, the resultant of the three positive charges on the ferric ion and the single negative charge which the electron represents.

To write the equation for the reduction of permanganate ion, we note that permanganate ion contains oxygen atoms, which are not present in the manganous ion formed by the reduction. This oxygen is not liberated as O_2; experiment shows that H_2O_2 is not formed in the reaction; therefore the only possible form in which the oxygen can exist after the reduction has taken place is water (hydroxyl ion might be formed as an intermediate in the reaction, but would be converted to water in the acid solution). But water contains hydrogen, the only source for which is oxonium ion or some other acid in the solution. For the sake of simplicity we shall write hydrogen ion, H^+, as a sort of symbol

133

for any acid, but shall keep in mind that hydrogen ion is not present in the free state in the solution but only in some form of combination. The 4 molecules of water require 8 hydrogen ions. We now have

$$MnO_4^- + 8H^+ \rightarrow Mn^{++} + 4H_2O.$$

This is balanced as to atoms but not as to charges. The net charge on the left is $8 - 1 = +7$; the charge on the right is $+2$. Writing in 5 electrons on the left gives us therefore the completely balanced equation

$$MnO_4^- + 8H^+ + 5e \rightleftarrows Mn^{++} + 4H_2O. \tag{2}$$

To combine this reduction with the oxidation of ferrous ion [Eq. (1)] we note that the latter must be multiplied term by term by 5 in order that it shall represent the production of the 5 electrons necessary in the permanganate reduction. Then simple algebraic addition with cancellation of the 5 electrons which appear on both sides leads to

$$MnO_4^- + 8H^+ + 5Fe^{++} \rightleftarrows Mn^{++} + 4H_2O + 5Fe^{+++}. \tag{3}$$

This equation has been arrived at by a process of elimination. It is the only equation which fits the known facts about the products of the reaction and the principle that neither atoms nor electrons appear out of nothingness or vanish in a chemical reaction. It is therefore not surprising that the equation leads to correct quantitative predictions about the reaction. Thus experiment shows that 1 mole of permanganate ion does react with exactly 5 moles of ferrous ion; that 5 moles of ferric ion and 1 mole of manganous ion are produced; and that 8 moles of acid are actually consumed during the course of the reaction of 1 mole of permanganate.

In one respect, the use of hydrogen ion instead of an actual acid, Eq. (3) is still incomplete. The complete equation must indicate this acid and account for the fate of the residue (the base, see page 15) left when hydrogen ion is removed from it. When the reaction takes place in a solution of a strong acid in water, the acid is oxonium ion, and the removal of 8 hydrogen ions from 8 oxonium ions leaves 8 water molecules which must appear among the products of the reaction. The equation therefore becomes for this case

$$MnO_4^- + 8OH_3^+ + 5Fe^{++} \rightleftarrows Mn^{++} + 12H_2O + 5Fe^{+++}. \quad (4)$$

If the reaction is carried out in aqueous acetic acid, similar reasoning leads to the equation

$$MnO_4^- + 8HC_2H_3O_2 + 5Fe^{++} \rightleftarrows Mn^{++} + 4H_2O + \\ 8C_2H_3O_2^- + 5Fe^{+++}. \quad (5)$$

The case in which the acid is water is of especial interest. It would apply if the reaction took place in alkaline solution. Here the removal of 8 hydrogen ions from the acid water leaves 8 hydroxyl ions, giving the equation

$$MnO_4^- + 8H_2O + 5Fe^{++} \rightleftarrows Mn^{++} + 4H_2O + 8OH^- + \\ 5Fe^{+++}. \quad (6)$$

It is an obvious simplification to cancel 4 water molecules leading to the final form

$$MnO_4^- + 4H_2O + 5Fe^{++} \rightleftarrows Mn^{++} + 8OH^- + 5Fe^{+++}. \quad (7)$$

At first sight this looks like a very different equation from Eq. (4), actually it means the same thing experimentally. In the one equation hydroxyl ions are produced, in the other oxonium ions are consumed; the two statements have with respect to most phenomena occurring in dilute aqueous solutions identical meanings (see page 90). The one exception, phenomena related to reaction rates, has no bearing here because all these complex oxidation-reduction reactions take place by means of a complicated series of intermediate steps. Information obtained from reaction-rate studies bears only on the mechanism of the slow step or steps whose rates determine that of the total reaction.

This method of writing an oxidation-reduction reaction is a perfectly general one. We may note a few more examples. In the first place Eq. (2) for the reduction of permanganate to manganous ion may be used as a step in writing the equation for the reaction of permanganate with any reducing agent which converts it to manganous ion. Thus the equation for the oxidation of iodide ion to iodine is

$$2I^- \rightleftarrows I_2 + 2e. \quad (8)$$

To combine it with the equation for the permanganate reduction, the latter equation must be multiplied term by term by 2, and the iodide equation must be multiplied in the same way by 5 in order that the number of electrons consumed and produced shall be the same when the equations are combined. The combination yields

$$2MnO_4^- + 16H^+ + 10I^- \rightleftarrows 2Mn^{++} + 8H_2O + 5I_2. \qquad (9)$$

The reactions of sulfide ion with nitrate ion furnish two examples which are both instructive and inherently important because they account for the solution of very insoluble sulfides in nitric acid. The two reactions occur simultaneously and are, so to speak, in competition with each other. In one of these sulfide ion is oxidized to sulfur

$$S^= \rightleftarrows S + 2e. \qquad (10)$$

If dilute nitric acid is used as the oxidizing agent, the nitrate ion is reduced to nitric oxide, NO. This is an experimental result, which cannot be predicted by any rules, and must be determined by experiment for each combination of oxidant and reductant. The reduction of nitrate ion might lead to NO_2, to N_2O, to N_2, to NH_3, or to other products, and indeed all of these substances can be obtained by reduction of nitrate ion under proper conditions.

Since nitric oxide, NO, contains 2 less atoms of oxygen than does nitrate ion, NO_3^-, 2 molecules of water must be formed in the reduction, and 4 hydrogen ions must be used to form this water. Writing down these facts, and summing up charges to determine the number of electrons consumed, the equation

$$NO_3^- + 4H^+ + 3e \rightleftarrows NO + 2H_2O \qquad (11)$$

is obtained. Since 3 electrons are used in the reduction of 1 nitrate ion, and 2 are formed by the oxidation of 1 sulfide ion, it follows that the oxidation of 3 sulfide ions will require 2 nitrate ions, and 2×4 hydrogen ions. The complete equation is therefore

$$2NO_3^- + 3S^= + 8H^+ \rightleftarrows 2NO + 3S + 4H_2O. \qquad (12)$$

In the other reaction sulfide ion is oxidized to sulfate ion

$$S^= + 4H_2O \rightleftarrows SO_4^= + 8H^+ + 8e. \qquad (13)$$

The equation is derived from the consideration that the 4 oxygen atoms in the sulfate ion can only have come from 4 molecules of water, and that the 8 hydrogen ions of these water molecules must thereby have appeared in the form of some acid, which we symbolize by H^+. The combination of this equation with Eq. (11) offers one new feature, the cancellation of hydrogen ions and water molecules. In order that the electrons shall cancel when the equations are combined, Eq. (13) must be multiplied by 3 and Eq. (11) by 8. The addition yields

$$8NO_3^- + 32H^+ + 3S^= + 12H_2O \rightleftarrows 8NO + 16H_2O + 3SO_4^= + 24H^+$$

which we, of course, simplify by canceling hydrogen ions and water molecules as far as possible.

$$8NO_3^- + 8H^+ + 3S^= \rightleftarrows 8NO + 3SO_4^= + 4H_2O. \qquad (14)$$

One more point about the writing of equations. The final equation must balance, in the sense that the number of atoms of any kind appearing among the reactants must be the same as the number of atoms of that kind among the products, and also in the sense that the net charge of reactants and products must be the same. In Eq. (14) there are 8 nitrogen atoms, 24 oxygens, 8 hydrogens, and 3 sulfurs on both sides of the equation. Further, the net charge on the left is $-8 + 8 - 6 = -6$, and the net charge on the right is -6. It is extremely important to check every reaction equation for balance and especially for electrical balance because an error in the derivation of the equation is more likely to lead to a lack of electrical balance than to a lack of atomic balance.

The Interpretation of Oxidation-reduction Equations.—We can derive two kinds of information from an oxidation-reduction equation, either of which would abundantly justify the trouble of writing the equation. In the first place the equation tells us immediately the proportions in which the various reactants take part in the reaction and in which the various products are formed. In the second place it tells us through the application of the law of chemical equilibrium the effect of any change in concentration of reactants or products upon the equilibrium of the reaction. Thus in the permanganate-ferrous reaction, the law of chemical equilibrium yields

$$\frac{[Mn^{++}][Fe^{+++}]^5}{[MnO_4^-][OH_3^+]^8[Fe^{++}]^5} = K. \tag{15}$$

Clearly the conversion of permanganate and ferrous ions to manganous and ferric ions is favored by high acidity, because the higher the concentration of oxonium ion the larger the quantity $[Mn^{++}][Fe^{+++}]/[MnO_4^-][Fe^{++}]$ must be if Eq. (15) is to be satisfied. Actually this reaction goes to completion within the precision of our measurements when the solution is acid, and the situation at lower acidities is complicated by the precipitation of ferrous, manganous, and ferric hydroxides, and by the occurrence of other reactions which consume a smaller proportion of hydrogen ion. Indeed the ability to predict the equilibrium in these complex oxidation-reduction reactions is of less value than would be expected, because the occurrence or nonoccurrence of reaction often depends upon reaction rates rather than upon reaction equilibrium. Therefore it is more likely to be a question whether the reaction is fast enough to be of any value, instead of whether the final state of equilibrium, if we could wait long enough for it, would represent any extensive reaction.

Thus in the nitrate-sulfide reactions [Eqs. (12) and (14)] nitrate ion does not oxidize sulfide ion at an appreciable rate unless the solution is strongly acid. For this reason sodium nitrate does not have the solvent action on difficultly soluble sulfides that nitric acid has. At the same time, however, NO does not reduce sulfur or sulfate ion as would necessarily be the case if the failure to react of the sulfide and nitrate ions depended solely upon an unfavorable equilibrium point in a mobile reaction system.

Unfortunately we cannot predict reaction rates or reaction mechanisms with any assurance from the overall equation alone. It is certain that the process of liberation of electrons from the reductant followed by reaction of the oxidant with the electrons which we have set up as a convenient picture to aid in writing equations does not represent the true course of the reaction. This follows partly from the convincing evidence of Faraday's laws (page 20) that free electrons do not exist in aqueous solution; partly from the fact that no oxidation-reduction reaction whose rate is measurable has properties which can be reconciled with this mechanism. Even so apparently simple a reaction as

$$2Fe^{+++} + 2I^- \rightleftarrows 2Fe^{++} + I_2 \tag{16}$$

has a complicated mechanism involving several steps.

The reaction of nitrate ion with sulfide ion like the reaction of nitrate ion with many reducing agents is strongly catalyzed by the reduction products of the nitrate. This is so much the case with the reaction with metals that mercury and copper practically do not react with nitric acid from which nitrous acid and nitrogen oxides have been carefully removed. The only conceivable interpretation of these results is a reaction mechanism involving several steps, in one of which some reduction product of nitric acid reacts with nitric acid to form a product which reacts rapidly with the metal whereas nitric acid itself reacts at a negligible rate. Such a series of reactions might be

$$4H^+ + 4NO_3^- + 2NO \rightleftarrows 3N_2O_4 + 2H_2O \tag{17}$$
$$N_2O_4 + 2Cu + 4H^+ \rightleftarrows 2Cu^{++} + 2NO + 2H_2O. \tag{18}$$

Nevertheless, it remains true as a matter of practical experience that most reactions which consume hydrogen ion actually do go more rapidly the higher the acidity of the solution. As we have seen, this is strikingly true of the reaction of nitrate ion with sulfide ion, which only takes place to a significant extent in acid solution. It is true of many permanganate reactions also. Thus the addition of permanganate to a solution of bromide ion acidified with a strong acid gives a practically instantaneous reaction according to the equation

$$2MnO_4^- + 16H^+ + 10Br^- \rightleftarrows 2Mn^{++} + 8H_2O + 5Br_2. \tag{19}$$

The purple color of the permanganate disappears and the brown color of the bromine takes its place. If the same experiment is performed in the presence of acetic acid instead of a strong acid, the reaction is very slow, and the disappearance of the permanganate color may require an hour or more.

Polar Number and Valence.—If sulfate ion is looked upon as a complex of S^{++++++} with $4O^=$ (and it has certain attributes of such a form of combination—see page 12), the number 6 of positive charges on the central sulfur atom is necessarily equal to the number of electrons set free by the oxidation in aqueous solution of elementary sulfur to sulfate ion. For the oxidation may be supposed to take place in the steps

$$S \rightleftarrows S^{++++++} + 6e \tag{20}$$
$$4H_2O \rightleftarrows 4O^= + 8H^+ \tag{21}$$
$$S^{++++++} + 4O^= \rightleftarrows SO_4^=. \tag{22}$$

Except for persulfate ion, which is really a special case, sulfate ion is the most highly oxidized sulfur compound, and it is a striking fact that the 6 electrons which must be lost in its formation correspond exactly to the 6 which must be lost if a sulfur atom is to be converted to an ion which has the same number of electrons as the next lower inert gas neon (see page 5). Similarly the equations

$$N_2 + 6H_2O \rightleftarrows 2NO_3^- + 12H^+ + 10e \tag{23}$$
$$P + 4H_2O \rightleftarrows PO_4^= + 8H^+ + 5e \tag{24}$$

show that the nitrogen and phosphorus ions which may be thought of as the nuclei of the nitrate and phosphate ions have the same numbers of electrons as the inert gases helium and neon, respectively. And the equation

$$Cl_2 + 8H_2O \rightleftarrows 2ClO_4^- + 16H^+ + 14e \tag{25}$$

shows that the chlorine ion which may be thought of as the central atom of perchlorate ion has the same number of electrons as neon. These results are in agreement with the idea that an atom can easily lose or gain enough electrons to attain the structure of an inert gas, but that further loss or gain is too difficult to occur in a chemical reaction (see page 5).

Persulfate ion is an apparent exception. To form it from sulfur requires the loss of 7 electrons per sulfur atom

$$2S + 8H_2O \rightleftarrows S_2O_8^= + 16H^+ + 14e \tag{26}$$

and the fact that it is one unit more positive than sulfate ion is demonstrated by its preparation by electrolytic oxidation of the latter

$$2SO_4^= \rightleftarrows S_2O_8^= + 2e. \tag{27}$$

The difficulty may be resolved by noting that persulfate ion is easily hydrolyzed to sulfate ion and hydrogen peroxide

$$S_2O_8^= + 2H_2O \rightleftarrows 2SO_4^= + H_2O_2 + 2H^+. \tag{28}$$

It is therefore entirely reasonable to consider that peroxide ion, $O_2^=$, as well as oxide ion is involved in the formation of this complex.

$$2S^{++++++} + O_2^= + 6O^= \rightleftarrows S_2O_8^=. \tag{29}$$

The number of electrons lost in the formation of a complex ion or other compound from the element may be called the *polar number* (a term suggested by Bray and Branch) or the *oxidation level* of the central atom of the complex. It has often been called the *valence* of that atom, but the word valence has been used in so many and such contradictory meanings that it has become a very vague and unsatisfactory term.

Cuprous Compounds.—The properties of elements of variable polar number offer some interesting features, for the intermediate oxidation levels can act both as oxidants and as reductants. Thus when the attempt is made to prepare a soluble ionized cuprous salt, say by the action of dilute sulfuric acid on cuprous oxide, there is obtained instead metallic copper and a cupric salt. Cuprous ion acts upon itself and is both oxidized and reduced.

$$2Cu^+ \rightleftarrows Cu + Cu^{++}. \tag{30}$$

The law of chemical equilibrium applied to this reaction tells us that in any solution in the presence of solid copper (in which the concentration of elementary copper may be considered constant) the equation

$$\frac{[Cu^{++}]}{[Cu^+]^2} = K \tag{31}$$

must be satisfied, the constant K being clearly a large number. (If metallic copper is absent, the ratio $[Cu^{++}]/[Cu^+]^2$ must be even larger.) That is to say, any aqueous solution containing copper compounds must contain a very much larger concentration of cupric than of cuprous ion. This requirement does not, however, in any way prohibit the stable existence of cuprous compounds provided they are of a kind which do not give rise to any large concentration of cuprous ion in solution.

In agreement with this it is found that very insoluble cuprous compounds like the hydroxide, the oxide, and the iodide, and very stable complexes like the chloride $CuCl_3^=$, and the cyanide, $Cu(CN)_3^=$, do not decompose in this way. Furthermore, the reaction of Eq. (30) is reversible, and cupric ion can actually be reduced to cuprous ion by copper metal provided some reagent is present which maintains the cuprous ion concentration at a very low level. One of the easiest ways to make a cuprous compound is, in fact, to reduce cupric chloride with copper in strong hydrochloric acid solution, the cuprous ion being tied up very firmly in the complex by the large chloride ion concentration. Other reducing agents might be used, hydrogen sulfide reduces cupric salts in the presence of strong hydrochloric acid, but the use of copper as a reductant has the advantage that the oxidation product of the reductant is the same as the desired reduction product of the oxidant.

Certain reagents act simultaneously as reducing agents and as precipitants or complex formers. Thus iodide ion added to a solution of a cupric salt precipitates cuprous iodide with liberation of iodine

$$2Cu^{++} + 4I^- \rightleftarrows 2CuI + I_2. \tag{32}$$

Cyanide ion likewise reduces cupric ion to form the very stable cuprocyanide complex. The reaction product varies with the acidity of the solution. Unless the solution is alkaline the reaction is

$$2Cu^{++} + 8CN^- \rightleftarrows 2Cu(CN)_3^= + (CN)_2. \tag{33}$$

Cyanide should never be added to a cupric salt solution which has not first been made alkaline, because of the volatile and extremely poisonous nature of cyanogen, $(CN)_2$. When the solution has been made alkaline with ammonia the reaction is

$$2Cu^{++} + 7CN^- + H_2O \rightleftarrows 2Cu(CN)_3^= + CNO^- + 2H^+, \tag{34}$$

which may be built up from the steps

$$Cu^{++} + e \rightleftarrows Cu^+, \tag{35}$$
$$CN^- + H_2O \rightleftarrows CNO^- + 2H^+ + 2e, \tag{36}$$
$$Cu^+ + 3CN^- \rightleftarrows Cu(CN)_3^=. \tag{37}$$

The student should note that this reaction is one which produces hydrogen ion, and that it should be favored by alkaline solution, as is the case. The value of this cyanide reaction in preventing the precipitation of copper sulfide so that cadmium ion can be tested for by sulfide precipitation in the presence of copper compounds is discussed on page 122.

Ferrous and Stannous Salts.—With iron the equilibrium is in the other direction. Ionized ferric salts are reduced quantitatively by metallic iron, the product of both oxidation and reduction being ferrous ion.

$$Fe + 2Fe^{+++} \rightleftarrows 3Fe^{++}. \tag{38}$$

Similarly with tin, chlorostannate ion is quantitatively reduced to stannous ion by metallic tin,

$$Sn + SnCl_6^= \rightleftarrows 2Sn^{++} + 6Cl^-. \tag{39}$$

Much the best way of preparing pure ferrous and stannous salt solutions is to treat the impure solution with iron or tin, respectively. By keeping the purified solution in contact with the metal it is protected against the oxidizing action of the atmosphere.

If alkali is added to the tin solution, stannous ion is converted to stannite ion, and chlorostannate ion to stannate ion. The former reaction tends to shift the equilibrium of the reaction in favor of the stannous compound, just as complex formation with cuprous ion favored the formation of cuprous compounds from cupric compounds and copper. But the formation of stannate ion tends to shift the equilibrium in the other direction, and the result of these opposing tendencies must depend upon the relative stabilities of the two complexes. Actually the stannate complex is so much more stable than the stannite that stannite ion reduces itself slowly to metallic tin. The reaction is

$$2Sn(OH)_3^- \rightleftarrows Sn(OH)_6^= + Sn \tag{40}$$

which may be built up from the steps

$$Sn(OH)_3^- + 3H^+ + 2e \rightleftarrows Sn + 3H_2O \tag{41}$$

$$Sn(OH)_3^- + 3H_2O \rightleftarrows Sn(OH)_6^= + 3H^+ + 2e. \tag{42}$$

It is only the slowness of this reaction which makes it possible to prepare stannite solutions and to use freshly prepared solutions as reagents.

Stannite ion will also reduce to the metal the small concentration of bismuth ion in a saturated solution of bismuth hydroxide. The reaction equation

$$2Bi(OH)_3 + 3Sn(OH)_3^- + 3H_2O \rightleftarrows 2Bi +$$
$$3Sn(OH)_6^= + 3H^+ \quad (43)$$

may be derived from Eq. (42) and the step

$$Bi(OH)_3 + 3H^+ + 3e \rightleftarrows Bi + 3H_2O. \quad (44)$$

Manganese Compounds.—In general, a similar effect of hydrogen ion concentration exists whenever oxide complexes are concerned. Permanganate ion may be reduced either to manganous ion or to manganese dioxide, depending on the acidity

$$MnO_4^- + 8H^+ + 5e \rightleftarrows Mn^{++} + 4H_2O \quad (45)$$
$$MnO_4^- + 4H^+ + 3e \rightleftarrows MnO_2 + 2H_2O. \quad (46)$$

The second reaction requires less hydrogen ion, and should be less markedly affected by decreasing acidity than is the first. In fact, permanganate is, in general, reduced to manganous ion in acid solution and to manganese dioxide in neutral and alkaline solutions.

Similarly, an oxidant may oxidize manganous ion to manganese dioxide or to permanganate ion. The possible reactions are

$$Mn^{++} + 2H_2O \rightleftarrows MnO_2 + 4H^+ + 2e \quad (47)$$

and

$$Mn^{++} + 4H_2O \rightleftarrows MnO_4^- + 8H^+ + 5e. \quad (48)$$

The first reaction can be made to take place in strongly acid solution by a sufficiently powerful oxidizing agent. Thus chlorate ion in concentrated nitric acid solution oxidizes manganous ion quantitatively to manganese dioxide

$$2ClO_3^- + Mn^{++} \rightleftarrows 2ClO_2 + MnO_2. \quad (49)$$

This equation may be derived from Eq. (47) and the step

$$ClO_3^- + 2H^+ + e \rightleftarrows ClO_2 + H_2O. \quad (50)$$

The reaction is important because no other metallic ion gives the same reaction, and this manganese dioxide precipitation offers the most satisfactory means of separating manganous ion from the otherwise similar ferrous, cobaltous, and nickelous ions.

The solubility of manganese dioxide is so low that it becomes the favored product of the oxidation of manganous ion as well as of the reduction of permanganate ion in neutral or alkaline solution. In such media manganous ion reacts with permanganate ion to form manganese dioxide and the reaction goes practically to completion

$$3Mn^{++} + 2MnO_4^- + 2H_2O \rightleftarrows 5MnO_2 + 4H^+. \quad (51)$$

Only the most powerful oxidizing agents such as bismuth dioxide, BiO_2, lead dioxide, PbO_2, and persulfate ion, $S_2O_8^=$, are capable of the oxidation of manganous ion to permanganate ion. Obviously, it requires an oxidant more powerful than the permanganate which is to be formed. The bismuth dioxide reaction may be written

$$BiO_2 + 4H^+ + e \rightleftarrows Bi^{+++} + 2H_2O \quad (52)$$

which, with the manganous-permanganate reaction, gives

$$Mn^{++} + 5BiO_2 + 12H^+ \rightleftarrows MnO_4^- + 5Bi^{+++} + 6H_2O. \quad (53)$$

Mercurous Salts.—The case of mercurous salts is peculiar. Mercurous ion has been shown definitely to be Hg_2^{++} instead of Hg^+. The equilibrium

$$Hg_2^{++} \rightleftarrows Hg + Hg^{++} \quad (54)$$

may be looked upon either as the dissociation of a complex of mercury and mercuric ion or as the reduction of one simple mercurous ion by another. This is one of those questions of polar-number assignment to which no certain answer can be given.

With soluble ionized salts the equilibrium is in favor of mercurous ion. Mercuric nitrate, a strong electrolyte, is reduced quantitatively by metallic mercury to mercurous nitrate, likewise a strong electrolyte. But the equilibrium may be displaced in favor of mercury and mercuric ion by any reagent which sufficiently decreases the concentration of mercuric ion, and a number of such reagents are known. Mercuric sulfide is extremely insoluble, and the addition of hydrogen sulfide to a solution of a mercurous salt precipitates a mixture of mercury and mercuric sulfide

$$Hg_2^{++} + S^= \rightleftarrows Hg + HgS. \tag{55}$$

Mercuric cyanide is an extremely weak electrolyte, and the addition of potassium cyanide to a mercurous salt gives mercuric cyanide and a precipitate of metallic mercury. The amido-mercuric compounds described on page 118 are likewise very stable, and ammonia reacts with mercurous compounds to give mercury and a mercuric-amido compound. The reaction is frequently used for the characterization of mercurous ion in the presence of silver ion. The two are precipitated together as the difficultly soluble chlorides, filtered, and treated with ammonia. The silver chloride dissolves forming the silver-ammonia complex ion, the mercurous chloride reacts

$$Hg_2Cl_2 \rightleftarrows Hg + HgCl_2, \tag{56}$$
$$HgCl_2 + 2NH_3 \rightleftarrows HgNH_2Cl + NH_4^+ + Cl^- \tag{57}$$

or, in sum,

$$Hg_2Cl_2 + 2NH_3 \rightleftarrows HgNH_2Cl + Hg + NH_4^+ + Cl^-. \tag{58}$$

Two insoluble substances are formed, mercury, and amido-mercuric chloride. The black color of the finely divided mercury proves the presence of mercurous ion in the original solution.

The Chemistry of Cobalt and Nickel.—The commonest cobalt compounds are derived from cobaltous ion, Co^{++}. Free or hydrated cobaltic ion Co^{+++} is not stable in aqueous solution, being in fact so powerful an oxidant that it slowly liberates oxygen from the solution.

$$4Co^{+++} + 2H_2O \rightleftarrows 4Co^{++} + 4H^+ + O_2. \tag{59}$$

There are many stable complexes derived from the triply positive ion (see page 126), and these are so much more stable than the corresponding cobaltous complexes that Eq. (59) is reversed. Thus the cobalto-cyanide ion is rapidly oxidized by molecular oxygen

$$4Co(CN)_6^\equiv + O_2 + 4H^+ \rightleftarrows 4Co(CN)_6^= + 2H_2O. \tag{60}$$

The cobaltous ammonia ion is likewise oxidized by oxygen, but the product is mainly a polynuclear peroxide-ammonia complex.

The situation is very different with nickel ion where the only known compound derivable from the triply charged ion is the oxide Ni_2O_3. Its existence may be attributed to low solubility.

The Analytical Chemistry of Cobalt and Nickel. *Direct Tests.*—The separation of cobaltous and nickel ions and the detection of cobaltous ion are best carried out by precipitating the cobalt as potassium cobaltinitrite, a salt of a cobaltic complex. The oxidant used to oxidize the cobaltous ion to the cobaltic state is the same nitrite ion which forms the complex. The reaction is

$$Co^{++} + 7NO_2^- + 2H^+ \rightleftarrows Co(NO_2)_6^= + NO + H_2O \quad (61)$$

which may be written by using the steps

$$Co^{++} \rightleftarrows Co^{+++} + e \quad (62)$$
$$NO_2^- + 2H^+ + e \rightleftarrows NO + H_2O \quad (63)$$
$$Co^{+++} + 6NO_2^- \rightleftarrows Co(NO_2)_6^=. \quad (64)$$

Hydrogen ion is consumed, and the reaction takes place only if the solution is moderately acid. If it is too acid, however, the nitrite ion is largely converted into the weakly ionized nitrous acid, and the cobaltous ion can be oxidized only if there is much nitrite ion present to convert cobaltic ion very completely into the complex. The conditions actually used, acetic acid and a large concentration of potassium nitrite, really give a nitrite buffer, which has the maximum hydrogen ion concentration compatible with a large nitrite ion concentration.

Strong acids decompose the complex by removing nitrite ion. The cobaltic ion then oxidizes nitrite to nitrate and returns itself to the cobaltous state. Alkalis decompose the complex by precipitating the very insoluble cobaltic hydroxide. When testing for cobaltous ion potassium nitrite is used, and the complex, if formed, is precipitated as the difficultly soluble potassium salt. The same precipitation may be used to test for potassium ion by making up a reagent solution from cobalt nitrate, sodium nitrite, and acetic acid.

This method of detecting cobaltous ion illustrates very well the danger of attempting direct tests, and the fact that it is impossible to find any reagent which can be added to an entirely unknown solution in the expectation of deciding immediately the question of the presence or absence of a particular ion. Thus a student, finding nickel and strontium in an unknown, and wishing to make a direct test for cobalt, might determine by experiment that strontium ion gives no precipitate with potassium nitrite. Knowing that nickel ion does not interfere, since the precipitation is the standard method of separating nickel and cobaltous ions, he might feel justified in assuming that the yellow precipitate which formed when he added potassium nitrite directly to the acetic acid solution of his unknown was sufficient proof of the presence of cobaltous ion. It is, in fact, insufficient because $K_2SrNi(NO_2)_6$ is yellow, difficultly soluble, and identical in appearance with potassium cobaltinitrite. To prove that nickel and strontium ions together do not interfere with the cobalt test, it is not sufficient to prove that neither does separately.

Nickel ion is usually detected by precipitation of the nickel salt of the weak organic acid dimethyl glyoxime. The test is as sure as any test known. If the characteristic pink precipitate of $Ni(C_4H_7O_2N_2)_2$ appears there can be no doubt of the presence of nickel ion, for the only other ion which gives a precipitate at all is the rather rare palladium, and the precipitate is very different in color from the nickel compound. The appearance of the pink precipitate proves the presence of nickel ion in the solution, but the failure of the precipitate to appear does not prove the absence of nickel ion in the solution.

Being the salt of a weak acid, nickel dimethyl glyoxime is not precipitated in acid solutions, except in very weakly acid ones. Being a nickel salt it is somewhat soluble in ammonia which converts the nickelous ion to the ammonia complex. If ammonia is used to neutralize the solution, excess must be avoided. The very fact that the solution must be neutral means that the precipitation cannot be carried out until ferric, aluminum, and chromic ions have been removed or tied up in complexes such as that with tartrate ion so that the hydroxides do not precipitate when the solution is neutralized. And cobaltous ion forms with dimethyl glyoxime a soluble compound very slightly ionized. So long as there is much cobaltous ion in a solution the dimethyl glyoxime combines with this rather than with the nickel ion, and this makes the possibility of missing nickel rather large unless the cobalt ion has first been removed. As a result of all these conditions nickel ion is usually tested for in a solution in which all other ions but the alkalis have been removed.

If it is desired to test a cobalt salt for the nickel salt from which it is so difficult to purify it, it is better to use another method of separation which depends upon the properties of the cyanide complexes of nickel and cobalt. If potassium cyanide is added to a solution containing nickel and cobaltous ions, the complex ions, $Ni(CN)_4^=$ and $Co(CN)_6^\equiv$ are formed. The latter is oxidized by atmospheric oxygen if the solution stands in the air; it will at any rate be oxidized when sodium hydroxide and bromine solutions are added. Sodium hypobromite is formed, and is a very powerful oxidant

$$2OH^- + Br_2 \rightleftarrows Br^- + BrO^- + H_2O \qquad (65)$$
$$BrO^- + 2Ni^{++} + 2H^+ \rightleftarrows Br^- + 2Ni^{+++} + H_2O. \qquad (66)$$

After the cobaltocyanide is oxidized to the stable cobalticyanide, the next most easily oxidized thing is the excess of cyanide ion. This goes to cyanate or even to carbon dioxide and nitrogen or ammonia, and it is therefore important not to add too much cyanide in forming the complexes, for much bromine will then be necessary. If the addition of bromine water is carried beyond this point, the nickel is oxidized, and black nickelic hydroxide precipitates.

Gold and Platinum Compounds: Aqua Regia.—No free or hydrated ions of the metals gold and platinum are known in solution, but there are many stable complex compounds. The commonest forms of combination are the chloraurates, $AuCl_4^-$, and the chloroplatinates, $PtCl_6^=$, which may be considered as containing triply positive gold and quadruply positive platinum, respectively. Both are formed by the action of aqua regia, a mixture of nitric and hydrochloric acids, on the metals. The nitrate ion is the oxidant

$$NO_3^- + 2H^+ + e \rightleftarrows NO_2 + H_2O \qquad (67)$$

but is quite ineffective without the presence of chloride ion to form the stable complexes.

Mercuric sulfide is another substance which is more soluble in *aqua regia* than in nitric acid alone, and the reason is again to be found in the formation of chloride complexes. The reaction to be desired is

$$HgS \rightarrow Hg^{++} + S^{=}. \tag{68}$$

Removal of the sulfide ion by oxidation with nitric acid is insufficient to make the solubility appreciable. The presence of chloride ion to remove the other product, mercuric ion, by forming with it the slightly ionized $HgCl_2$ and $HgCl_4^{=}$ causes a further increase in solubility so great that the precipitate is easily dissolved.

Hydrogen Peroxide.—When oxygen is reduced, the final product is water, or hydroxyl ion,

$$O_2 + 4H^+ + 4e \rightleftarrows 2H_2O \tag{69}$$

or

$$O_2 + 2H_2O + 4e \rightleftarrows 4OH^-. \tag{70}$$

The reduction can, however, be easily stopped at the intermediate stage of hydrogen peroxide, which is 2 electrons more negative than oxygen, instead of 4. The reaction

$$O_2 + 2H^+ + 2e \rightleftarrows H_2O_2 \tag{71}$$

can be carried out electrolytically by passing a current between inert electrodes immersed in a dilute sulfuric acid solution which is kept saturated with oxygen; it occurs also when the most diverse reductants act upon oxygen.

Hydrogen peroxide is therefore an intermediate oxidation level just as cuprous ion is. It can be oxidized to oxygen

$$H_2O_2 \rightleftarrows O_2 + 2H^+ + 2e \tag{72}$$

and dissolves manganese dioxide in acid solution by reducing it

$$MnO_2 + H_2O_2 + 2H^+ \rightleftarrows Mn^{++} + O_2 + 2H_2O. \tag{73}$$

Hydrogen peroxide can also be reduced

$$H_2O_2 + 2H^+ + 2e \rightleftarrows 2H_2O \tag{74}$$

and it is a valuable oxidizing agent.

The summation of the oxidation and the reduction is

$$2H_2O_2 \rightleftarrows O_2 + 2H_2O \tag{75}$$

which is the equation for the decomposition of hydrogen peroxide. The reaction is of the same type as the decomposition of cuprous salts,

$$2Cu^+ \rightleftarrows Cu + Cu^{++}. \tag{76}$$

That hydrogen peroxide exists at all is due to the slowness of this reaction. The equilibrium point at ordinary temperatures represents practically complete decomposition, and hydrogen peroxide is truly a very unstable substance. Hydroxyl ion greatly increases the rate of decomposition, certain organic compounds decrease the rate greatly. Acetanilide is often used in medicinal hydrogen peroxide as a stabilizer.

That hydrogen peroxide is an acid is shown by the existence of such salts as sodium peroxide and barium peroxide, but the soluble salts are very extensively hydrolyzed and hydrogen peroxide must be considered a very weak acid. Equations for the reactions of sodium peroxide may be written either in terms of peroxide ion, $O_2^=$, or of the hydrogen peroxide proceeding from it by the hydrolysis,

$$O_2^= + 2H_2O \rightleftarrows H_2O_2 + 2OH^-. \tag{77}$$

Of these sodium peroxide reactions a most important example is the oxidation of chromite ion to chromate.

$$O_2^= + 4H^+ + 2e \rightleftarrows 2H_2O \tag{78}$$
$$CrO_2^- + 2H_2O \rightleftarrows CrO_4^= + 4H^+ + 3e \tag{79}$$
$$2CrO_2^- + 3O_2^= + 4H^+ \rightleftarrows 2CrO_4^= + 2H_2O. \tag{80}$$

The equation seems to indicate a reaction which consumes hydrogen ion, which should be aided by increased acidity, whereas the reaction proceeds only in alkaline solution. This shows the care with which such interpretations should be made. What the equation really indicates is that an increase in acidity would favor the oxidation of the chromite ion if all the other concentrations were kept constant when the acidity was increased. But it is impossible to increase the acidity without decreasing the concentrations of both chromite and peroxide ions.

The reaction has great importance in analytical chemistry. Chromic ion is so similar to aluminum ion in its properties that a separation is impossible unless the chromium is transferred to a different oxidation level. Aluminate ion is unaffected by peroxide ion, and is so different from chromate ion that a separation becomes easy when the chromium is in the chromate form.

One of the reasons why peroxide is such a valuable reagent is the ease with which excess may be removed. Boiling an alkaline solution for a few minutes causes complete decomposition, and one product, oxygen, escapes, and is a normal constituent of. any solution in contact with the air in any case; the other product of the decomposition is the solvent water. If the excess peroxide were not removed the solution obtained by oxidizing chromite with peroxide could not be made acid, because peroxide in acid solution reduces chromate to chromic ion. The reaction is

$$3H_2O_2 + 2CrO_4^= + 10H^+ \rightleftarrows 3O_2 + 2Cr^{+++} + 8H_2O \quad (81)$$

but it goes through the unstable intermediate perchromic acid, $H_3CrO_8(H_2O)_2$, which is intensely blue in color.

Polysulfides.—In some ways similar to the peroxides are the polysulfides, which are formed by such reactions as

$$S^= + S \rightleftarrows S_2^=, \quad (82)$$
$$S^= + 4S \rightleftarrows S_5^=. \quad (83)$$

These are reversible, and the decreased sulfide ion concentration produced by the addition of acid to a polysulfide solution causes the precipitation of sulfur. The polysulfides are oxidants, and can be reduced to sulfide ion

$$S_2^= + 2e \rightleftarrows 2S^= \quad (84)$$
$$S_5^= + 8e \rightleftarrows 5S^=. \quad (85)$$

The sodium or ammonium sulfide solution used to separate the copper and tin groups often contains some polysulfide ion (produced by dissolving sulfur in the sodium or ammonium sulfide) to oxidize stannous and antimonous sulfides to the higher oxidation level (see page 124). The reaction of oxidation is, for instance

$$Sn^{++} + S_2^= \rightleftarrows Sn^{++++} + 2S^= \quad (86)$$

or

$$SnS + S_2^= \rightleftarrows SnS_2 + S^= \tag{87}$$

or

$$SnS + S_2^= \rightleftarrows SnS_3^=. \tag{88}$$

Polyhalides.—Similar are the polyhalides. Iodine is much more soluble in potassium iodide solutions than in water, and the increased solubility has been shown to be due chiefly to the formation of the tri-iodide ion, I_3^-. Tribromides, from Br_3^-, are also known, likewise mixed compounds like ICl_2^-.

From the results of this comparison one may group together peroxide, polysulfide, and polyhalide as similar addition compounds of neutral element and ion. Peroxides are unique only in that their reactions are so sluggish that they only decompose slowly under conditions which make them really unstable.

From another point of view pentasulfide ion, $S_5^=$, is tetrasulfo-sulfate ion, just as $SO_4^=$ is tetra-oxo-sulfate ion. Pentasulfide ion bears the same relation to sulfate ion that $AsS_4^\equiv$ does to $AsO_4^\equiv$. There is even one step in the transition; thiosulfate ion, $S_2O_3^=$, may be considered monosulfo-trioxo-sulfate ion.

Looked at from its relation to sulfate ion, pentasulfide ion appears as a sulfide complex ion in which the central atom is likewise sulfur but a highly oxidized sulfur with a polar number of 6. Looked at from its relation to the polyhalides, pentasulfide is likely to be thought of as a loose complex of 1 sulfide ion with 4 neutral sulfurs. Looked at from its relation to peroxide, it should be thought of as composed of 5 equivalent sulfur atoms carrying a negative charge, for the oxygens in peroxide are considered to be equivalent. These compounds furnish therefore excellent examples of the mixed nature of the linkages in complex compounds.

Suggestions for Reading

General: The references on atomic structure and chemical valence cited in Chap. I; JETTE, "Oxidation-reduction Reactions in Inorganic Chemistry," New York, 1927.

Reaction mechanisms: REINMUTH, *J. Chem. Education*, **6**, 527 (1929); **7**, 1180; 1689 (1930); BRAY, *loc. cit.*

Exercises

1. Write equations for all of the oxidation-reduction reactions encountered in your laboratory work.

2. Aluminum metal reacts with alkaline nitrate solutions, the products being ammonia and aluminate ion.   Write the equation.

3. In the following reactions state which substances are oxidized and which reduced.

$$Al^{+++} + 4OH^- \rightleftarrows AlO_2^- + 2H_2O.$$
$$Hg_2^{++} + 2NH_3 + Cl^- \rightleftarrows Hg^{''} + HgNH_2Cl + NH_4^+.$$
$$2HgCl_2 + Sn^{++} \rightleftarrows Hg_2Cl_2 + Sn^{++++} + 2Cl^-.$$
$$Mn^{++} + H_2O_2 \rightleftarrows MnO_2 + 2H^+.$$
$$Ba^{++} + H_2O_2 \rightleftarrows BaO_2 + 2H^+.$$
$$2Ag + Cl_2 \rightleftarrows 2AgCl.$$
$$Ag^+ + Cl' \rightleftarrows AgCl.$$

CHAPTER VII

OXIDATION POTENTIALS

On the Quantitative Measure of Oxidizing and Reducing Power.—In the previous chapter we have spoken several times of powerful oxidizing agents and of powerful reducing agents, and we now wish to give these vague terms a quantitative meaning. Consider an oxidant-reductant pair such as ferric ion–ferrous ion. If an electron in the reductant is loosely held, there will be a large tendency for this electron to be transferred to any oxidant which may be present, even if this is one which is difficult to reduce. Under these conditions we should certainly say that the reductant of the pair is a powerful reducing agent. We should also have to admit that the oxidant formed by the removal of an electron from the reductant is a weak oxidizing agent, because a loosely held electron in the reductant necessarily means that the oxidant has little tendency to add an electron to form the reductant. On the other hand a firmly bound electron in the reductant would make the reductant a weak reducing agent and the oxidant a powerful oxidizing agent.

Suppose some chemically inert metallic conductor, which we shall call an *electrode* (a piece of platinum, gold, or carbon) is introduced into the solution containing the oxidant-reductant pair. The metal contains electrons, the electrons which are responsible for its conducting properties (see page 19), and these electrons can be transferred to the solution provided there is something there, some oxidant to which they can attach themselves. This happens whenever the electrode serves as cathode in electrolysis. On the other hand, electrons can be transferred from a reductant in the solution to the electrode, and this process occurs inevitably whenever the electrode serves as anode.

If now the electrons in the reductant are loosely bound, if therefore the reductant is a powerful one and the oxidant a weak one, some electrons will be transferred from solution to electrode, and there will be an increase in the concentration of electrons in the electrode. If, on the other hand, the oxidant is strong and the reductant weak, the reverse process will occur, electrons will be transferred from electrode to solution, and the concentration of electrons in the electrode will decrease. Now we are unable to measure this increase or decrease in electron concentration, which would clearly represent a satisfactory criterion of oxidizing and reducing power; but we can compare the effect on two different electrodes, because electrons will tend to flow from the electrode of higher to that of lower electron concentration, and the flow of electrons is an electrical current. This makes it possible to compare two different oxidant-reductant systems. That one contains the more powerful reductant and the weaker oxidant in contact with which an inert electrode has the higher electron concentration.

· The Galvanic Cell.—Suppose we have two electrodes, one immersed in a solution containing ferric and ferrous ions, the other in a solution containing iodine and iodide ions, and suppose the electron concentration to be higher in the second than in the first. If the two electrodes are brought into metallic contact, there will be a flow of electrons, in itself too small to be detected, from the iodine electrode to the ferric-ferrous electrode. The iodide ions will tend to replenish the supply of electrons in the corresponding electrode, the ferric ions will tend to remove the added electrons from the electrode immersed in that solution; but neither process can continue for the following reason: To the extent that flow does take place, the iodine-iodide solution loses iodide ions at the electrode, but it does not lose the cations which are necessarily present with them. The solution therefore becomes positively charged, and this positive charge soon reaches the point where further loss of electrons to the electrode is impossible. Similarly, the reaction of ferric ions at the other electrode tends to leave unbalanced negative ions in the ferric-ferrous solution and to confer on it a negative charge.

These effects may be avoided by bringing the two solutions into electrolytic contact by a column of sodium chloride or other electrolyte (the ferric and iodide solutions must not be brought into direct contact because they would react). A convenient setup is shown in Fig. 9. One beaker contains the ferric-ferrous solution, the other the iodine-iodide solution. The inverted U-tube, with its ends loosely plugged with cotton, contains sodium chloride solution and is called a salt bridge.

If the wires leading from the electrodes are connected, a negative current flows from the iodine-iodide electrode to the ferric-ferrous electrode through the wires. This is easily shown by interposing a galvanometer as indicated. The flow of electricity is accompanied by reaction according to Faraday's laws (see

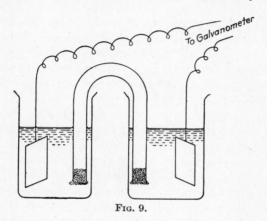

Fɪɢ. 9.

page 20); for every 96,500 coulombs one mole of iodide ion is oxidized to iodine and one mole of ferric ion is reduced to ferrous. The total chemical process is simply

$$2Fe^{+++} + 2I^- \rightleftarrows 2Fe^{++} + I_2 \tag{1}$$

which is exactly what would occur if the ferric ion and the iodide were brought together in the same solution.

Indeed this correspondence is a necessary one. In both cases the essential thing is a flow of electrons from iodide ions to ferric ions, in the one case directly from atom to atom, in the other through the metallic conductors. But the direction of such a flow of electrons is not dependent upon the path by which it takes place, any more than is the flow of water. If water flows spontaneously from one reservoir to another through one pipe, it can flow spontaneously only from the first to the second through any kind of a pipe. It never flows uphill unless it is pumped.

Oxidation Potentials.—If an electrical potential from outside is applied to a cell of the sort we have just described, in such a way that the outside potential is opposed to the spontaneous flow of current from the cell, the current will decrease as the potential increases, will pass through zero, and will then begin to flow in the opposite direction. When this happens, the direction of the reaction will also be reversed; in the case we have been considering iodine will be reduced to iodide ion and ferrous ion will be oxidized.

The electrical potential which just suffices to balance the chemical reaction in a cell in such a way that if the potential is

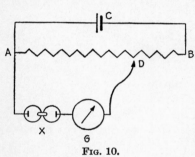

Fig. 10.

decreased a little, reaction takes place in one direction, and if the potential is slightly increased, reaction takes place in the opposite direction, is a most important quantity. It clearly is a measure of the tendency of the reaction to occur; it can be positive or negative, just as the tendency of the reaction may be in the one direction or in the other; when it is large, it is difficult to stop the reaction, when it is small, it is easy. This potential is called the potential of the cell.

For the measurement of the potentials of cells a potentiometer is used. A simplified diagram is shown in Fig. 10. A constant and known potential E_c is applied, for instance from a storage battery of large capacity C, to the ends of a resistance AB. The position of the contact D is varied until the galvanometer G shows that no measurable current flows through the circuit which includes the cell X and the galvanometer. The potential drop through the resistance AD is then just sufficient to balance the tendency of the reaction in cell X to take place. This potential E_x is related, according to familiar electrical laws, to the potential E_c and the resistances R_c of AB and R_x of AD by the equation

$$E_x = E_c \frac{R_x}{R_c}. \tag{2}$$

For many purposes of not too high precision a fairly sensitive high-resistance voltmeter connected between the points A and D will give a satisfactory value of the potential without the necessity of knowing the quantities E_c, R_x, and R_c.

The potential of a cell in one half of which the electrode reaction is

$$2OH_3{}^+ + 2e \rightleftarrows H_2 + 2H_2O \tag{3}$$

the solution being saturated with hydrogen at 1 atmosphere pressure, and the oxonium ion concentration being 1 mole per liter (this is called a normal hydrogen electrode) is called the oxidation potential of the oxidant-reductant system present in the other half of the cell. Such oxidation potentials have the extremely important property that the difference between any two of them is equal to the potential of a cell containing the two oxidant-reductant systems in question.

Thus the oxidation potential of a solution containing 0.1 M ferric ion and 0.1 M ferrous ion is +0.75 volt. The positive sign means that when the cell potential is measured, the positive side of the opposing potential from the potentiometer must be applied to the electrode immersed in the ferric-ferrous solution, and the negative side to the hydrogen electrode. Similarly the oxidation potential of a dilute solution of iodine and potassium iodide is in the neighborhood of +0.54, the positive sign having the same significance as in the other case.

Now the characteristic additive property of oxidation potentials leads to this result: that a cell one-half of which contains the ferric-ferrous solution, the other the iodine-iodide solution will have a potential of $0.75 - 0.54 = 0.21$ volt, and that the electrode in the ferric-ferrous solution will be the positive one. A little consideration will show that this must be so, otherwise it would be possible to construct a perpetual motion from a combination of the three cells which can be constructed from the three half-cells, ferric-ferrous, iodine-iodide, and hydrogen-oxonium ion. (The principle that a perpetual motion is impossible is so thoroughly established that the whole science of thermodynamics, one of the most valuable tools of the chemist, consists in working out the corollaries of that impossibility.)

If, then, we know the oxidation potential of any oxidant-reductant pair, we know also the potential of the cell formed by the combination of this pair with any other pair of known potential. More important than this, we know whether the oxidant in the first pair will oxidize the reductant in the second pair or whether the reaction will occur in the reverse direction when the two oxidant-reductant systems are brought together in the same solution. Thus the fact that the potential of the ferric-ferrous system is more positive than that of the iodine-iodide system means not only that the electrode in the ferric-ferrous solution in a cell involving these two systems will be the positive one, but it assures us that if the ferric-ferrous solution is mixed with the iodine-iodide one, the reaction that occurs will be

$$2Fe^{+++} + 2I^- \rightarrow 2Fe^{++} + I_2 \tag{4}$$

and not the reverse. The reasoning involved is the following: The positive potential of the ferric-ferrous system means that the tendency of the system is for the positive current to flow through a metallic conductor from the electrode in that system to the other electrode. This means that the electrons tend to flow in the opposite direction and that they must be supplied by the iodide ions

$$2I^- \rightarrow I_2 + 2e \tag{5}$$

and consumed by the ferric ions

$$Fe^{+++} + e \rightarrow Fe^{++}. \tag{6}$$

The reaction which accompanies the spontaneous flow of current must therefore be in the direction shown in Eq. (4).

But as we have seen (page 157), the direction of reaction must be the same when the two oxidant-reductant systems are mixed as is the case in the cell. Therefore we have the general rule: When solutions containing two oxidant-reductant systems are mixed, that system which has the more positive oxidation potential will furnish the oxidant, and that system which has the more negative oxidation potential will furnish the reductant in the reaction which ensues. In the case we have been discussing the more positive ferric-ferrous system furnishes the oxidant ferric ion, the more negative iodine-iodide system furnishes the reductant iodide ion in the reaction, Eq. (4), which occurs when the two systems are brought together.

To a certain extent these relations are approximate because there are electrical potential differences at the junction of two solutions of different compositions, which appear in the total potential measured. The consequent errors are not very important for the kind of discussion we are now concerned with; they may be very serious in accurate work. Their magnitude can be greatly decreased by having some electrolyte present in relatively large concentration in both half-cells and in the salt bridge. This electrolyte may, or may not, take part in the electrode reactions; so long as its concentration is constant throughout the cell and considerably larger than the concentration of the other electrolytes present, the junction potentials will be negligible.

There is an unfortunate disagreement among chemists on the assignment of plus and minus signs to oxidation potentials. It is perfectly possible to call all those potentials positive which we have called negative, and to call those potentials negative which we have called positive, and to carry through a consistent system on this basis. In terms of this system a large negative potential means a powerful oxidizing agent, a large positive potential a powerful reducing agent. While this system is used by an important group of chemists, the one here presented possesses on the whole the widest acceptance and has certain advantages of consistency.

The Effect of Concentration upon the Potential.—The direction in which a reversible chemical reaction takes place depends upon the concentrations of the various reactants and products; the oxidation potential must also be a function of concentration. We can more easily illustrate the form of this dependence than state it exactly. Let us confine our attention to a temperature of 25°C. Then the oxidation potential of the ferric-ferrous system has been found to follow the equation,

$$E_{Fe^{+++}, Fe^{++}} = E^\circ_{Fe^{+++}, Fe^{++}} + \frac{0.059}{1} \log \frac{[Fe^{+++}]}{[Fe^{++}]}. \quad (7)$$

The quantity $E^\circ_{Fe^{+++}, Fe^{++}}$ is called the molar potential of the oxidant-reductant system. It is the value possessed by the potential when the concentrations of ferric and ferrous ion are both unity (this follows from the equation; in that case the ratio $[Fe^{+++}]/[Fe^{++}]$ is one and its logarithm zero, hence $E_{Fe^{+++},\,Fe^{++}} = E°_{Fe^{+++},\,Fe^{++}}$). It represents the inherent nature of the particular oxidant-reductant system; the value is large and positive for systems involving characteristically powerful oxidizing agents;

TABLE VII.—MOLAR POTENTIALS AT 25°C.

Electrode Reaction	$E°$
$K^+ + e \rightleftarrows K$	-2.922
$Ba^{++} + 2e \rightleftarrows Ba$	-2.90
$Ca^{++} + 2e \rightleftarrows Ca$	-2.87
$Na^+ + e \rightleftarrows Na$	-2.713
$Mg^{++} + 2e \rightleftarrows Mg$	-2.40
$Zn^{++} + 2e \rightleftarrows Zn$	-0.758
$Fe^{++} + 2e \rightleftarrows Fe$	-0.44
$Cr^{+++} + e \rightleftarrows Cr^{++}$	-0.40
$Cd^{++} + 2e \rightleftarrows Cd$	-0.398
$Ni^{++} + 2e \rightleftarrows Ni$	-0.24
$SbO^+ + 2OH_3^+ + 3e \rightleftarrows Sb + 3H_2O$	-0.21
$Sn^{++} + 2e \rightleftarrows Sn$	-0.14
$Pb^{++} + 2e \rightleftarrows Pb$	-0.12
$2OH_3^+ + 2e \rightleftarrows H_2 + 2H_2O$	0
$Ti^{++++} + e \rightleftarrows Ti^{+++}$	0.0
$CuCl + e \rightleftarrows Cu + Cl^-$	$+0.129$
$Cu^{++} + 2e \rightleftarrows Cu$	$+0.344$
$O_2 + 2H_2O + 4e \rightleftarrows 4OH^-$	$+0.400$
$Fe(CN)_6^= + e \rightleftarrows Fe(CN)_6^≡$	$+0.489$
$I_2 + 2e \rightleftarrows 2I^-$	$+0.536$
$MnO_4^- + e \rightleftarrows MnO_4^=$	$+0.66$
$Fe^{+++} + e \rightleftarrows Fe^{++}$	$+0.748$
$Hg_2^{++} + 2e \rightleftarrows 2Hg$	$+0.799$
$Ag^+ + e \rightleftarrows Ag$	$+0.800$
$Mo(CN)_8^= + e \rightleftarrows Mo(CN)_8^≡$	$+0.82$
$2Hg^{++} + 2e \rightleftarrows Hg_2^{++}$	$+0.901$
$HVO_3 + 3OH_3^+ + e \rightleftarrows VO^{++} + 5H_2O$	$+0.9$
$AuCl_4^- + 3e = Au + 4Cl^-$	$+1.00$
$Br_2 + 2e = 2Br^-$	$+1.066$
$O_2 + 4OH_3^+ + 4e = 6H_2O$	$+1.23$
$MnO_2 + 4OH_3^+ + 2e = Mn^{++} + 6H_2O$	$+1.33$
$Cl_2 + 2e = 2Cl^-$	$+1.359$
$Ce^{++++} + e = Ce^{+++}$	$+1.6$
$PbO_2 + 4OH_3^+ + SO_4^= + 2e \rightleftarrows PbSO_4 + 6H_2O$	$+1.68$
$Co^{+++} + e = Co^{++}$	$+1.82$

it is large and negative for systems involving characteristically powerful reducing agents. Table VII contains some important molar potentials. The quantity 0.059 is a theoretical constant whose value may be derived from thermodynamics. This constant is proportional to the absolute temperature. The quantity in the denominator before the *log* sign is called the *valence factor*. This is the number of electrons involved in the electrode reaction. In this case the reaction is given by Eq. (6), one electron is involved, and the valence factor is unity. Instead of the concentrations of ferric and ferrous ions, we might write the activities (see page 64), but little would really be gained because the error involved in using concentrations is about the same as the unavoidable one due to junction potentials (see page 161).

Where one concentration is automatically maintained constant, we do not write that constant concentration in the equation, but modify the meaning of the molar potential to take account of the omission. Thus the equation for the silver-silver ion system is written

$$E_{Ag^+, Ag} = E^\circ_{Ag^+, Ag} + \frac{0.059}{1} \log [Ag^+] \qquad (8)$$

and the quantity $E^\circ_{Ag^+, Ag}$ is the potential when the concentration of silver ion is unity and the concentration of silver is that present in solid silver.

For the cupric ion-copper system the equation involves a valence factor of two because the reaction is

$$Cu^{++} + 2e \rightleftarrows Cu. \qquad (9)$$

The equation for the potential is therefore

$$E_{Cu^{++}, Cu} = E^\circ_{Cu^{++}, Cu} + \frac{0.059}{2} \log [Cu^{++}]. \qquad (10)$$

If two molecules of a given kind take part in the electrode reaction, it has been found that the concentration of that substance must be squared in the potential formula. Thus with the iodine-iodide system for which the electrode process is

$$I_2 + 2e \rightleftarrows 2I^- \qquad (11)$$

the equation for the potential is

$$E_{I_2, I^-} = E^\circ_{I_2, I^-} + \frac{0.059}{2} \log \frac{[I_2]}{[I^-]^2}. \qquad (12)$$

When one of the substances involved in the electrode reaction is a gas with which the solution is maintained saturated, it is customary to write the equation for the potential in terms of the pressure of the gas. Thus the equation for the hydrogen electrode reaction

$$2OH_3^+ + 2e \rightleftarrows H_2 + 2H_2O \tag{13}$$

is written

$$E_{OH_3^+, H_2} = E^\circ_{OH_3^+, H_2} + \frac{0.059}{2} \log \frac{[OH_3^+]^2}{p_{H_2}} \tag{14}$$

and $E^\circ_{OH_3^+, H_2}$ is the potential when the concentration of oxonium ion is unity and the solution is saturated with hydrogen gas at a pressure of 1 atmosphere. The concentration of water does not appear in Eq. (14) because it is effectively constant in dilute aqueous solution and the value of $E^\circ_{OH_3^+, H_2}$ is defined accordingly. It may be noted that $E^\circ_{OH_3^+, H_2}$ is zero from the nature of our definition of oxidation potential (see page 159).

In all of these equations the oxidant is written in the numerator, the reductant in the denominator. This is obviously necessary if the equation is to agree with the fact that an increase in the concentration of oxidant must increase the oxidizing power and hence the potential of the system. The concentration of each substance which enters into the electrode reaction must appear in the equation for the potential unless the concentration is for some reason maintained constant. If a substance appears on the same side of the reaction equation as the oxidant its concentration appears in the numerator of the potential equation, if on the other side in the denominator. Thus the equation for the permanganate-manganous potential for which the reaction is

$$MnO_4^- + 8OH_3^+ + 5e \rightleftarrows Mn^{++} + 12H_2O \tag{15}$$

must be

$$E_{MnO_4^-, Mn^{++}} = E^\circ_{MnO_4^-, Mn^{++}} + \frac{0.059}{5} \log \frac{[MnO_4^-][OH_3^+]^8}{[Mn^{++}]}. \tag{16}$$

Some Corollaries.—These equations have some obvious and useful corollaries. When the ratio oxidant/reductant is greater than 1, the actual potential is more positive than the molar potential, $E°$, because the logarithm of a number greater than 1 is a positive quantity. The greater the ratio, the more positive the potential. If the valence factor is 1, the potential is 0.059 volt more positive than the molar potential when the ratio is 10, it is 0.354 volt more positive when the ratio is 1,000,000. The concentration ratio would have to be nearly 10^{17} to raise the potential 1 volt above the molar potential. If the valence factor is 2, the changes in potential are, of course, only one-half as great. On the other hand, the potential is less positive than the molar potential when the ratio oxidant/reductant is less than 1, because the logarithm of a number less than 1 is a negative quantity. The decrease in potential is 0.059 when the ratio is one-tenth, the valence factor being unity, and so on.

No solution containing a given oxidant can be completely free from the corresponding reductant; for instance, a solution containing ferric ion must contain some ferrous ion. This follows from the formula in this way: if the concentration of ferrous ion is zero and the concentration of ferric ion is not zero, the ratio $[Fe^{+++}]/[Fe^{++}]$ is infinite, its logarithm is likewise infinite and so is the potential. This is an impossibility because an infinite oxidation potential would be sufficient to oxidize something in the solution; it could certainly produce the reaction

$$4OH^- \rightleftarrows O_2 + \quad 2H_2O + 4e \qquad (17)$$

if no reaction requiring a lower potential is available. A finite concentration of ferrous ion with a zero concentration of ferric ion is likewise impossible, because the ratio $[Fe^{+++}]/[Fe^{++}]$ would then be zero, and its logarithm, and therefore the potential, would be minus infinity. If nothing more easily reducible is present, oxonium ion can always be reduced to hydrogen by Eq. (13). Of course, the necessary minimum concentration of ferrous ion in a ferric salt solution or of ferric ion in a ferrous salt solution may be too small for direct detection.

The Concentration Cell.—A galvanic cell in which the two half-cells contain the same oxidant-reductant system, but at different concentrations is called a concentration cell. Consider a cell in which two copper electrodes are immersed in two copper salt solutions which are connected by a salt bridge. Let the concentrations of cupric ion in the two solutions be represented by

$[Cu^{++}]_1$ and $[Cu^{++}]_2$.   The potential of this cell, as of any other, is equal to the difference of the potentials which would be obtained if each half-cell were measured against a molar hydrogen electrode, that is, to the difference of the oxidation potentials. These oxidation potentials are, respectively,

$$E_1 = E°_{Cu^{++}, Cu} + \frac{0.059}{2} \log [Cu^{++}]_1 \qquad (18)$$

and

$$E_2 = E°_{Cu^{++}, Cu} + \frac{0.059}{2} \log [Cu^{++}]_2 \qquad (19)$$

for the two half-cells.   The potential, E, of the concentration cell is therefore given by

$$E = E_1 - E_2 = \frac{0.059}{2}\{\log [Cu^{++}]_1 - \log [Cu^{++}]_2\}. \qquad (20)$$

Since the difference of the logarithms of two numbers is equal to the logarithm of the ratio of the numbers, this equation reduces to

$$E = \frac{0.059}{2} \log \frac{[Cu^{++}]_1}{[Cu^{++}]_2}. \qquad (21)$$

It will be noted that the molar potential $E°_{Cu^{++}, Cu}$ has been canceled out.   The potential of a concentration cell depends therefore only upon the ratio of the concentrations and the valence factor.   Except for the valence factor it does not depend upon what substances are involved, it depends only upon the numerical values of the concentrations.

The positive electrode in the concentration cell is the one in the solution with the higher concentration of oxidant.   That is, if $[Cu^{++}]_1 > [Cu^{++}]_2$, then $E > 0$ and the positive electrode is in solution 1; if $[Cu^{++}]_1 < [Cu^{++}]_2$, then $E < 0$ and the negative electrode is in solution 1.   If $[Cu^{++}]_1 = [Cu^{++}]_2$, the ratio $[Cu^{++}]_1/[Cu^{++}]_2$ is 1, its logarithm is 0, and so is the potential. This is obviously a necessary result.   If the concentration cell is short-circuited, copper deposits from the more concentrated solution, it dissolves as cupric ion in the more dilute solution, and anions migrate through the salt bridge.   Hence the total effect is simply to transfer cupric salt from the concentrated to the dilute solution.   This is the same result that would be obtained as a result of diffusion if the two solutions were brought into contact with each other.

If a cell is set up containing copper electrodes in a dilute copper sulfate solution with the same concentration in the two half-cells the potential is, of course, zero. If sodium hydroxide is now added to one side, a considerable difference in potential appears, the electrode in the solution containing the sodium hydroxide being negative. We now have in this solution only the small concentration of cupric ion in the saturated solution of cupric hydroxide. If sodium sulfide is added, the blue hydroxide is converted to the black sulfide, which can occur only if the resulting saturated cupric sulfide solution contains a smaller concentration of cupric ion than the cupric hydroxide solution did. The potential of the cell increases accordingly, because the ratio of the cupric ion concentration in the cupric sulfate solution to that in the other solution to which the reagents have been added has increased. If potassium cyanide is added, the sulfide dissolves. Therefore the cupric ion concentration of the resulting solution must be even less than that of the sulfide solution to which the cyanide was added. Again the potential shows an increase in accord with Eq. (21).

One of the most important applications of the concentration cell is in the measurement of unknown ion concentrations. If we have a known concentration of cupric ion in one half-cell, and an unknown one in the other, and measure the potential of the cell, Eq. (21) enables us to calculate the unknown concentration. Thus the only method available for the determination of the solubility product constants of such insoluble substances as cupric sulfide or the equilibrium constants for the formation of stable complex ions like $Ag(CN)_2^-$ depends upon the use of a concentration cell. In the experiment we have just described we could have determined the concentration of cupric ion in the saturated cupric sulfide solution, and if we knew the sulfide ion concentration of the solution, the product of the two ion concentrations would be the solubility product constant of cupric sulfide.

Electrometric Measurements of pH.—For this purpose a concentration cell is used in which the electrode reaction is

$$2OH_3^+ + 2e \rightleftarrows H_2 + 2H_2O. \tag{22}$$

In order to make this reaction take place at a measurable rate, the electrodes must carry a catalyst, the finely divided platinum which can be obtained by electrodeposition from a chloroplatinate solution being a suitable one.   Obviously we cannot hope to measure the electrical potential required to stop a reaction (which is the definition of the oxidation potential) if the reaction does not take place at a significant rate.

The potential of such a concentration cell is given by the equation

$$E = \frac{0.059}{2} \log \frac{[OH_3^+]_1{}^2 p_2}{[OH_3^+]_2{}^2 p_1} \tag{23}$$

which is easily derived from Eq. (14).   If the solutions in both half-cells are saturated with hydrogen at the same pressure (usually 1 atmosphere), this equation simplifies to

$$E = \frac{0.059}{1} \log \frac{[OH_3^+]_1}{[OH_3^+]_2}. \tag{24}$$

Since the pH of the solution is given by

$$pH = -\log [OH_3^+] \tag{25}$$

Eq. (24) may be put in the form

$$E = 0.059(pH_2 - pH_1). \tag{26}$$

If a concentration cell with hydrogen electrodes is set up in which one half-cell contains a dilute solution of a strong acid of known concentration, and the other half-cell contains a dilute solution of alkali of known concentration (both solutions containing the same large concentration of sodium chloride or other salt to minimize the otherwise very large junction potentials) the value of the water constant $[OH_3^+][OH^-]$ can be calculated from the cell potential (this will be the value of the water constant in the presence of the salt, and will differ because of the salt effect from the value which prevails in pure water).   The concentration of hydroxyl ion in the alkali solution is known from the known concentration of alkali, the concentration of oxonium ion is known in the dilute solution of strong acid.   From the concentration-cell formula and this known oxonium ion concentration we calculate the oxonium ion concentration in the alkali solution, and the product of this by the hydroxyl ion concentration is the water constant.

By similar methods it is possible to determine the ionization constants of any weak acid or base whose ionization is appreciable, and which does not contain, as for instance nitric acid does, an oxidant with a potential sufficiently high to react with the hydrogen on the electrode.

For practical purposes a concentration cell is not usually employed directly. A half-cell containing the solution of unknown oxonium ion concentration and a hydrogen electrode is measured against a saturated calomel electrode, which is an easily prepared half-cell whose potential is constant and reproducible. Let us call this potential E. Now the potential of a similar combination of hydrogen and calomel electrodes in which the hydrogen half-cell contains 1 M oxonium ion has been carefully studied, and may be taken to be -0.246 (junction potentials and salt effects introduce considerable uncertainty). The potential of a concentration cell containing 1 M oxonium ion in one half-cell and the unknown solution on the other would necessarily, because of the additive property of cell potentials (see page 159), be equal to the difference of the potentials measured when each half-cell is measured against the calomel electrode. We thus obtain

$$E + 0.246 = 0.059 \log [\text{H}^+]. \tag{27}$$

The Daniell Cell.—If a copper electrode is placed in a solution of copper sulfate, and a zinc electrode in a solution of zinc sulfate, and if the solutions are connected by a salt bridge, a very well-known cell is obtained. This, the Daniell cell, develops a potential of about 1.1 volts. The copper electrode is the positive one, and the reaction which takes place when current flows is

$$\text{Zn} + \text{Cu}^{++} \rightarrow \text{Zn}^{++} + \text{Cu}. \tag{28}$$

If sodium hydroxide is added to the copper sulfate solution, decreasing the cupric ion concentration, the cell potential decreases. If sodium sulfide is then added to the copper side the potential becomes nearly zero, and if, finally, potassium cyanide is added the potential swings across and the copper electrode becomes negative. The reaction when current flows is now

$$Cu + Zn^{++} \rightarrow Cu^{++} + Zn. \qquad (29)$$

The decrease in the cupric ion concentration has made the copper more active than the zinc, and it is displacing the latter from solution.

If sodium hydroxide (to prevent evolution of hydrocyanic acid) and potassium cyanide are now added to the zinc solution, the potential may again be brought approximately to zero. The potentials of the two metals, and hence their reducing activities, are now equal.

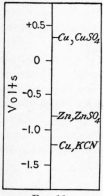

Fig. 11.

Figure 11 will serve to make clear the potential relationships. The potential of copper in a 0.5 M copper sulfate solution is about +0.3 volt, that of zinc in a 0.5 M zinc sulfate solution is about −0.8 volt, giving a total of 1.1 volts for the Daniell cell. When sodium hydroxide is added to the copper salt the potential decreases and comes nearer to that of the zinc. When sodium sulfide is added, the copper potential becomes still more negative because of the still lower concentration of cupric ion. It is now negative, and practically equal to the potential of the zinc in the zinc sulfate solution. When potassium cyanide is added the copper potential moves still further toward negative values reaching about −1.2 volts, the point marked Cu, KCN in the diagram. The copper is now more negative than the zinc. When cyanide is now added to the zinc sulfate solution the zinc potential also moves toward the negative side, but the shift is not so great as with copper because the zinc-cyanide complex is not so stable as the copper-cyanide complex. The potential attained is not very different from that of the copper in the presence of excess cyanide ion.

This has an important application. To plate a metal from solution requires that a sufficiently negative potential be put upon the object to be plated to reduce the ions of the metal to be deposited. From the above diagram it will be seen that the potential required to reduce cupric ion is much less negative than the potential required to reduce zinc ion if both are in a sulfate solution. If a solution contains cupric and zinc sulfates, the copper will plate out alone until the decrease in cupric ion concentration has shifted the copper potential toward the negative as far as the zinc potential. When this has happened and it has become possible for the zinc to plate out, the total copper concentration of the solution is extremely small and any copper that plates out will be negligible. But if the solution from which the electrodeposit is made contains copper and zinc-cyanide complexes in the presence of excess cyanide ion, the copper and the zinc potentials are practically the same. Therefore, the metal that plates out will be a mixture of copper and zinc. This is the technical method of brass plating.

It will be seen that the position of a metal in the electromotive series is not rigidly fixed, but depends upon the concentration of its ions in solution. In the presence of cyanide ion, copper is as active a metal as zinc, because copper ion forms a more stable compound with cyanide ion than does zinc ion.

Equilibrium in an Oxidation-reduction Reaction.—The question whether copper will reduce zinc ion or zinc reduce cupric ion amounts to the determination of the equilibrium condition for the reaction

$$Zn + Cu^{++} \rightleftarrows Zn^{++} + Cu. \tag{30}$$

For reactions always take place in such a way as to approach equilibrium. If therefore the condition for equilibrium is known, it is possible to predict in what direction any given reaction mixture can react.

The condition for equilibrium is that the two potentials

$$E_{Cu^{++}, \, Cu} = E°_{Cu^{++}, \, Cu} + 0.0296 \log [Cu^{++}] \tag{31}$$
$$E_{Zn^{++}, \, Zn} = E°_{Zn^{++}, \, Zn} + 0.0296 \log [Zn^{++}] \tag{32}$$

be equal. For if the potentials are equal the tendencies of cupric and zinc ions to take on electrons are equal and just balance so that no reaction can take place. The E's can only be equal if the quantities on the right sides of the equations are equal. That is, at equilibrium

$$E_{Cu^{++}, Cu} = E_{Zn^{++}, Zn} \tag{33}$$

$$\therefore \ E^{\circ}_{Cu^{++}, Cu} + 0.0296 \log [Cu^{++}] = E^{\circ}_{Zn^{++}, Zn} +$$
$$0.0296 \log [Zn^{++}] \tag{34}$$

and

$$\log \frac{[Cu^{++}]}{[Zn^{++}]} = \frac{E^{\circ}_{Zn^{++}, Zn} - E^{\circ}_{Cu^{++}, Cu}}{0.0296}. \tag{35}$$

From this equation and the values of the molar potentials given in Table VII it may be calculated that the ratio $[Cu^{++}]/[Zn^{++}]$ must have the value 5×10^{-38} at equilibrium. This is the equilibrium constant for the reaction of Eq. (30), the constant concentrations of the metals being included in the constant. A solution containing cupric and zinc ions in this ratio, say a zinc ion concentration of 0.1 M and a cupric ion concentration of 5×10^{-39} would react neither with copper nor with zinc, for the solution is already in equilibrium and is incapable of further reaction. If a solution contains equal concentrations of cupric and zinc ions so that the ratio of cupric ion concentration to zinc ion concentration is 1, reaction can only take place in the direction of reducing this ratio, and approaching the equilibrium value of 5×10^{-38}. The only possible reaction is

$$Zn + Cu^{++} \rightarrow Zn^{++} + Cu; \tag{36}$$

the reverse is impossible. If, therefore, zinc metal is introduced into a solution containing equal concentrations of cupric and zinc ions, zinc will go into solution and copper will be precipitated. The process will continue until the cupric ion concentration has been decreased and the zinc ion concentration increased to the point where the condition for equilibrium is satisfied. If copper metal is introduced into a solution with equal concentrations of cupric and zinc ions nothing can happen.

Similarly, if the ratio of the cupric ion concentration to the zinc ion concentration is less than 5×10^{-38} the solution will be capable of reacting with metallic copper, dissolving it and precipitating zinc, but it will be incapable of reacting with zinc metal. The only possible reaction is

$$Cu + Zn^{++} \rightarrow Cu^{++} + Zn \tag{37}$$

which will increase the ratio, and the reaction can continue until the ratio rises to the equilibrium value.

The Removal of the Reaction Product.—The only way in which the reducing activity of copper can be increased is by decreasing the concentration of cupric ion; it is impossible to increase the concentration of copper. There is further value in the method of making copper a more powerful reducing agent by adding to the solution a reagent which combines with cupric ion to form a precipitate or a complex. Such an addition provides not merely that the concentration of cupric ion shall be low but that it shall remain low when reaction takes place.

The reducing potential of copper is infinite $(-\infty)$ when it is in contact with a solution containing a zero concentration of cupric ion. This may be taken to mean that under such conditions copper is capable of reducing any oxidant. Placed in contact with a solution containing 0.1 M zinc ion the copper should reduce zinc ion, unless of course there is some more easily reducible oxidant present. But as soon as 5×10^{-39} moles per liter of cupric ion had appeared in the solution, the reaction would be at equilibrium and would cease. The amount of zinc that would be displaced would be likewise 5×10^{-39} moles for every liter of solution, and would be entirely negligible. If, however, cyanide ion or some other reagent which forms a sufficiently stable complex with copper ion is present a considerable quantity of copper will dissolve, forming the complex and displacing zinc, before the necessary cupric ion concentration for equilibrium is established.

Even when the concentrations of both oxidant and reductant can be varied, it is often possible to obtain a much greater effect by decreasing the concentration of the product of the reaction than by increasing the concentration of the reactant. For if one has a solution of a given ion at ordinary reagent concentration, say 0.1 M, the concentration can be increased at most ten to a hundred times, whereas it may be reduced in any ratio whatsoever if only suitable reagents can be found.

Some examples of the effect of reagents upon the ferric-ferrous system will illustrate these principles. If sodium hydroxide is added to a solution containing highly ionized ferric and ferrous salts the concentrations of both ferric and ferrous ions decrease, for both hydroxides are difficultly soluble; but the concentration of ferric ion reaches a much lower value than the concentration of ferrous ion because ferric hydroxide is less soluble than ferrous hydroxide. This difference in solubility is known from the fact that a much smaller hydroxyl ion concentration is necessary to precipitate ferric hydroxide than to precipitate ferrous hydroxide. The ratio $[Fe^{+++}]/[Fe^{++}]$ decreases therefore as the solution is made alkaline, and the potential becomes less positive. This means that ferric ion is a much weaker oxidizing agent in alkaline than in acid solutions, but it also means that ferrous ion is a much more active reducing agent. This may be illustrated by the fact that an alkaline suspension of ferrous hydroxide is rapidly oxidized by atmospheric oxygen, while a strongly acid solution of a ferrous salt is unaffected by oxygen.

Similarly, the fact that the potential of an equimolar mixture of ferricyanide and ferrocyanide ions is somewhat more negative than the potential of an equimolar mixture of ferric and ferrous ions (see Table VII) may be taken to indicate that the ferricyanide ion is somewhat more stable than the ferrocyanide ion.

That pyrophosphate ion $(P_2O_7^{=})$ forms a stable complex ion with ferric ion may be demonstrated by the fact that the addition of a solution of pyrophosphate acidified with acetic acid to a solution of a ferric salt decreases the ferric ion concentration to the point where the addition of thiocyanate ion gives no red color. (This is a very delicate test for ferric ion.) The molar potential of the ferric-ferrous system is slightly greater than that of the iodine-iodide system. The addition of a ferric salt to an iodide solution causes some reaction

$$2Fe^{+++} + 2I^{-} \rightleftarrows 2Fe^{++} + I_2$$

and the solution takes on the brown color of iodine solutions (really of I_3^{-}). The addition of acidified pyrophosphate to this solution causes the iodine color to disappear because the decreased ferric ion concentration decreases the potential of the ferric-ferrous system, and makes ferrous ion so much more powerful a reducing agent that it now reduces the iodine almost completely. But not entirely, for the solution still gives a faint blue upon the addition of starch.

We have met other examples of the same sort of thing in the consideration of complex oxidation-reduction reactions.

Some Limitations.—If the reaction

$$Fe^{+++} + e \rightleftarrows Fe^{++}$$

has come to a state of equilibrium with an electrode, or with the iodine-iodide system, or with some other oxidant-reductant system, ferric ion is being reduced at a rate which is equal to that at which ferrous ion is being oxidized. In the case of this system these rates are large. If, therefore, the rate of reduction of ferric ion is decreased by a decrease in the ferric ion concentration, it is possible for the net rate of oxidation of ferrous ion (the total rate of oxidation minus the rate of the reverse reaction) to become very large.

But the removal of the ferric ion could never make the net rate of oxidation of ferrous ion greater than the total rate of oxidation under the original equilibrium conditions. If this rate and that of the equal reverse reaction had been very small, it would have been impossible to make the oxidation of ferrous ion proceed at a significant rate by suppressing the reverse reaction. The only way to make the oxidation of ferrous ion rapid, if this were the case, would be to apply a high positive potential to the electrode or to use an oxidizing agent of high potential.

Such sluggish reactions, whose spontaneous rates are extremely small, and which can only be forced to rates of practical value by the application of potentials very different from the equilibrium values are particularly common among oxidant-reductant systems in which oxygen complexes are concerned. Thus the potential at which chromate ion acts as an effective oxidizing agent is certainly much less positive than the equilibrium value of the chromate-chromic ion potential. Correspondingly, the concentration of chromic ion has no measurable effect upon the oxidizing action of chromate ion. The reverse reaction, the oxidation of chromic ion to chromate ion, proceeds at a rate so slow that suppressing it makes no difference that can be detected.

The potential of an inert electrode in solutions of sluggish systems such as these is the potential at which the oxidant or reductant reacts at a significant rate with the impurities of the electrode. Since the reverse reaction proceeds here too at a negligible rate, it is not surprising that the concentration of chromic ion has no significant effect upon the potential of an inert electrode in a chromate solution.

Overvoltage.—Both the hydrogen and the oxygen evolution reactions are sluggish in the sense we have just discussed. In the former case we have however seen (page 168) that finely divided platinum is a catalyst. It necessarily catalyzes the reaction in both directions, for catalysts do not change the equilibrium constant of a reaction. For this reason hydrogen is more easily evolved on a surface of catalytically active platinum than on most other metals. On a platinized electrode hydrogen appears when the potential reaches the equilibrium value for the system, or one so near the equilibrium value as to be indistinguishable from it. Theoretically, the reaction also takes place upon a mercury or lead surface at the same potential, but the rate at which hydrogen is produced does not reach a detectable value until the potential is as much as a volt more negative.

The true potential for the system is the potential at which oxonium ion is reduced to hydrogen as fast as hydrogen is oxidized to oxonium ion. On a surface of mercury or lead this rate is so low that it is only when the rate has been enormously increased by making the electrode much more negative that the hydrogen formed can be detected.

The difference in potential between the true value for the system and the value at which the reaction rate becomes large enough so that the products of the reaction can be detected is called the "overvoltage." It is because of the existence of this that it is possible to use in aqueous solution reagents with a potential more negative than the true hydrogen potential. A piece of pure zinc or one coated with a mercury alloy by amalgamation is scarcely attacked by dilute acids, although the zinc potential may be more than three quarters of a volt more negative than the hydrogen potential. But if the zinc is connected to a platinized electrode, the zinc dissolves, the electrons furnished by the process

$$Zn \rightleftarrows Zn^{++} + 2e$$

move to the platinum where they react with oxonium ions

$$2OH_3^+ + 2e \rightleftarrows H_2 + 2H_2O$$

at a rate much greater than is possible on the zinc surface. For the same reason the introduction of platinum black into a chromous salt or one of cobaltocyanide causes evolution of hydrogen. Theoretically, this evolution was already taking place at a very slow rate. On the platinum surface the reduction becomes so much more rapid that the reaction,

$$2Cr^{++} + 2OH_3^+ \rightleftarrows 2Cr^{+++} + H_2 + 2H_2O$$

now goes rapidly.

The rate of the oxygen reaction is likewise greatly dependent upon the material of the electrode and oxygen overvoltages can also be measured. There is, however, no known catalyst for this reaction which possesses nearly the effectiveness of suitably prepared platinum for the hydrogen evolution reaction.

Suggestions for Reading

General: GETMAN-DANIELS, *op. cit.*, ch. XVII.
Calculations: ENGELDER, *op. cit.*, ch. IX.

Exercises

1. In a silver concentration cell the concentration of silver ion is 0.1 M on one side, 10^{-6} M on the other. What is the potential of the cell?
2. What does the fact that mercury metal dissolves easily in HI solution, hydrogen being evolved, and does not dissolve in HCl solution prove about the relative stabilities of the mercuric chloride and mercuric iodide complexes?
3. When an acid solution of a cupric salt is shaken with finely divided iron, the iron displaces the copper quantitatively. Would iron displace mercury under the same conditions? Would iron displace lead under the same conditions?
4. The addition of pyrophosphate ion makes the potential of a ferrous salt solution more negative, makes the ferrous ion a more powerful reducing agent. Does this mean that a given quantity of ferrous ion will reduce a greater quantity of iodine in the presence of pyrophosphate ion?
5. Does it mean that a greater number of molecules of iodine are reduced for each ferrous ion oxidized when pyrophosphate is present?
6. Using the results of exercises 5 and 6 of Chap. V, calculate the potentials of systems composed of silver metal and of the following solutions: 0.01 M $Ag(NH_3)_2^+$; the same plus 0.5 M NH_3; 0.1 M $Ag(CN)_2^-$; the same plus 0.1 M CN^-.
7. The potential of a hydrogen concentration cell is 0.180. The oxonium ion concentration in one half-cell is 0.01, the other half-cell contains a buffer solution containing equal concentrations of a weak acid and its sodium salt. What is the ionization constant of the acid?

8. If zinc metal reacts with a 0.1 M solution of Cu^{++} until equilibrium is established, what will be the concentration of Zn^{++}? What will be the concentration of Cu^{++}? What would be the concentration of Cu^{++} in a solution originally containing 0.1 M Cu^{++} from which Cu had been precipitated by the addition of lead metal?

9. Predict whether iron metal would react with a solution containing 0.1 M ferrous ion and 0.1 M cadmium ion; with a solution containing 0.1 M ferrous and 0.0036 M cadmium ion; with a solution containing 0.1 M ferrous ion and 0.00036 M cadmium ion. Would cadmium metal react with any of these solutions?

PART II
EXPERIMENTS

A. INTRODUCTION

The Purpose of Inorganic Qualitative Analysis.—A qualitative analysis might be expected to have either one of two different aims. It might attempt to determine what chemical individuals make up a given material, whether this be a mixture or a single substance: this is called "proximate analysis." Alternatively it might attempt to discover what elements are present regardless of their form of combination: this is called "ultimate analysis." As ordinarily conducted, however, inorganic qualitative analysis has come to be a search for the ionic constituents of a substance or mixture, and it thus partakes of the nature of both proximate and ultimate analyses. Thus we make tests for chloride and for chlorate ions and perhaps for other ions containing chlorine, but we do not attempt a general test for the element chlorine nor do we make tests for the specific substances sodium chloride, potassium chloride, and so on. We have tests for sulfide, sulfite, and sulfate ions, if not for sulfur in general; for nitrate, nitrite, and ammonium ions, if not for nitrogen. But we cannot, short of the application of X-rays or other crystallographic methods, distinguish a mixture of potassium chloride and sodium nitrate from one of potassium nitrate and sodium chloride.

Separations.—The student often approaches the study of qualitative analysis with the idea that there exist "direct tests," specific reagents which react in perfectly definite ways to prove the presence or absence of a given constituent. In reality one reaction is never enough to characterize a given ion constituent, several reactions are always necessary. The formation of a white precipitate upon the addition of silver nitrate solution is a property of chloride ion, but it is not a sufficient test either for its presence or for its absence. Many other difficultly soluble silver salts can be precipitated by silver nitrate, and the presence of ammonia, on the other hand, prevents the precipitation of silver chloride. Making the solution acid prevents the precipitation of some of these and converts any ammonia to ammonium ion,

181

and is a necessary part of the preparation of the solution for the silver nitrate test. But there still remain a number of common ions which precipitate a silver salt in acid solution. A white precipitate might contain cyanide or thiocyanate instead of, or in addition to, chloride, and a black precipitate of silver sulfide might or might not contain silver chloride with its white color completely masked.

The identification of chloride ion requires the precipitation of a white silver salt in an acid solution that has undergone a previous treatment which makes certain that no ion but chloride capable of giving the silver nitrate reaction in acid solution can still be present. The chloride ion must first be separated from interfering ions, and such separations form the most important subject matter of inorganic analytical chemistry.

Similarly we shall find that our only positive reagents for sodium ion also produce a precipitate with practically all of the metallic ions except potassium ion. The negative property of not giving precipitates with a series of other reagents by the successive application of which these other interfering ions may be removed from a solution is therefore of equal importance for the detection of sodium ion with the positive property of giving a precipitate with potassium antimonate reagent.

On Common Elements.—It is a direct consequence of these facts that the complexity of a method of analysis increases very rapidly with the number of ions to be tested for. Not merely that new tests are necessary; the separations necessary as a preparation for both old and new tests become more and more numerous and laborious. The subject matter of a course in qualitative analysis must, therefore, be restricted to a reasonable number of ions. The compounds of certain elements may be excluded on the basis of rarity and expense, and certain ions of the more common elements may be eliminated on this ground or on that of instability. With all these reservations, it remains impossible in a course of reasonable length to study all the ions which may reasonably be expected to appear in industrial materials or to form the subject matter of scientific investigations.

The only possible aim of instruction in qualitative analysis as such is therefore to impart an understanding of the important types of analytical separation and to offer an opportunity for practice in the techniques involved. Even if this is done with a restricted number of ions, the extension to a wider and more general field will require an increased number of operations of known type, and based upon known principles, rather than the study of entirely new methods. The difference between an analysis for what are usually called the "commoner elements" and a complete analysis is that in the latter case the same sort of operations must be carried out a greater number of times.

The subject matter of the Course of Laboratory Instruction and of the Method of Analysis which follow (Sections *B* and *D*) includes the methods of testing for the ions of a limited number of metallic elements. The choice is partly based upon tradition, but is largely justified by the fact that almost all of the important principles and methods used in any qualitative analysis are illustrated.

Quantitative Considerations.—A purely qualitative analysis is impossible; the question, present or absent, can never be answered. The methods of qualitative analysis determine whether the amount of a given constituent present is greater or less than the least quantity which the test used can detect, and the result means nothing unless something is known about the delicacy of the test. This varies from test to test. A test or separation must, of course, be reasonably sensitive if it is to have any usefulness whatsoever. The methods of Section *D* are of sufficient delicacy to permit the detection of 0.0001 equivalent or less of any ion tested.

But a test may also be too sensitive. Thus the yellow color which sodium compounds impart to a flame is so sensitive a reaction that it is a matter of great difficulty to obtain reagents or other materials which do not give the test. And one of the most confusing occurrences that a student of analytical chemistry meets is the formation of a green colloidal solution or even a black precipitate upon the addition of hydrogen sulfide to a solution which responds to no other tests for ions which possess dark-colored sulfides. This arises from the presence of traces of iron compounds whose quantity is too small to respond to the other tests.

The Estimation of Quantity.—Since a consideration of quantity cannot be escaped, it is usually worth while to determine roughly how much of an ion is present from the intensity of color reactions or the size of precipitates. The small extra effort results in an analysis of much greater value, and the training is excellent preparation for more accurate quantitative methods. For the purposes of such estimation the unknowns with which we shall work in Section *B* are made up so that the concentration of each ion to be tested for is either 0.5, 0.1, or 0.01 equivalent per liter. The student is instructed to use 10 cc. of the unknown for the analysis; therefore the precipitates obtained represent either 0.005, 0.001, or 0.0001 equivalent of the ion. (It should be thoroughly understood that the size of the precipitate depends upon the amount, not the concentration of the ion concerned. Except for minor variations as much barium chromate will be obtained from 5 cc. of 0.1 *N* barium salt as from 50 cc. of 0.01 *N* barium salt.)

In order to decide which of these concentrations of any ion is present in an unknown the student must be prepared to make up comparison tests from the reagents of known concentration in his chemical outfit. Thus he may compare the bulk of the precipitate of barium chromate obtained in the analysis of 10 cc. of an unknown with the precipitate obtained from the equivalent of 10 cc. of 0.1 *N* barium salt. It is desirable that the precipitation of the known barium chromate take place in a volume, at a temperature, and in the presence of amounts of salts as nearly as possible the same as those which prevailed in the precipitation of the unknown because all of these factors may influence the particle size and therefore the apparent bulk of a precipitate. Reference to P. **26** of the Method of Analysis shows that the obvious way to make the comparison test is to mix 1 cc. of the normal barium chloride of the chemical outfit (which contains the same amount of barium ion as 10 cc. of a 0.1 *N* solution) with 14 cc. of water, 2 cc. of 6 *N* acetic acid, and 5 cc. of 6 *N* ammonium acetate, and to precipitate in hot solution with potassium chromate according to the method of that paragraph.

It is usually possible to decide whether the amount of the known precipitate is approximately the same as that of the unknown, or is 10 times less or 5 times greater. (This is best done by observing the bulk of the precipitate after settling from solution but without filtration.) In case of doubt other comparison tests corresponding to the 0.5 and 0.01 N concentrations can be made (to make a comparison test for 0.01 N solution it is necessary to first dilute the normal reagent in some known proportion because the 0.1 cc. of normal solution which would be equivalent to 10 cc. of 0.01 solution is too small a quantity to be measured with sufficient precision).

In certain cases (Ni^{++}, Na^+, K^+) the final test for an ion is made upon a definite fraction of the material contained in the unknown. This fact must, of course, be taken into account in making comparison tests.

After the student has had some experience with the characteristic test for any ion he should be able to recollect the bulk of the precipitate or the intensity of the color well enough to dispense with a comparison test when that ion is again found present.

On the Technique of Qualitative Analysis.—The manipulative operations involved in this work offer no difficulty; they involve merely mixing of solutions, filtration, and evaporation. Nor does qualitative analysis require the pains to prevent loss of material which the student of quantitative analysis must learn. The loss of one or two per cent of the solution being analyzed through incomplete rinsing of containers, inadequate washing of precipitates, or splashing is of no importance for the precision at which we aim, even if such losses are repeated several times on the same material before the final test for an ion is made.

But a satisfactory analysis does require a certain amount of judgment in drawing conclusions from the considerable amount of information which accumulates during the course of an analysis. It also requires what is for a student untrained in chemical operations a somewhat surprising amount of pains to avoid contamination of the solutions during the analysis. Thus the student must learn to wash all containers by several washings until they are really chemically clean, and then to rinse with distilled water from a wash bottle. (It is an excellent idea to put some permanganate solution or other highly colored material in a flask or beaker and to see how many washings are necessary to get rid of the color.) He must learn to keep all containers covered with watch glasses or otherwise protected whenever possible. (This is to avoid contamination from dust, which in a laboratory consists chiefly of iron rust, of zinc compounds from paint, and of calcium and magnesium compounds from plaster.) He must learn never to return to a solution a stirring rod which he has laid for a moment on the dirty desk top; he must learn not to allow the ground-glass portion of the stopper of a reagent bottle to touch the desk top or other contaminated surface; he must learn never to return to a reagent bottle any solution which has been poured out of it; he must learn to return stoppers to bottles immediately lest the stoppers from two bottles be interchanged; he must learn to use distilled water instead of tap water for all dilutions. All these and other precautions against contamination must become so much a matter of habit that they are observed automatically.

Finally he must adopt a questioning attitude toward the materials he is working with. Reagents may have become contaminated through his own carelessness or they may have been of insufficient purity to begin with. (The filter papers usually sold for use in qualitative analysis are entirely unsuited for the purpose. They contain so much iron and calcium that any acid solution filtered through one of them will give tests for these elements. A more expensive paper which has been washed with hydrochloric acid is indispensable for any serious analytical work.) Therefore the student should be prepared to "run a blank" on his materials and reagents, that is, to make an analysis or a portion of an analysis on a sample of pure water to see if he gets negative tests.

On Efficiency in the Laboratory.—Another habit which the student of chemistry should acquire as early as possible is that of working efficiently. This does not mean hurried or careless work, there is nothing more inefficient than a hasty analysis with uncertain results. It is usually followed by a hurried repetition with results contradictory to those of the first, leaving the analyst worse off than before he started. One analysis should always be sufficient. But efficiency does require some forethought and planning of the work, it requires that two or more operations which do not mutually interfere be carried out simultaneously as often as possible, it especially abhors the situation in which an analyst waits without occupation while a long evaporation or other operation which requires little attention is completed.

Working with several materials at once requires careful labeling if confusion is to be avoided. A supply of labels or a glass-marking pencil should be kept handy and used liberally.

Another requirement for efficiency is correct note taking. To have any value notes must be taken immediately; they should record every significant occurrence; and every precipitation or color and every failure to obtain a reaction are significant for the result of analysis; but they should be as brief as possible. Especially they should be treated as the analyst's own record and not as a copy book for exhibition.

Some Special Techniques: Saturation with Hydrogen Sulfide.—The reagent hydrogen sulfide is used as a gas, and we assure ourselves that a sufficient amount has been added by saturating the solution with it. This is most efficiently accomplished by placing the solution in a conical flask provided with a two-hole rubber stopper carrying outlet and inlet tubes. Attach the inlet tube to the source of H_2S, and pass a current of the gas through the flask long enough to displace most of the air. Then close the outlet and keep the liquid well agitated until saturation is shown to be complete by the marked decrease or cessation of the flow of gas entering the flask. (If the gas bubbles through water in a tube or flask before entering the saturation flask, its rate of flow can be estimated from the rate of bubbling.) The large gas-liquid interface, and the mixing of the liquid produced by the shaking, make the saturation very rapid, and there is the further advantage that very little of the toxic H_2S escapes into the laboratory air. If the gas is generated from the reaction of acid with ferrous sulfide it is extremely important that it be filtered through a column of two or more inches of cotton to remove the fine spray of solution carrying iron salts from the generator.

The only way to be certain that enough hydrogen sulfide has been dissolved in a solution to complete the precipitation of a sulfide is to filter and add more hydrogen sulfide to the filtrate. This precaution should never be omitted in a sulfide precipitation.

Filtration.—The filtrations of qualitative analysis may be carried out with a great saving of time by the use of suction. The stem of the funnel is inserted in a rubber stopper in the neck of a heavy-walled Erlenmeyer flask provided with a side arm to which is attached a rubber tube from a water-suction pump. The tip of the filter paper must be supported, for instance by a perforated gold cone in the apex of the funnel. (Gold is attacked by aqua regia, by bromine water, by acid solutions of chlorates, and by any solution containing simultaneously a moderately strong oxidizing agent and a halide ion; see page 149.) If the quantity of filtrate is small, it is best to receive it in a test tube inserted in the suction flask.

It is most important to disconnect the rubber tube from the flask or otherwise "break the vacuum" before turning off the supply of water to the pump. Otherwise water from the pump will be sucked back through an inevitably dirty connecting tube into the filtrate. Difficulty from this source can be most safely avoided by using a safety bottle between filter flask and pump to catch any water sucked back.

If any further operations are to be carried out on a filtrate, the precipitate should be washed with a small portion of water (or of dilute reagent if so directed), and the filtrate from this washing should be added to the main filtrate. This reduces the loss of material from the filtrate to a low enough value for the present kind of work. To reduce the losses to the part or so per thousand which quantitative analysis strives to attain would require many careful repetitions of the washing process and could only be made sure of by testing the washings for some ion present in the original filtrate.

When further operations are to be carried out on the precipitate it is sometimes necessary to wash more thoroughly than this to prevent interference by substances present in the liquid adhering to precipitate and filter paper. It is always desirable to wash a precipitate on which further work is to be done into as small a portion as possible of the tip of the paper. This is done with a fine stream of water from the wash bottle.

To transfer a precipitate to a beaker for further treatment, tear off those portions of the filter paper to which little or no precipitate adheres; if possible, transfer the precipitate directly from the paper to the wall of the beaker; if not, add the reagent to the precipitate and paper, and after the precipitate has dissolved, either remove the paper with a stirring rod, squeezing out the solution, or filter through a fresh paper.

B. THE COURSE OF LABORATORY INSTRUCTION

1. Prepare 0.1 N test solutions of $Pb(NO_3)_2$ and of $BaCl_2$. Test 10 cc. portions with K_2CrO_4, H_2SO_4, $(NH_4)_2CO_3$ and H_2S. Which of these reagents offers a possible separation?

2. Dilute 10 cc. portions of 0.5 N, 0.1 N, and 0.01 N $Pb(NO_3)_2$ to 100 cc., add 1 cc. of 6 N ammonium acetate solution (to prevent the formation of a colloidal suspension), and saturate the solutions with H_2S. Note the relative amounts of precipitate produced by the different quantities of lead ion. Make certain that the precipitation is complete (see page 187).

3. Dilute 10 cc. portions of 0.5 N, 0.1 N, and 0.01 N $BaCl_2$ to 25 cc., and precipitate with 3 cc. of 3 N K_2CrO_4. Note carefully the relative sizes of the precipitates.

4. Unknown No. 1 may contain lead and barium ions but no other cations. To 10 cc. of the unknown add 5 cc. of 6 N HNO_3 (to avoid formation of colloidal lead sulfide), dilute to 100 cc., saturate with H_2S, and estimate the concentration of lead ion in the unknown from the size of the precipitate if any appears. Filter, evaporate the filtrate to 20 cc., make alkaline with NH_3, add 3 cc. of 3 N K_2CrO_4, and estimate barium ion from the size of the precipitate if any.

5. Test solutions of $Cd(NO_3)_2$ with H_2S, with H_2SO_4, and with K_2CrO_4.

6. To 10 cc. of 0.01 N $Pb(NO_3)_2$ add 5 cc. of 16 N HNO_3, then 3 cc. of 18 N H_2SO_4. If a precipitate forms, filter. Evaporate the filtrate or the clear unfiltered solution to fumes of SO_3. (The dense white fumes of SO_3 are very different in appearance from the steam and nitric acid fumes which appear during the evaporation, but it is possible for one unfamiliar with their appearance to be confused. Be sure you evaporate far enough.) Cool the sulfuric acid residue thoroughly, and add carefully to 10 cc. of H_2O.

7. Dilute a mixture of 10 cc. of 0.1 N $Cd(NO_3)_2$ and 10 cc. of 0.1 N $BaCl_2$ to 100 cc. and precipitate with H_2S. Filter with suction, and wash the precipitate thoroughly. Transfer the precipitate to a beaker, and dissolve in a little 6 N HCl.   Add a few drops of 6 N H_2SO_4 to the solution.

8. Precipitate a small amount of $PbSO_4$, filter, and wash. Pour a few cubic centimeters of 3 N ammonium acetate several times through the paper containing the precipitate.   Acidify this solution with acetic acid, and test with K_2CrO_4.   Repeat the experiment using $BaSO_4$ instead of the $PbSO_4$.

9. Make solutions of $BaCl_2$ and of $Ca(NO_3)_2$ alkaline with NH_3, and test with K_2CrO_4, with $K_2C_2O_4$, and with Na_2SO_4. Filter off the $CaSO_4$ if any forms, and add alcohol to the filtrate or solution.

10. Test 10 cc. of 0.1 N NH_4Cl by P. **33** of Section D.

11. Unknown No. 2 may contain lead, cadmium, barium, calcium, and ammonium ions.   (*a*) Test for ammonium ion on a 5 cc. portion by P. **33** of Section D.   (*b*) Add 5 cc. of 6 N HCl to 10 cc. of unknown, dilute to 100 cc., and saturate with H_2S.   Filter.   (*c*) Wash precipitate thoroughly with hot water, then dissolve in hot 6 N HNO_3 (see page 139 and P. **6** Section D).   Separate, estimate, and confirm lead ion by P. **6.** (*d*) To the filtrate from the $PbSO_4$, *c*, add NH_3 until just alkaline, dilute to 100 cc. and precipitate CdS with H_2S.   (*e*) Evaporate the filtrate from *b* to 25 cc., make alkaline with NH_3, add 3 cc. of 3 N K_2CrO_4, and estimate barium.   Filter if there is a precipitate.   (*f*) To the filtrate from *e* add 3 cc. of 3 N $K_2C_2O_4$ to precipitate CaC_2O_4, and estimate calcium.

12. Make up a solution containing 0.05 N $Zn(NO_3)_2$ and 0.3 N HCl, and saturate with H_2S.   Repeat with a solution containing 0.001 N $Cd(NO_3)_2$ and 0.3 N HCl.

13. Make up three solutions, each containing 0.001 N $Zn(NO_3)_2$. The first contains 0.1 N HCl, the second 0.1 N acetic acid, the third 0.1 N acetic acid and 0.1 N ammonium acetate.   Determine approximately the maximum oxonium ion concentration which permits a satisfactory precipitation of ZnS.

14. Make a solution of 0.1 N $Ni(NO_3)_2$ alkaline with NH_3, and divide into two parts.   To one add HCl until decidedly acid, then saturate with H_2S.   Saturate the other with H_2S, then add as much HCl as was added to the other portion.

15. Determine whether $BaCrO_4$ precipitates from dilute HCl solution.   Precipitate $BaCrO_4$ according to the method of **26**

of Section D by mixing 10 cc. of 0.1 N $BaCl_2$, 5 cc. of water, 2 cc. of 6 N acetic acid, and 5 cc. of 6 N ammonium acetate, and precipitating in hot solution with K_2CrO_4 as there described. Filter, and examine the filtrate to determine whether the precipitation is analytically complete (*i.e.*, complete enough to prevent interference with a subsequent test for strontium ion).

16. Repeat the second part of **15** using 10 cc. of normal $Sr(NO_3)_2$ instead of the $BaCl_2$. Make the solution, or the filtrate, if there is a precipitate, alkaline with NH_3, then add 5 cc. more. Filter and add to the filtrate 15 cc. of 95 per cent alcohol.

17. Treat a few cubic centimeters of 3 N K_2CrO_4 with an equal volume of alcohol.

18. To a 5 cc. portion of 0.1 N $Mg(NO_3)_2$ add 2 cc. of normal Na_2HPO_4 and 2 cc. of 6 N NH_3. The precipitate is $Mg_3(PO_4)_2$. To another portion of $Mg(NO_3)_2$ add 2 cc. of normal Na_2HPO_4 and 2 cc. of 6 N ammonium acetate, and let stand a few minutes. The precipitate here is $MgNH_4PO_4$. Filter and add excess of NH_3 to the filtrate. Compare the appearance of the different precipitates.

19. To 5 cc. of 0.1 N $Ca(NO_3)_2$ add Na_2HPO_4, ammonium acetate, and NH_3 as in the previous experiment. Compare the appearance of this precipitate with that of the two magnesium phosphates.

20. Unknown No. 3 may contain lead, cadmium, zinc, barium, strontium, calcium, magnesium, and ammonium ions. (*a*) Test for ammonium ion by D **33**. (*b*) Neutralize 10 cc. of the unknown to litmus, if it is not already neutral, then add 5 cc. of 6 N HCl, and dilute to 100 cc. Saturate with H_2S, and filter. (*c*) and (*d*) Dissolve the precipitate from *b* and estimate lead and cadmium as in Unknown No. 2. (*e*) Heat filtrate from *b* until H_2S is driven off, cool, neutralize with NH_3, make alkaline, and saturate with H_2S. Estimate Zn from the precipitate of ZnS, and filter. (*f*) Make filtrate from *e* just barely acid with HCl, evaporate to 15 cc., add 2 cc. of 6 N acetic acid, and 5 cc. of 6 N ammonium acetate, heat to boiling, and precipitate with K_2CrO_4 according to D **26**. (*g*) Estimate strontium ion by D **27**. (*h*) Estimate calcium ion by D **28**. (*i*) Estimate magnesium ion by D **29**.

21. Test 2 cc. portions of 0.3 N and 0.03 N $NaNO_3$ (see **32** of Section D) with 2 cc. of potassium antimonate reagent.

Allow the well-stoppered test tube to stand at least 24 hours. Note carefully the appearance of the precipitate, especially its crystalline properties and adherence to the walls of the tube.

22. Test portions of $Pb(NO_3)_2$ and of $Ca(NO_3)_2$ solution with the antimonate reagent. Note appearance of the precipitates. Nearly all cations but potassium and ammonium give similar precipitates with this reagent.

23. Test the antimonate reagent with litmus.

24. Test 5 cc. of 0.067 N KNO_3 with sodium cobaltinitrite reagent. Repeat with NH_4NO_3. Heat a few crystals of KCl in a crucible. Is it volatile below red heat? Repeat with NH_4Cl.

25. Test the cobaltinitrite reagent with litmus. What is the effect of HCl upon the reagent? Of NaOH?

26. To 10 cc. of 0.1 N $Ca(NO_3)_2$ add 1 cc. of ammonium carbonate reagent. Filter and to the filtrate add 15 cc. of the reagent and 15 cc. of alcohol. Repeat with $Mg(NO_3)_2$.

27. To 10 cc. portions of 0.01 N, 0.001 N, and 0.0001 N $Fe(NO_3)_3$ add 10 cc. of normal NH_4SCN. To part of each solution now add a few cubic centimeters of HCl, drop by drop. Test solutions of $CrCl_3$ and of $Co(NO_3)_2$ with thiocyanate.

28. Investigate similarly the sensitivity of the test for ferric ion obtained by making the solution alkaline with NH_3 and saturating with H_2S. See if the precipitation of $Fe(OH)_3$ is equally sensitive.

29. Test solutions of $Fe(NO_3)_3$, of $Ni(NO_3)_2$, and of $Co(NO_3)_2$ with $K_4Fe(CN)_6$, and note carefully the colors of the precipitates. Add NaOH solution to the ferric ferrocyanide.

30. Add excess of 6 N NaOH to portions of 0.1 N $AlCl_3$ and of 0.1 N $Zn(NO_3)_2$. Add a volume of 6 N ammonium acetate twice that of the NaOH used to each solution. Treat portions of $Fe(NO_3)_3$ and $Ni(NO_3)_2$ solutions with excess of NaOH, filter through a hardened paper, and test the filtrate with H_2S for completeness of precipitation.

31. To 10 cc. of 0.1 N $Fe(NO_3)_3$ add 2 cc. of 6 N ammonium acetate and NH_3 in excess. Filter and test filtrate for completeness of precipitation.

32. Add 5 cc. of 15 N NH_3 to 5 cc. of 0.1 N $AlCl_3$. Filter, boil off the excess NH_3, and add 1 cc. 6 N ammonium acetate.

33. Add ammonium sulfide to a solution of $AlCl_3$. Repeat with $Fe(NO_3)_3$.

34. To 10 cc. portions of 0.1 N solutions of $Mg(NO_3)_2$, of $Ni(NO_3)_2$, and of $Zn(NO_3)_2$ add 6 N NH_3 in excess. To other 10 cc. portions of the same solutions add 2 cc. of 6 N ammonium acetate, then add NH_3 in excess.

35. Dilute a portion of conc. Na_2SiO_3 300 times, acidify with HCl, then make alkaline with NH_3, and boil. This aping of the properties of $Al(OH)_3$ is due to peculiar colloidal properties of silicic acid.

36. To 10 cc. portions of 0.01 N solutions of $AlCl_3$, $Fe(NO_3)_3$, and $CrCl_3$, and of the diluted Na_2SiO_3 used in **35,** add 1 cc. of 6 N acetic acid, 2 cc. of 6 N ammonium acetate, and 5 cc. of a 0.1 per cent solution of the ammonium salt of aurin tricarboxylic acid; mix thoroughly, and observe the results. Make each solution alkaline with ammonium carbonate reagent, and observe.

37. To 10 cc. of 0.025 N $Ni(NO_3)_2$ add 2 cc. of 6 N ammonium acetate solution, and make the solution just alkaline with NH_3. Add 4 cc. of a 0.1 N dimethyl-glyoxime solution. What is the effect of acid and what is the effect of a large excess of NH_3 upon this precipitation?

38. Add 2 cc. of 6 N HCl to 10 cc. of 0.1 N $AgNO_3$. Heat, filter, cool the filtrate, and observe. Repeat with $Pb(NO_3)_2$ instead of $AgNO_3$. Treat the precipitate of AgCl on the paper with 6 N NH_3. Acidify with HNO_3 the solution obtained.

39. Filter a cold saturated solution of $PbCl_2$, and test the filtrate with H_2S.

40. Unknown No. 4 may contain silver, lead, cadmium, zinc, aluminum, ferric, nickel, barium, strontium, calcium, magnesium, sodium, potassium, and ammonium ions. (*a*) Test for ammonium ion as in previous unknowns. (*b*) Neutralize 10 cc. of the unknown to litmus then add 2 cc. of 6 N HCl. Heat to dissolve $PbCl_2$, and filter hot. Wash with hot water several times, adding the wash waters to the filtrate. (*c*) Pour a 5-cc. portion of NH_3 several times through the filter, then acidify this solution with HNO_3 to test for Ag^+. (*d*) To the combined filtrates from *b* add 3 cc. of 6 N HCl, dilute to 100 cc. and saturate with H_2S. Filter. (*e*) Dissolve the precipitate from *d* and estimate lead and cadmium as in previous unknowns. (*f*) Heat the filtrate from *d* to remove H_2S, make decidedly alkaline with NH_3, and boil. Observe the precipitate which may be $Al(OH)_3$ or $Fe(OH)_3$, then saturate with H_2S and heat to boiling.   Filter rapidly with suction and wash the precipitate with hot water containing a little freshly prepared ammonium sulfide.   (*g*) Remove the gold cone, replace the filter paper in the funnel, sprinkle a little solid $KClO_3$ over the precipitate, and pour a 5- to 10-cc. portion of hot 6 *N* HCl repeatedly through the filter until the precipitate is dissolved. Evaporate the filtrate nearly to dryness, add 10 cc. of H_2O, enough NaOH to make the solution alkaline, then 10 cc. more of 6 *N* NaOH.   Filter through a hardened filter paper, and wash the precipitate which may contain $Fe(OH)_3$ and $Ni(OH)_2$ thoroughly with hot water.   (*h*) Dissolve the precipitate from *g* in a few cubic centimeters of HCl, then pour the solution into four times its volume of 6 *N* NH_3.   Estimate iron from the $Fe(OH)_3$ precipitate, and filter.   (*i*) To one-fourth of the filtrate from *h* made just alkaline with NH_3 add 10 cc. of 0.1 *N* dimethyl glyoxime.   Wait 15 min. and estimate nickel ion from the red precipitate of nickel dimethyl glyoxime.   (*j*) To the filtrate from *g* which contains $Al(OH)_4^-$ and $Zn(OH)_4^=$ add 20 cc. of 6 *N* ammonium acetate.   Boil until the volume of the solution is reduced one-half.   Estimate aluminum ion from the precipitate, filter and then confirm the precipitate by the test with aurin tricarboxylic acid given in *D* **18**.   (*k*) Saturate the filtrate from *j* with H_2S, and estimate zinc ion from the ZnS.   (*l*) Treat the filtrate from *f* by *D* **25** to *D* **32** for the detection and estimation of the alkaline earths and alkalis.

41. Analyze a known solution containing chromic, cobalt, and manganous ions, all at 0.1 *N* concentration, starting at **16**, Section *D*.

42. Analyze a known solution containing bismuth, copper, cadmium, mercuric, arsenate, antimonous, and chlorostannate ions, all at 0.1 *N* concentration, by the method of Section *D*.

43. Unknowns No. 5 and 6 may contain any of the ions provided for in Section *D*.   Analyze these as there directed, estimating concentrations as in previous unknowns.

C. QUESTIONS ON THE EXPERIMENTS

1. Describe in detail how you prepared the test solutions.

2. How can you ascertain that the precipitation is complete?   Why is it important to be certain on this point?

3. Is 3 cc. of 3 N K_2CrO_4 a sufficient amount? How do you know?

5. How can you test for cadmium ion when a solution contains lead ion?

6. It is very difficult to precipitate lead sulfate in the presence of nitrate ion. The same thing is not true of barium and strontium sulfates. What hypothesis can you think of to account for these phenomena? (Consult the table of solubility products.)

7. How do you account for the presence of barium ion in this solution?

8. Explain these reactions.

9. How do you account for the effect of the alcohol in this experiment?

10. Explain this reaction, and state under what conditions it may be taken as a sufficient test for ammonium ion.

12. Explain how you can make up a solution from normal $Zn(NO_3)_2$ and 6 N HCl that is simultaneously 0.05 N in zinc ion and 0.3 N in HCl. Is a satisfactory separation of zinc and cadmium ions possible by precipitating CdS from 0.3 N HCl? Why are these concentrations of zinc and cadmium ions used to decide this question?

13. Explain your conclusion in this experiment.

14. Explain the difference in the results produced by adding the same two reagents in reverse order.

15. Why is a mixture of acetic acid and ammonium acetate used here instead of acetic acid alone? What is such a mixture called?

16. Why is a repetition of the precipitation of $BaCrO_4$ under essentially the same conditions as the first precipitation of any value in identifying barium ion? Under what conditions should this "confirmatory test" be carried out? Why does the color of the solution change in this experiment when NH_3 is added? Why does a precipitate appear? Are the two phenomena related?

17. What bearing does the result of this experiment have on the test for strontium ion?

18. Explain the reactions involved in this experiment. Why is $MgNH_4PO_4$ more suitable for analytical work than $Mg_3(PO_4)_2$? State and explain the conditions necessary for the optimum precipitation of $MgNH_4PO_4$.

19. What additional reason for preferring $MgNH_4PO_4$ to $Mg_3(PO_4)_2$ does this experiment bring out?

20. (*b*) Why is the unknown just neutralized? (*h*) Why is only a small quantity of oxalate added at first in a cold solution, with a larger amount added later in hot solution if a precipitate appears? (*i*) Explain the confirmatory test for Mg^{++}.

21. Explain the choice of amount and concentrations of $NaNO_3$ solution in this experiment.

22. Under what conditions only may the precipitation with potassium antimonate be used as a valid test for sodium ion?

23. Explain the result of this test. Why is not potassium antimonate alone used in making up this reagent? What is the effect of acid upon the reagent?

24. Explain how potassium and ammonium ions may best be separated.

25. Explain these results.

26. Is magnesium carbonate more or less soluble than calcium carbonate? What is the composition of the reagent used here? Would there be any advantage in the use of sodium carbonate instead of ammonium carbonate in the precipitation of magnesium? Any disadvantage?

27. Is a red color with thiocyanate a sufficient test for ferric ion? Explain the effect of HCl upon the sensitivity of the test for ferric ion. What is the formula of the red substance?

29. Explain the effect of the NaOH.

30. Explain the various reactions occurring in these experiments. How can you best separate aluminum and zinc ions from ferric and nickel ions?

32. Why is $Al(OH)_3$ dissolved by NH_3? How may the solution be minimized?

33. Why does $Al(OH)_3$ and not Al_2S_3 precipitate? Why does Fe_2S_3 and not $Fe(OH)_3$ precipitate?

34. Explain the reactions involved. How can you best separate zinc and nickel ions from aluminum and ferric ions?

35. Why is the presence of silicate a possibility in unknowns to which none is deliberately added?

36. Why is a confirmatory test for aluminum ion necessary? What other ions must be absent if this confirmatory test is to be reliable?

37. Explain the effect of acid and of a large excess of ammonia on the precipitation.

38. Would you expect AgCl to be more soluble in HNO_3 than in water? Explain. Why is a further test than the precipitation of a chloride necessary to characterize silver ion? Explain the solution of the precipitate in NH_3 and its reprecipitation with HNO_3. Would $PbCl_2$ dissolve in NH_3?

39. Does chloride ion give a quantitative precipitation of lead ion?

40. (*f*) Why is the H_2S expelled by boiling before adding the NH_3, which is followed by addition of H_2S? (*g*) What is the function of the $KClO_3$ in this procedure? Why must the gold cone be removed? Write equations for the reactions which occur upon addition of the NaOH. (*h*) Explain the separation of ferric and nickel ions which occurs here. (*i*) Why is only one-fourth of the solution used? (*j*) Explain the reaction of the ammonium acetate. What is the purpose of evaporating the solution to one-half?

41. Why is it important to have ammonium salt present in **16**? What complications would the presence of phosphate ion involve? What is the purpose of the sodium peroxide in **17**? Why is a very large excess of NaOH employed? Why is a special test for chromate ion made with lead ion, although the separation is carried out by precipitation of barium chromate? Most of the difficulty in **21** results from the addition of too much KNO_2. Why does this cause trouble?

42. Explain the function of the HNO_3 and of the HCl in **4**. What is the purpose of the detailed directions for adding diluted NH_3 in **4**? Why does the reagent in **5** contain NaOH? Write equations for the reactions involved in **5**. Why is it necessary not to let the solution stand too long in **6**? Would a pale gray color in the confirmatory test in **7** be sufficient evidence for Bi^{+++}? Explain. Could precipitation with ferrocyanide be used to separate cupric and cadmium ions? Explain why iron reduces cupric ion but not cadmium ion in **9**. What would happen in the confirmatory test in **9** if iron compounds were not thoroughly washed out? What would be the reaction of NH_3 with arsenic group sulfides if these were present in **9**? Explain the effect of the ammonium chloride in **10**. Why are copper and bismuth likely to be present in the precipitate in **10**? Why is sulfur likely to precipitate in **12**?

D. THE METHOD OF ANALYSIS

1. The Separation of the Silver Group from the Other Groups. Add to the unknown, which if alkaline has first been acidified with 6 *N* HCl, 2 cc. of 6 *N* HCl. If there is a precipitate, filter, and wash the precipitate with a small portion of normal HCl. This precipitate may contain AgCl, Hg_2Cl_2, or $PbCl_2$. The filtrate contains the other groups, and is reserved for **4** (see page 72).

2. The Detection of Lead Ion.—Wash the precipitate from **1** with 10 cc. of boiling water, pouring the same portion repeatedly through the filter, and heating each time. Add to the solution thus obtained 2 cc. of 6 *N* HNO_3 and 2 cc. of 3 *N* K_2CrO_4. A yellow precipitate of $PbCrO_4$ demonstrates the presence of lead ion in the unknown. Even if no test for lead ion is obtained here, considerable quantities of lead ion may nevertheless be present, and will appear at later stages of the analysis (**6**) (see page 207).

3. The Separation and Detection of Silver and Mercurous Ions.—Wash the residue left by the hot water in **2** with several further portions of hot water. Then pour 5 to 10 cc. of 6 *N* NH_3 over the filter, and catch the solution which filters through. Pour it back through the filter several times if the reaction seems to be incomplete. A black residue on the filter demonstrates the presence of mercurous ion in the unknown. Acidify the filtrate. A white precipitate of AgCl demonstrates the presence of silver ion in the unknown (see pages 117, 146).

4. The Separation of the Copper and Tin Groups from the Other Groups.—To the filtrate from **1** add 5 cc. of 12 *N* HCl and 2 cc. of 16 *N* HNO_3, and evaporate just to dryness under the hood, taking care not to overheat the residue. Add 5 cc. of 12 *N* HCl and again evaporate just to dryness. Add 10 cc. of

6 N HCl, saturate with H_2S, heat to boiling, and pass in a stream of H_2S for 5 min. Then add slowly and with active agitation to avoid local excesses of ammonia a mixture of 5 cc. of 6 N NH_3 and 85 cc. of water. Again saturate with H_2S. Filter, reserving the filtrate for **16**, and wash the precipitate thoroughly with hot water. The precipitate may contain PbS, Bi_2S_3, CuS, CdS, HgS, As_2S_5, Sb_2S_5, SnS_2, and S. If it is pure white it consists only of S and may be neglected (see pages 75, 207).

5. The Separation of the Copper Group from the Tin Group.— Transfer the precipitate from **4** to a beaker, add 10 cc. of sodium sulfide-hydroxide reagent, and heat nearly to boiling for a few minutes. Then add 10 cc. of water and filter, reserving the filtrate, which may contain $HgS_2^=$, $AsS_4^\equiv$, $SbS_4^\equiv$, and $SnS_3^=$, for **10**. The precipitate, which may contain PbS, Bi_2S_3, CuS, and CdS, should be washed thoroughly with hot water (see pages 123, 208).

6. The Detection of Lead Ion.—The undissolved residue from **5** is treated with boiling 6 N HNO_3 sufficient to dissolve. Completion of the solution may be recognized by the coagulation of the sulfur formed by the oxidation into a few large lumps, which may nevertheless be black because of enclosed sulfides. Filter, add 3 cc. of 18 N H_2SO_4 to the filtrate, and evaporate under the hood until heavy white fumes of SO_3 appear. Cool and pour slowly with cooling into 10 cc. of water. Allow to stand 5 min. A white precipitate appearing within this time is $PbSO_4$, and indicates the presence of lead ion in the unknown. If there is a precipitate filter, reserving the filtrate for **7**, wash the precipitate with a small amount of water, then pour a portion of 3 N ammonium acetate several times through the filter containing the precipitate. Make the solution thus obtained decidedly acid with acetic acid, and add a few drops of K_2CrO_4 solution. A yellow precipitate of $PbCrO_4$ demonstrates the presence of lead ion in the unknown (see pages 72, 139, 208).

7. The Detection of Bismuth Ion.—Make the filtrate from **6** alkaline with NH_3. A white precipitate of $Bi(OH)_3$ indicates the presence of bismuth ion in the unknown. Filter, reserving the filtrate for **8**, wash the precipitate with water, and then pour over the precipitate on the filter a solution of sodium stannite, freshly prepared by adding 6 N NaOH with cooling to normal $SnCl_2$ solution until the precipitate first formed redissolves. An intense black color on the filter, due to the formation in finely divided form of metallic Bi, demonstrates the presence of bismuth ion in the unknown (see pages 144, 208).

8. The Detection of Cupric Ion.—If more than a very small concentration of cupric ion is present, the filtrate from **7** will be visibly blue from the cupric-ammonia ion. To make the detection still more sensitive or to confirm the blue color as being certainly due to cupric-ammonia ion, a small portion of the solution may be acidified with acetic acid. A drop or two of normal $K_4Fe(CN)_6$ will give a pink or red precipitate if cupric ion was present. The concentration of the cupric ion is best estimated from the color of the ammoniacal solution.

9. The Separation of Cupric and Cadmium Ions and the Detection of Cadmium Ion.—The main portion of the filtrate from **7**, to which no ferrocyanide has been added, is made just acid with H_2SO_4. If no cupric ion was found in **8**, saturate the solution with H_2S. If cupric ion was found in **8** add 5 cc. more $6\ N\ H_2SO_4$, and about 1 cc. of powdered Fe. Boil about 2 minutes or longer if necessary to completely remove the blue color, filter, and immediately saturate the filtrate with H_2S. In either case a yellow precipitate of CdS indicates the presence of cadmium ion. Reserve the precipitate, and, if much arsenic, antimony, or tin are found present in **12**, wash the supposed CdS thoroughly with hot water to remove iron compounds, then pour repeatedly through the filter containing the precipitate a portion of hot $6\ N\ NH_3$, which dissolves the tin-group sulfides but not CdS. If the yellow precipitate remains undissolved the presence of cadmium ion in the unknown is confirmed (see pages 177, 178).

10. The Separation of Mercuric Ion from the Ions of Arsenic, Antimony, and Tin.—To the filtrate from **5** add 15 cc. of $3\ N$ ammonium chloride, and heat just to boiling. Filter, without suction, refiltering through the same paper if the filtrate is not clear. Reserve the filtrate for **12**. The precipitate may contain HgS together with small amounts of CuS and Bi_2S_3. It may also contain much or all of the tin, if much mercury and little tin is present. If therefore the ammonium chloride precipitate is large, wash it well with hot water, heat it nearly to boiling with 5 cc. of $6\ N$ HCl, and filter, reserving the precipitate for **11.**   Evaporate the filtrate to half its volume to remove H_2S, dilute again to the original volume, and make a confirmatory test for tin by reaction with $HgCl_2$ after reduction with Sb exactly as described in **15** (see pages 124, 208).

11. The Detection of Mercuric Ion.—The supposed HgS precipitate from **10** is dissolved in 6 N HCl by adding solid $KClO_3$, a little at a time, to the hot solution, until the precipitate dissolves (see **6**).   Filter, evaporate to destroy excess of chlorate, dilute to 10 cc., and add normal $SnCl_2$ a little at a time.   A white precipitate turning gray (Hg_2Cl_2 and Hg) demonstrates the presence of mercuric ion in the unknown (see pages 150, 208).

12. The Separation of Arsenic from Antimony and Tin.— Add sufficient (about 15 cc.) 6 N HCl to the filtrate from **10** to give a blue reaction on Congo red paper, and allow the solution to stand for a minute or two.   There will in any case be a precipitate.   If this is pure white, it consists solely of the sulfur produced by the decomposition of the small amounts of polysulfide always present in the sodium sulfide-hydroxide reagent; and the absence of the ions of arsenic, antimony, and tin is demonstrated.   If it is yellow or orange, filter with suction, wash thoroughly, and suck as dry as possible.   Transfer, with as little of the filter paper as possible, to a test tube, add exactly 10 cc. of 12 N HCl, place the tube in a beaker of water, and heat for 10 min. at a temperature such that the solution in the test tube boils very gently.   Then pass H_2S through the solution for 1 min., add gradually with stirring 3 cc. of water and filter immediately, reserving the filtrate containing the ions of antimony and tin for **14.**   The undissolved residue contains any arsenic as sulfide (see pages 75, 124, 152, 208).

13. The Detection of the Ions of Arsenic.—Wash the residue from **12** with water, then treat it in a beaker for several minutes with a mixture of 5 cc. of 3 N NH_3 and 10 cc. of 3 N NH_4Cl. Filter, and make the filtrate strongly acid with HCl.   If no precipitate forms at first warm.   A yellow precipitate demonstrates the presence of the ions of arsenic in the unknown (see page 208).

14. The Separation of Antimony and Tin and the Detection of the Ions of Antimony.—Dilute the filtrate from **12** to a volume of 55 cc.   Put in a flask, warm nearly to boiling, and place the flask in a beaker of boiling water.   Pass in H_2S slowly for 10 min. at this temperature. An orange precipitate of Sb_2S_5 demonstrates the presence of the ions of antimony in the unknown. Filter while hot, reserving the filtrate for **15.** If very much tin is found in **15,** or if the precipitate does not have the characteristic color of Sb_2S_5, dissolve it in NH_3, filtering out any undissolved material, remove the NH_3 by evaporation, and carry out a second precipitation of the Sb_2S_5 under the same conditions of volume, HCl concentration, and temperature as the first precipitation (see pages 75, 125, 208).

15. The Detection of the Ions of Tin.—To the filtrate from **14** add just 4 cc. of 6 N NH_3, cool, and saturate with H_2S. If there is no immediate precipitate cork the flask and let it stand 10 min. A heavy yellow precipitate of SnS_2 is sufficient to demonstrate the presence of the ions of tin in the unknown. If the precipitate is small in quantity or not distinctly yellow in color, evaporate the solution without filtering to about half its volume, add about ½ cc. of powdered Sb, boil a few minutes, filter, and add the filtrate immediately to a mixture of 10 cc. of 0.2 N $HgCl_2$ and 2 cc. of 6 N HCl. An immediate white precipitate of Hg_2Cl_2 confirms the presence of the ions of tin in the unknown (see page 208).

16. The Separation of the Aluminum and Iron Groups from the Alkaline-earth and Alkali Groups.—Boil the filtrate from **4** until the dissolved H_2S has been completely expelled, then make it decidedly alkaline with NH_3, and boil. Observe carefully whether a precipitate forms, and note its color if there is one. If there is no precipitate aluminum, ferric, and chromic ions are absent, and subsequent steps for their separation from other ions and detection may be omitted. In any case saturate with H_2S, and heat to boiling. If there is a precipitate, filter rapidly with suction and reserve the filtrate for **25.** Wash the precipitate, which may contain white $Al(OH)_3$ and ZnS, flesh colored MnS, green $Cr(OH)_3$, and black Fe_2S_3, FeS, NiS, and CoS, with hot water containing a little ammonium sulfide (see pages 75, 100, 116, 209).

17. The Separation of the Aluminum and Iron Groups.—Pour a 5- to 10-cc. portion of 6 N HCl through the filter. If the precipitate is dark-colored and does not dissolve readily, remove the gold cone, replace the filter paper in the funnel, sprinkle a little solid $KClO_3$ over the precipitate, heat the HCl solution and pour it repeatedly through the filter until the precipitate is dissolved except for a residue of sulfur. Filter, and evaporate the filtrate nearly to dryness. Add 10 cc. of water and just enough 6 N NaOH to produce a precipitate or to make the solution alkaline. Add this solution slowly with stirring to 10 cc. of 6 N NaOH to which about $\frac{1}{2}$ to 1 cc. of Na_2O_2 has just been added. Add another $\frac{1}{2}$ cc. of Na_2O_2 if it seems to be necessary to complete the conversion of a large amount of undissolved green $Cr(OH)_3$ or dissolved green $Cr(OH)_4{}^-$ ion to yellow $CrO_4{}^=$ ion in solution. Boil the solution a minute or two, filter through a hardened filter paper, and treat the filtrate, which may contain $Al(OH_4)^-$, $Zn(OH)_4{}^=$, and $CrO_4{}^=$ ions, immediately by **18.** The precipitate may contain brown to black hydrates of MnO_2, $Fe(OH)_3$, and $Co(OH)_3$, and green $Ni(OH)_2$. Wash it thoroughly with hot water, and reserve it for **21** (see pages 76, 112, 151, 209).

18. The Separation of Aluminum Ion from Zinc and Chromate Ions.—Add 20 cc. of 6 N ammonium acetate to the filtrate from **17.** If the absence of a precipitate with NH_3 alone in **16** proved the absence of aluminum and chromic ions, omit the rest of this paragraph and the whole of **19** and proceed directly to test for zinc ion by **20.** Otherwise, boil the solution until the volume is reduced approximately one-half. A white precipitate of $Al(OH)_3$ indicates the presence of aluminum ion in the unknown. Filter, reserving the filtrate, which contains any zinc and chromate, for **19.** Wash the precipitate with hot water, then dissolve it by pouring 5 cc. of normal HCl at the boiling temperature several times through the filter. Make the solution thus obtained alkaline with NaOH, and filter out any precipitate which does not dissolve in a small excess of 6 N NaOH. Acidify the solution with 6 N acetic acid, add 5 cc. of a 0.1 per cent solution of the ammonium salt of aurin tricarboxylic acid, mix thoroughly, and let stand a minute or two. Then make alkaline with ammonium carbonate-ammonia reagent. A red precipitate persisting after the solution is made alkaline confirms the presence of aluminum ion in the unknown (see pages 109, 116, 210).

19. The Separation of Chromate and Zinc Ions and the Detection of the Ions of Chromium.—Acidify the filtrate from

18 with acetic acid and observe its color.   If it is entirely color-less the ions of chromium were absent in the unknown.   In this case make the solution alkaline with NH_3 and proceed directly to **20**.   If, however, the solution is yellow or orange confirm the presence of dichromate ion by adding to one tenth of the solution 1 to 2 cc. of N $Pb(NO_3)_2$.   A yellow precipitate of $PbCrO_4$ demonstrates the presence of the ions of chromium in the unknown.   The concentration of the chromium is best estimated from the color of the dichromate solution.   If dichro-mate is present it must be removed before testing for zinc ion. Heat the major portion of the solution, to which no lead ion has been added, to boiling, and add 10 cc. of N $BaCl_2$.   Filter out the precipitate of $BaCrO_4$, make the filtrate alkaline with NH_3 and use it in **20** (see page 210).

20.   The Detection of Zinc Ion.—Saturate with H_2S the solution to be tested for zinc ion, which must be alkaline with NH_3. A white precipitate of ZnS demonstrates the presence of zinc ion in the unknown.   If the precipitate is gray or black from traces of iron or cobalt sulfides, filter it off, wash with water, warm with a few cubic centimeters of 6 N HCl, filter again, and boil the filtrate to remove H_2S.   Make alkaline with NaOH, add a little Na_2O_2, and boil a minute or two.   Filter if there is a precipitate, and saturate the filtrate with H_2S.   A white precipitate of ZnS confirms the presence of zinc ion in the unknown (see page 210).

21.   The Separation and Detection of the Ions of Manganese.— Spread the filter paper containing the precipitate from **17** out in a beaker.   Add 5 to 10 cc. of 16 N HNO_3.   If the precipitate does not dissolve add solid KNO_2, in *very small* portions, with constant stirring until the precipitate is completely dissolved. Pour the solution into a conical flask, avoiding the introduction of filter paper.   Heat to boiling, and place the flask in a beaker of boiling water.   Add about 1 cc. of solid $KClO_3$.   If a precipi-tate forms within 3 min., add more $KClO_3$ and continue warming until the formation of precipitate ceases.   Filter through an asbestos filter prepared by pouring a suspension of asbestos fibers into a funnel, whose apex has been plugged loosely with glass wool, until a good filter surface is formed, then washing the filter thoroughly with water using suction.   Reserve the filtrate, which contains any ferric, nickel, and cobalt ions, for **22**. The precipitate is hydrated MnO_2, and its formation demonstrates the presence of the ions of manganese in the unknown (see pages 144, 210).

22. The Separation and Detection of the Ions of Iron.—If the precipitate obtained with ammonium sulfide in **16** was white, the ions of iron, nickel, and cobalt were absent in the unknown, and **22, 23,** and **24** may be omitted and the filtrate from **21** rejected. Otherwise pour the filtrate from **21** into four times its volume of 6 N NH_3, and make sure that the resulting solution is alkaline. A brown precipitate of $Fe(OH)_3$ indicates the presence of ferric ion, but a brown precipitate is not sufficient, because any manganese which escaped precipitation in **21** will produce a brown precipitate here. Filter, reserving the filtrate, which may contain cobalt and nickel ions, for **23**, and wash the precipitate thoroughly with hot water. Pour 5 cc. of 6 N HCl several times through the filter, then add to the solution a few cubic centimeters of normal $K_4Fe(CN)_6$. A deep-blue solution or precipitate demonstrates the presence in the unknown of ferric or ferrous ion (see pages 117, 210).

23. The Separation of Cobalt and Nickel Ions and the Detection of Cobalt Ion.—Evaporate the filtrate from **22** to about half its volume, acidify with acetic acid, add 5 cc. more, then add about 3 cc. of solid KNO_2. Let stand 15 min. A yellow precipitate of $K_3Co(NO_2)_6$ demonstrates the presence of cobalt ion in the unknown. Filter, and use the filtrate in **24** (see page 147).

24. The Detection of Nickel Ion.—Make one quarter of the filtrate from **23** just alkaline with NH_3, add 10 cc. of 0.1 N dimethyl glyoxime, and let stand 15 min. A red precipitate demonstrates the presence of nickel ion in the unknown (see pages 148, 211).

25. The Separation of the Alkaline-earth from the Alkali Group.—Evaporate the filtrate from **16** to 10 cc. and filter if it is not perfectly clear. Add 15 cc. of ammonium carbonate-hydroxide reagent and 15 cc. of alcohol. If there is a large precipitate add 15 cc. more of each. Shake frequently for at least $\frac{1}{2}$ hr., or better, let stand over night. Filter, reserving the filtrate for **30**. It contains any sodium or potassium ion present in the unknown and large amounts of ammonium salts. The precipitate may contain carbonates of barium, strontium, calcium, and magnesium. Treat it by **26** (see pages 96, 211).

26. The Separation from Other Alkaline-earth Ions and Detection of Barium Ion.—Dissolve the precipitate from **25** by pouring 10 cc. of 6 N acetic acid repeatedly through the filter. Evaporate the solution just to dryness. Dissolve the residue in 15 cc. of water and 2 cc. of 6 N acetic acid, add 5 cc. of 6 N ammonium acetate, and heat nearly to boiling. Add drop by drop with stirring 3 cc. of 3 N K_2CrO_4, and keep hot for 5 min. A yellow precipitate of $BaCrO_4$ indicates the presence of barium ion in the unknown. If there is much precipitate add 2 cc. more of the K_2CrO_4 in the same way. Filter even if the solution appears clear, reserve the filtrate which contains the other alkaline-earth ions for **27**, and wash the soluble K_2CrO_4 out of the paper, when a yellow precipitate will be much more easily visible than it was in the yellow solution. If much strontium ion is found in **27**, confirm the presence of barium ion by dissolving the supposed $BaCrO_4$ in hot 6 N HCl, evaporating to dryness, taking up with water, acetic acid, and ammonium acetate, and precipitating with K_2CrO_4 just as in the first part of this paragraph. The second precipitation of $BaCrO_4$ confirms the presence of barium ion in the unknown (see pages 69, 211).

27. The Separation from Calcium and Magnesium Ions and Detection of Strontium Ion.—Make the filtrate from **26** alkaline with NH_3 and add 5 cc. more of 6 N NH_3. Heat nearly to boiling, and add 15 cc. of alcohol. Cool and let stand 5 min. A yellow precipitate of $SrCrO_4$ demonstrates the presence of strontium ion in the unknown. Filter, and reserve the filtrate, which may contain calcium and magnesium ions, for **28** (see page 44).

28. The Separation of Calcium and Magnesium Ions and the Detection of Calcium Ion.—Dilute the filtrate from **27** with 50 cc. of water, add 3 cc. of 3 N $K_2C_2O_4$, and let stand 15 min. A white precipitate of CaC_2O_4 indicates the presence of calcium ion in the unknown. If there is no precipitate, use the solution directly for **29**. If there is a precipitate heat the solution nearly to boiling, add about 5 cc. more of the $K_2C_2O_4$, and keep hot for 5 min. Filter immediately, retaining the precipitate, and use the filtrate for **29**. If much magnesium ion is found in **29** wash the supposed CaC_2O_4 with water, dissolve in a few cubic centimeters of 6 N HCl, make alkaline with NH_3, adding 5 cc. in excess, dilute to 75 cc. and repeat the precipitation of CaC_2O_4 by the method used in the first part of this paragraph. A white precipitate confirms the presence of calcium ion in the unknown (see pages 77, 211).

29. The Detection of Magnesium Ion.—Add 5 cc. of 15 N NH_3 and 25 cc. of normal Na_2HPO_4 to the filtrate from **28**, and let the solution stand for $\frac{1}{2}$ hour or more. A crystalline white precipitate of $MgNH_4PO_4$ which frequently adheres to the walls of the flask demonstrates the presence of magnesium ion in the unknown. If the precipitate is not definitely crystalline, filter on a small paper and wash with several small portions of alcohol. Dissolve the precipitate by pouring a 5 cc. portion of 2 N H_2SO_4 several times through the paper. To the solution thus obtained add 1 cc. of an alkaline solution of p-nitro benzene azo resorcine, and make the solution alkaline with 6 N NaOH. A sky-blue precipitate appearing within a few minutes demonstrates the presence of magnesium ion (see pages 96, 211).

30. The Removal of Ammonium Salts.—Evaporate the filtrate from **25** to dryness in a small casserole, and heat over a direct flame until further strong heating gives no more fumes of ammonium salts. When the dish is cold, dissolve the residue in 3 cc. of water, and filter through a very small filter (see pages 77, 211).

31. The Detection of Potassium Ion.—Dilute one-third of the solution from **30** to 5 cc., and add 5 cc. of sodium cobaltinitrite reagent. Let stand at least 10 min. A yellow precipitate of potassium or mixed potassium and sodium cobaltinitrite indicates the presence of potassium ion. Further certainty can be attained by heating the solution with the precipitate until the color changes from the yellow of the $Co(NO_2)_6^=$ to the pink color of cobaltous ion. Cool, and add 5 cc. more of the cobaltinitrite reagent. If the yellow precipitate forms again the presence of potassium ion is demonstrated (see pages 147, 212).

32. The Detection of Sodium Ion.—To the remaining two-thirds of the solution from **30** add 2 cc. of potassium antimonate reagent, and let the solution stand in a stoppered tube, overnight if possible. A white crystalline precipitate of $NaSb(OH)_6$ demonstrates the presence of sodium ion in the unknown (see pages 27, 110, 212).

33. The Detection of Ammonium Ion.—Mix 5 cc. of the original unknown and 5 cc. of 6 N NaOH in a small beaker provided with a cover glass. Attach a moist piece of red litmus paper to the underside of the cover glass. Warm the solution gently but do not allow it to boil, lest the extremely alkaline solution spatter up on the test paper. A blue color on the litmus paper demonstrates the presence of ammonium ion in the unknown (see page 77).

E. SPECIAL NOTES ON THE METHOD OF ANALYSIS

On 2. Lead chloride is moderately soluble, and may or may not precipitate in the silver group, depending upon the concentration of lead ion, the temperature, and the time of standing. Lead chromate is the least soluble of the chromates, and precipitates even in dilute nitric acid solution.

On 4. The evaporation with HCl and HNO_3 oxidizes arsenic, antimony, tin, and iron to the higher oxidation level, forming chiefly H_3AsO_4 and its ions, $SbCl_6^-$, $SnCl_6^=$, and Fe^{+++}. The oxidation is necessary in order that the sulfides of tin and antimony which precipitate later shall be SnS_2 and Sb_2S_5 which dissolve easily and completely in the sulfide-hydroxide reagent in **5.** SnS is insoluble in this reagent and Sb_2S_3 is not very soluble. Also the sulfoantimonite is largely decomposed by the addition of ammonium chloride in **10**; the sulfoantimonate is not.

From an arsenate solution arsenic sulfide is precipitated quantitatively only if the solution is strongly acid. Nitrate ion, which in such solutions oxidizes hydrogen sulfide rapidly, must be absent. In the evaporation with *aqua regia* in **4** the excess of nitrate is reduced by the chloride, and the unknown is easily obtained in an HCl solution from which the precipitation of arsenic sulfide is quick and complete. If an arsenite solution were evaporated with HCl much arsenic would be volatilized as $AsCl_3$, but the nitric acid oxidizes the arsenic and prevents this.

The caution, not to overheat the residue from the evaporation, is to prevent the loss of mercury through the volatility of $HgCl_2$.

The dilution and partial neutralization give the 0.3 N oxonium ion concentration necessary for the separation of the rest of the copper and tin groups from the other groups.

It is important to avoid local excesses of NH_3 during the partial neutralization, because the NiS or CoS whose precipitation they permit do not redissolve in the acid.

On 5. The reagent is $4 N$ Na_2S and N $NaOH$.

On 6. If any HgS has remained from **5**, it will remain undissolved by nitric acid under the conditions used. The nitric acid must be removed by evaporating until the fumes of the less volatile sulfuric acid show that the removal of the more volatile nitric acid is complete. This is to prevent the interference of nitric acid with the precipitation of $PbSO_4$.

There is a basic bismuth sulfate which is capable of precipitating even under the strongly acid conditions used for the precipitation of lead sulfate. Fortunately, it supersaturates and precipitates slowly if the solution is kept cold and is not allowed to stand too long.

On 7. A confirmatory test is necessary, for the precipitation of a gelatinous white hydroxide is not a very characteristic test. Copper and cadmium remain dissolved as complex ammonia ions.

It is advisable to filter the solution to which the NH_3 has been added and to make the stannite test on the filter paper, even if no precipitate of $Bi(OH)_3$ is visible. A blank confirmatory test on a piece of clean filter paper should be run, as there is frequently some discoloration due to the decomposition of the reagent in the absence of bismuth ion.

On 10. If only small amounts of copper and bismuth are present, almost all of them may appear in this precipitate (see page 124). If it is desired to test for them, part of the solution obtained by heating the precipitate with HCl may be made alkaline with NH_3. Copper is indicated by a blue solution, bismuth by a precipitate which may be confirmed by the stannite test.

On 11. HCl and $KClO_3$ dissolve HgS for the same reason that HCl and HNO_3 do. Sn^{++} reduces $HgCl_2$ to white insoluble Hg_2Cl_2 and further to Hg. The precipitate is white with small amounts of Sn^{++}, and turns gray or black with further addition, because finely divided Hg is black. This is a very characteristic reaction.

On 12. The polysulfide whose decomposition by acid gives the sulfur precipitate arises from oxidation by atmospheric oxygen of the sulfide.

The sulfoarsenate is decomposed only by a relatively high acidity. The Congo red reaction assures this, since the indicator changes color in the pH range from 3 to 5.

On 13. The NH_3-NH_4^+ solution is sufficiently alkaline to dissolve As_2S_5 (to form a mixture of oxy-sulfo arsenates, see page 125). It will not dissolve any appreciable quantity of Sb_2S_5 or SnS_2.

On 14. The ammonia dissolves the antimony sulfide and any tin sulfide that may have precipitated, but no mercuric sulfide or sulfides of the copper group if these are present. The second precipitation of Sb_2S_5 under identical conditions assures the absence of interference from tin.

On 15. Both the lowering of the temperature and the decrease in the acidity favor the precipitation of SnS_2. When the solution containing the precipitate is evaporated, the rise in temperature, the increase in the concentration of HCl, and the removal of H_2S as gas all favor the solution of the SnS_2.

The potential of Sb against a chloride solution is sufficiently negative to reduce the tin to the stannous oxidation level. The Sn^{++} is recognized by its property of reducing $HgCl_2$. Since the $HgCl_2$ is in excess the reduction proceeds only to the white Hg_2Cl_2.

On **16.** Ammonium salt must be present at this point to keep the hydroxyl ion concentration so low that $Mg(OH)_2$ will not precipitate. Sufficient NH_4Cl is formed by the neutralization of the 10 cc. of acid added in **4,** so that no more ammonium salt need be added.

A brown precipitate of hydrated manganese dioxide may appear upon addition of NH_3 (see page 117).

Care should be exercised, in filtering this precipitate, to expose it to the air as little as possible. Sulfide ion in alkaline solution is oxidized by oxygen quite rapidly, and the removal of sulfide ion by the oxidation may cause the solution of a considerable part of the precipitate if it is too much exposed to the air. The addition of a little ammonium sulfide to the wash liquor helps to prevent this solution of the precipitate.

Ammonium polysulfide dissolves NiS in considerable amount forming a deep-brown solution of uncertain composition. Since ammonium sulfide solutions which have stood for any length of time in contact with air always contain polysulfide, the precipitation is carried out by adding hydrogen sulfide to the ammoniacal solution rather than by adding ammonium sulfide. Similarly, the ammonium sulfide in the wash water should be freshly prepared from NH_3 and H_2S. If in spite of these precautions the filtrate from **16** is dark-colored, acidify it with HCl, heat to coagulate the precipitate, and filter. Add the precipitate to the main precipitate obtained in **16;** make the filtrate alkaline with NH_3, and reserve for **25.**

While the alkaline-earth hydroxides do not precipitate at the hydroxyl ion concentration used here, and the alkaline-earth sulfides never precipitate from aqueous solution, the precipitate may contain alkaline-earth phosphates, oxalates, or borates, if the corresponding anions are present. In this case, special means have to be used for the detection of the alkaline-earth ions in the aluminum and iron group precipitate, as well as in the filtrate.

On **17.** If sodium hydroxide alone were used in this separation the solution of the chromic hydroxide might be very incomplete, as it is firmly occluded by the iron-group hydroxides. If zinc and chromic ions both were present, both might fail to dissolve in the sodium hydroxide, remaining as zinc chromite. It would be necessary to test for zinc and chromium in both precipitate and filtrate. The addition of sodium peroxide dissolves the chromium completely by oxidizing it to chromate, which must be done in any case before aluminum and chromium can be separated. Unfortunately, however, the cobaltic hydroxide and manganese dioxide also formed by oxidation occlude zinc very seriously unless a large excess of sodium hydroxide is used. But a large excess of sodium hydroxide dissolves cobaltous hydroxide to a marked extent, forming a blue solution, from which cobaltic hydroxide is not precipitated by sodium peroxide. If, however, the solution to be tested is added to a large excess of sodium hydroxide solution containing sodium peroxide the cobalt is oxidized before it can dissolve to form the blue compound, and the large excess of sodium hydroxide provides for the solution of the zinc hydroxide to such an extent that the separation is satisfactory. Such small amounts of cobalt as do dissolve can easily be allowed for in the further tests and separations to be carried out on the filtrate.

On **18.** $Al(OH)_3$ is precipitated from the aluminate solution by adding a large excess of NH_4^+ to combine with the OH^- and then boiling most of the NH_3 formed out of the solution.

After dissolving the supposed $Al(OH)_3$ in HCl the addition of NaOH removes traces of ferric ion not completely removed in **17** or introduced since that separation.

Al^{+++}, Fe^{+++}, and Cr^{+++} form red lakes with aurin tricarboxylic acid in an acetate buffer. Colloidal silicic acid, which is a likely contaminant of any solution kept in glass, and Zn^{++} do not. The chromium lake is decomposed when the solution is made alkaline, the aluminum lake remains unchanged, in spite of the fact that the lake is not formed in alkaline solution. Red compounds of calcium are decomposed with formation of $CaCO_3$ by the ammonium carbonate. If, therefore, the removal of iron is assured, this test is a reliable one for aluminum ion.

On **19.** $PbCrO_4$ is much yellower than $BaCrO_4$ and much less likely to have its color masked by the precipitation of sulfate arising from the oxidation of sulfide in **17.** Its precipitation is therefore used as a test for $CrO_4^=$. If present the $CrO_4^=$ is however precipitated as $BaCrO_4$ because Ba^{++} does not interfere with the test for Zn^{++} in the filtrate as Pb^{++} would.

On **20.** A white precipitate with H_2S in alkaline solution is sufficient to characterize Zn^{++}. ZnS is the only common white sulfide. Sulfur might precipitate in acid solution but in alkaline solution soluble polysulfides and thiosulfates are formed instead of precipitated sulfur. If a dark precipitate is obtained further procedures to separate iron and cobalt are necessary.

On **21.** The aim of this procedure is to get the precipitate dissolved in concentrated HNO_3 with the minimum effort, then to reprecipitate the MnO_2. MnO_2 and $Co(OH)_3$ dissolve in nitric acid only when reducing agents are present. These may be organic compounds derived from the filter paper or added NO_2^-. If the HNO_3 acts too long on the paper or if too much KNO_2 is added the ClO_3^- later added is reduced and the manganese remains unprecipitated.

On **22.** Pouring the strongly acid solution into a large excess of NH_3 provides a high concentration of both NH_3 and NH_4^+ which favors the conversion of Ni^{++} and Co^{++} into the complex ammonia ions instead of their precipitation as hydroxides and helps to prevent occlusion by the $Fe(OH)_3$.

If phosphates of the alkaline earths have been precipitated in **16,** they will come through to this point, and will precipitate with the $Fe(OH)_3$ if the procedure of **22** is followed. If, therefore, phosphate was found in the unknown, a portion of the filtrate from **21** is tested for Fe^{+++} with SCN^- and the phosphate is precipitated from the main portion of the solution by nearly neutralizing it, and adding a large excess of sodium or ammonium acetate and enough Fe^{+++} so that the red color of colloidal Fe_2O_3 shows that more than enough iron is present to precipitate all $PO_4^=$ as colorless $FePO_4$. If then the solution is boiled the excess of iron is precipitated as hydroxide or basic acetate (see page 99). Since the $PO_4^=$ has been removed the filtrate can then be made alkaline with ammonia without any alkaline-earth compound precipitating. H_2S then precipitates CoS and NiS, and the filtrate can be investigated for alkaline earths carried down in the aluminum and iron-group precipitate.

On 24. Only one quarter of the solution is used because the test is sufficiently sensitive, and the reagent is expensive. This fact should be remembered in estimating the concentration of Ni^{++} in the original unknown.

On 25. It is most important that sufficient time be given for this slow precipitation to complete itself because even small amounts of alkaline earths interfere with the test for Na^+ by producing a gelatinous precipitate. The reagent is $6 N$ $(NH_4)_2CO_3$ and $6 N$ NH_3.

On 26. If the concentration of Sr^{++} is so large that $SrCrO_4$ precipitates in this procedure, the second precipitation will be carried out in a solution containing only that fraction of the total Sr^{++} which precipitated the first time, and a second precipitation of $SrCrO_4$ is most unlikely.

On 28. Ca^{++} is first tested for under conditions of temperature and $C_2O_4^=$ concentration which give rise to a precipitate of CaC_2O_4 even with a small amount of Ca^{++}, and which make very improbable the precipitation of MgC_2O_4 even when much Mg^{++} is present, but which are not sufficient for the complete removal of Ca^{++} when much is present. If Ca^{++} is thus shown to be present its complete removal is assured by the addition of more $C_2O_4^=$ and by increasing the temperature, regardless of the possible precipitation of part of the Mg^{++}. The slowness with which MgC_2O_4 precipitates plays an important part in this separation.

On 29. The precipitation of $MgNH_4PO_4$ is likely to be slow in any case. Oxalate ion retards it, alcohol accelerates it. Agitation helps. The crystalline nature of the precipitate is of considerable assistance, for the other alkaline earths give phosphates under the conditions used which are amorphous and gelatinous. The confirmatory test depends upon the formation of an intensely blue salt or lake of the dyestuff, which is a very weak acid. None of the other alkaline earths ions interfere when present in reasonable concentrations. [See RUIGH, *J. Am. Chem. Soc.* **51**, 1456 (1929).] The dyestuff reagent sometimes decomposes on standing. It should be checked against known magnesium solutions.

On 30. It is much more difficult to remove ammonium salts completely than the student usually appreciates. Long and intense heating is required. Failure to remove is fatal to the potassium test and even interferes with the sodium test. The addition of 5 cc. of $16 N$ HNO_3 and 3 cc. of $12 N$ HCl to the solution before the evaporation facilitates the removal by oxidizing ammonium ion to nitrogen.

On **31.** The reagent is $0.3\ N$ $Na_3Co(NO_2)_6$, $3\ N$ $NaNO_2$, normal acetic acid. It sometimes decomposes on standing, and should always be tested on a known solution of K^+ before using. Decomposition goes to Co^{++} and the change to the pink color of this from the yellow brown of $Co(NO_2)^=$ is a fairly good criterion of usability.

This decomposition goes to completion if the solution is boiled, and any precipitate of $K_3Co(NO_2)_6$ or $(NH_4)_3Co(NO_2)_6$ is thereby dissolved. If the precipitate is the ammonium salt, the NH_4^+ reacts with the NO_2^-

$$NH_4^+ + NO_2^- \rightarrow N_2 + 2H_2O$$

and is destroyed. A renewed precipitate upon the addition of more reagent to the cooled solution can only be $K_3Co(NO_2)_6$.

On **32.** Antimonic acid is extremely weak and its precipitation by hydrolysis can be prevented only by the presence in the reagent of KOH. The reagent is $0.1\ M$ $KSb(OH)_6$ and $0.5\ N$ KOH. The solution to be tested must be free from acids. Furthermore almost all metallic ions give gelatinous precipitates with the reagent, so that their complete removal is a necessary prerequisite to the test for Na^+. The reagent is somewhat erratic in behavior. The student should check it against known sodium solutions.

F. FURTHER ANALYTICAL METHODS

Preparation of Solutions for Analysis for the Ions of the Metals. The quantity of substance taken for analysis must lie within reasonable limits. If too small an amount is taken, the sensitivity of the tests suffers; if too large an amount of an ion is present, it may not be completely separated and will interfere with tests for other ions. The quantity must furthermore be known with a moderate precision if any estimate of the approximate quantitative composition of the material is to be made. In most cases a reasonable sample is 1 g., but only 0.5 g. of most alloys should be taken and not more than 0.25 g. of a light metal alloy (which may be recognized by its low density). If the material to be investigated is a solution, a measured portion should be evaporated to dryness and the residue weighed in order that a suitable volume may be taken for the analysis.

If the material is soluble in water or in dilute HNO_3 or HCl, make up a solution, and analyze starting with **1** of the Method of Analysis. If the material does not dissolve in dilute acids, treat it with HCl and HNO_3 by **4.** If a clear solution is obtained with the 10 cc. of HCl after the second evaporation (heat to ensure the solution of any $PbCl_2$), proceed with the analysis.

If not, filter out the residue, and continue the analysis with the filtrate. The residue may be AgCl, an alkaline-earth or lead sulfate, CaF_2, silica, a silicate, or it may be Al_2O_3, Cr_2O_3, SnO_2, or SnS_2, which are extremely difficult to dissolve as they exist in nature or if they have been strongly heated. AgCl will dissolve in NH_3 and may be thus identified. The sulfates and CaF_2 will be metathetized at least partially by boiling with 10 cc. of 3 N Na_2CO_3 solution, more completely by successive treatments with several portions of Na_2CO_3, and the carbonates of the metals formed may then be dissolved in dilute acid, and the solution added to that previously obtained for analysis. A residue unacted upon by these treatments must be treated with hydrofluoric acid or subjected to a sodium carbonate fusion. For these methods the reader is referred to more extensive treatises on qualitative analysis.

If the material for analysis contains organic matter (which may be recognized by the fact that a small portion of it chars and fumes when heated in a miniature test tube), this must be removed before analysis to prevent interference (see exercise **7**, Chap. V). For this purpose the sample is heated with 10 cc. of 18 N H_2SO_4 until well charred. The solution is cooled, a few cubic centimeters of 16 N HNO_3 are added, and the mixture is gradually heated to SO_3 fumes. If it chars, it is cooled, HNO_3 is added and the process is repeated until the strongly heated solution is light colored. Evaporate to dryness, and treat the residue as you would any inorganic material.

Test for Phosphate Ion.—Since the method of analysis for the metallic ions must be modified when phosphate is present, this must be tested for during that analysis. Boil 5 cc. of the filtrate from **4** until H_2S has been removed, and add it to a mixture of 5 cc. of 6 N HNO_3 and 5 cc. of molybdate reagent (90 g. of ammonium molybdate and 240 g. of NH_4NO_3 dissolved in 100 cc. of 6 N NH_3 and diluted to 1 liter). Warm gently and let stand for 5 to 10 min. A yellow precipitate indicates the presence of phosphate ion. The precipitate is the ammonium salt of a complex acid and has the approximate composition $(NH_4)_3PO_4$-$(MoO_3)_{12}$. Arsenate gives a similar precipitate, but has been removed at this point of the analysis. Only a small portion of the unknown is required because the test is very sensitive, and is furthermore desirable because the precipitate is only formed when the ratio of molybdate to phosphate is large.

If phosphate is found present, the method of analysis of the aluminum and iron group must be modified as described in the note on **22** on page 210.

Preparation of the Solution for Analysis for the Anions.— Treat 2.5 g. of the substance to be analyzed with 25 cc. of 3 N Na_2CO_3 solution, boiling the mixture several minutes if a clear solution is not obtained. This treatment precipitates most of the metallic ions as carbonates or hydroxides, and their removal is an advantage in the analysis for the anions. It also metathetizes many water-insoluble substances with the formation of insoluble carbonate and the soluble sodium salt of the anion present in the original solid. A typical reaction is

$$PbSO_4 + CO_3^= \rightleftarrows PbCO_3 + SO_4^=.$$

The substances which do not liberate their anion to the solution under this treatment are: many sulfides (see under Sulfide Ion, page 215); many phosphates, but phosphate is tested for in the course of the analysis for the metallic ions; the halides of silver, but these may be recognized by special test if silver ion has been found present (see under Chloride Ion, below); and the silicates and other materials which require treatment with HF or carbonate fusion to prepare a solution for the analysis for the metallic ions.

Sulfate Ion.—Acidify a portion of the carbonate solution with HCl, dilute two or three times with water (to avoid precipitation of $BaCl_2$ or $Ba(NO_3)_2$), and add normal $BaCl_2$. A white precipitate of $BaSO_4$ indicates the presence of sulfate ion. The only probable interference is from fluosilicate ion.

Chloride Ion.—Acidify a small portion of the carbonate solution with HNO_3. If sulfide is present boil until it is completely removed, then cool. Add a few drops of N $AgNO_3$. A precipitate may contain chloride, cyanide, ferrocyanide, or thiocyanate, which are white, pale-yellow bromide, yellow iodide, or orange ferricyanide. For further distinction between these possibilities the reader must consult more extensive treatises.

Nitrate Ion.—(*a*) Mix 2 cc. of the carbonate solution with 10 cc. of water and 3 cc. of 6 N NaOH. If ammonium ion has been found present, boil until the NH_3 has been completely driven off, then cool. Add aluminum turnings, zinc dust, or Devarda's alloy. These reduce the nitrate ion to ammonia which may be tested for with litmus in the vapors as in the method of analysis for the metallic ions. Various organic nitrogen compounds, nitrite ion, cyanide ion, thiocyanate ion, ferrocyanide and ferricyanide ions also give the reaction. The last four may be removed by shaking the carbonate solution with silver carbonate or sulfate before making the test. Nitrites are practically certain to contain nitrate ion in any case. An estimate of quantity is possible in terms of the intensity of the coloration of the litmus and the time required for the development of the color.

Carbonate Ion.—Any solid containing an appreciable amount of carbonate will effervesce when dilute acid is added. To be certain of its presence, place about 0.5 g. of solid substance in a test tube, add 10 cc. of 3 per cent H_2O_2 to oxidize sulfite and 5 cc. of 6 N HCl, and quickly close the tube with a stopper carrying a delivery tube which reaches below the surface of some clear freshly prepared $Ba(OH)_2$ solution in another container. Heat gently to drive the CO_2 over into the $Ba(OH)_2$ where it precipitates $BaCO_3$. It is practically indispensable to run a blank to take account of the absorption of CO_2 from the air by the $Ba(OH)_2$ solution.

Sulfide Ion.—When any metallic ions except aluminum, chromium, the alkaline earths, or the alkalis are present, the color and solubility of the material will be sufficient to demonstrate the presence of sulfide ion. Otherwise an acidified solution may be treated with a few drops of $AgNO_3$, when sulfide ion will produce a black or dark-brown precipitate.

APPENDICES

APPENDIX A

THE LECTURE EXPERIMENTS

Chapter I

Page 6. A bead and wire model of the sodium chloride lattice and of other lattice types if possible should be exhibited to the class.

Page 8. The conductivity of fused salts may be demonstrated with KNO_3. An iron crucible is mounted in a wire triangle on a ring stand over a Meeker burner. A copper wire is held in an insulated clamp in the center of the crucible. Crucible and wire are connected to the 110-volt direct-current circuit through a 25-watt lamp. The crucible is filled with KNO_3 which has been melted in the crucible previously and allowed to solidify in it. When the KNO_3 is melted by heating with the burner, the light glows brilliantly.

Page 11. Exhibit 0.05 N solutions of $CuSO_4$, $Cu(NO_3)_2$, $CuCl_2$, and $CuCr_2O_7$. The last is prepared by mixing equal volumes of 0.1 N $CuSO_4$ and 0.1 N $K_2Cr_2O_7$.

To demonstrate the additivity of colors rectangular museum glasses 4.5 × 7 × 14.5 cm. are suitable. One contains 0.1 N $CuSO_4$, a second 0.1 N $K_2Cr_2O_7$, and two more are filled with 0.05 N $CuCr_2O_7$. These are now held in front of a window or a ground-glass pane illuminated by an electric light in such a way that the class may observe the identity of the light which has traversed the $CuSO_4$ and $K_2Cr_2O_7$ in succession with that which has traversed the two glasses filled with the $CuCr_2O_7$.

Page 13. A solution of HCl in benzene is prepared by passing gaseous HCl into benzene, and the solution is preserved in contact with $CaCl_2$. A portion of this solution is placed in a beaker, and two platinum electrodes connected to the 100-volt direct-current circuit through a 25-watt lamp are introduced. The lamp remains dark. Water is now poured in, which extracts the HCl from the benzene and forms a hydrochloric acid solution which conducts excellently. The lamp glows brilliantly.

Page 19. A U-tube about 17 cm. high and of 2-cm. bore is provided with a tubulature and stopcock at the bottom of the bend as shown in Fig. 2. The tubulature is connected through a rubber tube to a leveling bulb, and the bulb, rubber tube, and glass tube are filled to the exclusion of air bubbles with a $CuCr_2O_7$ solution. This is prepared by mixing equal volumes of N $CuSO_4$ and N $K_2Cr_2O_7$ and adding a few drops of H_2SO_4 to prevent hydrolysis. The U-tube and connecting tube above the stopcock are rinsed out and enough normal H_2SO_4 is introduced into the U tube to fill the curved part. The stopcock is now opened just enough to allow the $CuCr_2O_7$ to flow gently in under the H_2SO_4 preserving a sharp plane of separation. When a sufficient height is attained, the stopcock is closed, small platinum electrodes are dipped into the H_2SO_4, one in each leg of the tube, and a current of about 0.25 ampere is allowed to flow. (A 25-watt lamp is used in series with the 110-volt direct-current line.) Five or ten minutes should be sufficient to demonstrate the migration.

Chapter II

Page 24. Shake up approximately equal volumes of $CHCl_3$ and bromine water in a large separatory funnel.

Page 25. Draw off the aqueous layer from the previous experiment and shake the $CHCl_3$ solution with water.

Page 26. Hydrated sodium acetate or hydrated sodium thiosulfate may be melted in a flask either alone or with the addition of a little water. If the flask is loosely plugged with cotton and allowed to cool slowly, crystallization is unlikely to take place. As a demonstration, a stirring rod is dipped into the dry crystalline salt concerned, tapped to remove any but invisible dustlike crystals, and dipped into the supersaturated solution. Rapid and almost complete solidification takes place.

Page 27. Mix equal volumes of 0.05 N $NaNO_3$ and potassium antimonate reagent, and rub the walls of the vessel with a stirring rod to show the acceleration of the crystallization.

Page 28. Precipitate $Al(OH)_3$ from 0.1 N $AlCl_3$ with a small excess of NH_3. Divide into two parts. Treat one with HCl and the precipitate dissolves immediately. Boil the other portion 15 min., keeping up the volume by the addition of water. Cool and add HCl. The precipitate will not be completely dissolved at the end of 1 hour.

Add small portions of the saturated solutions of sodium acetate, $AgNO_3$, and $NaNO_3$ to separate portions of a saturated solution of silver acetate.

Page 42. Experiment 7 (page 189) may be cited or used to illustrate occlusion.

Page 44. Mix 60 cc. of 0.1 N $Sr(NO_3)_2$ and 10 cc. of 3 N K_2CrO_4, make alkaline with ammonia, then add about half the volume of the solution of ethyl alcohol.

Mix equal volumes of 3 N K_2CrO_4 and alcohol, and compare the precipitate of K_2CrO_4 thus obtained with that of $SrCrO_4$ previously obtained.

Chapter III

Page 47. Add N $AgNO_3$ to 6 N ammonium acetate until a precipitate of silver acetate appears. Add a similar amount of $AgNO_3$ solution to 6 N acetic acid, showing that no precipitate appears.

Add a few drops of 0.1 per cent methyl orange solution to a portion of 0.01 N HCl and to one of 0.01 N acetic acid. Test the two solutions with litmus.

Precipitate some $SrCrO_4$ from N $Sr(NO_3)_2$ and 3 N K_2CrO_4. Show that it dissolves upon addition either of 6 N HCl or of 6 N acetic acid. Add 10 cc. of 3 N K_2CrO_4 to 50 cc. of 0.1 N $BaCl_2$, and divide into two parts. To one add 5 cc. of 6 N HCl, to the other 5 cc. of 6 N acetic acid.

Page 53. Precipitate some ZnS from a 0.1 N $Zn(NO_3)_2$ solution with H_2S. Repeat the experiment with the previous addition of enough HCl to prevent the precipitation.

Add a few cubic centimeters of 6 N acetic acid to a portion of 0.1 N $FeSO_4$, and pass in H_2S. Then add ammonium acetate until FeS precipitates.

Page 54. To the solution (page 53) containing Zn^{++}, HCl, and H_2S add ammonium acetate solution and if necessary more H_2S to precipitate ZnS.

Precipitate $Mg(OH)_2$ from 0.5 N $Mg(NO_3)_2$ with 6 N NH_3. To another portion of magnesium salt solution add one quarter its volume of 6 N ammonium acetate solution, then NH_3.

Page 60. A conductivity board apparatus of the sort described by Noyes and Blanchard, *J. Am. Chem. Soc.*, **22**: 737 (1900), may be used with HCl, NaCl, acetic acid, and sodium acetate to emphasize the discrepancy between the conductivity of acetic acid actually observed and the value calculated on the basis of the principle of additivity.

Page 62. Make up a 0.001 N $Fe[Fe(SCN)_6]$ solution containing 0.01 N HNO_3 by mixing solutions of $Fe(NO_3)_3$, NH_4SCN, and HNO_3. A number of portions are placed in test glasses, one is kept as a reference, and various solid salts, such as NH_4Cl, KNO_3, $BaCl_2$, and Na_2SO_4 are added to the others. Strong HCl or HNO_3 may also be used. To demonstrate the qualitative validity of the predictions of the law of chemical equilibrium, normal $Fe(NO_3)_3$ and normal NH_4SCN may be added to other portions.

Page 75. Acidify a 0.1 N solution of $Mn(NO_3)_2$ with a small amount of acetic acid, and saturate with H_2S. No precipitate appears. Add 6 N ammonium acetate and continue to pass in H_2S. No precipitate appears. Make alkaline with NH_3 and MnS precipitates.

Repeat with 0.1 N $Co(NO_3)_2$. No precipitate appears in the acetic acid solution but CoS precipitates when ammonium acetate is added.

Acidify a 0.1 N solution of $Zn(NO_3)_2$ with acetic acid and pass in H_2S. ZnS precipitates. Add 6 N HCl until the precipitate just dissolves. Add a little normal $Cd(NO_3)_2$ and yellow CdS precipitates. Dissolve by adding 12 N HCl. Add a little normal $Cu(NO_3)_2$ and CuS precipitates.

Mix a portion of normal $Cu(NO_3)_2$ with 10 volumes of 12 N HCl and saturate with H_2S. No CuS appears, but sulfur is precipitated.

Mix a portion of normal H_3AsO_4 with 10 volumes of 12 N HCl and saturate with H_2S. As_2S_5 precipitates.

Page 76.   Experiment **14** (page 190) may be repeated to demonstrate the slow solution of NiS.

Chapter IV

Page 84.   Add 6 N ammonium acetate to a portion of 0.1 N acetic acid colored red by methyl orange until the color changes to yellow.   Now test with litmus paper to show that the solution is nevertheless acid.

Add 6 N ammonium acetate to 0.1 N NH_3 colored red by phenolphthalein until the solution is colorless.

Add 6 N ammonium acetate to a portion of 0.1 N HCl colored red with methyl orange until the color changes to yellow.

Add 3 N Na_2CO_3 to a portion of 0.1 N $AlCl_3$.   Add 6 N $(NH_4)_2S$ to a portion of 0.1 N $AlCl_3$.

Page 95.   Precipitate some $Mg(OH)_2$, then redissolve it by adding an ammonium salt.

Page 96.   To 50 cc. of 0.1 N $MgCl_2$ in a test glass add 5 cc. of 3 N Na_2CO_3. A precipitate appears.   Add 3 cc. 6 N ammonium acetate.   The precipitate dissolves because the NH_4^+ combines with the OH^- and the decrease in OH^- concentration permits a further decrease in CO_3^- concentration by hydrolysis.   Add 50 cc. of 15 N NH_3.   A faint precipitate appears because of the increased concentrations of OH^- and CO_3^- Add 50 cc. of alcohol and the precipitate increases greatly.

Experiment **18** (page 191) may be carried out on a larger scale as a lecture experiment.

Page 98.   Add $(NH_4)_2S$ to $AlCl_3$ solution.   Pass H_2S through $AlCl_3$ solution to demonstrate that $Al(OH)_3$ is not precipitated.

Page 99.   Add 10 cc. of 6 N ammonium acetate to 50 cc. of 0.1 N $AlCl_3$. Heat part of the solution to boiling and show precipitation.   Test the supernatant liquid with litmus paper.

Chapter V

Page 103.   Exhibit samples of various hydrated and anhydrous cobaltous and cupric salts, and compare with the colors of the dilute solutions.

Page 105.   Add 6 N NaOH to 0.1 N $ZnCl_2$ a little at a time so that a precipitate of $Zn(OH)_2$ is first formed then dissolved.

Page 106.   Add 3 N Na_2S to the zincate solution prepared in the previous experiment.

Page 109.   Prepare a $NaAl(OH)_4$ solution from 0.1 N $AlCl_3$ and a small excess of 6-normal NaOH.   Precipitate $Al(OH)_3$ from one portion of this by passing in H_2S, from another by adding 6 N ammonium acetate.

Page 111.   Add several volumes of 6 N NaOH to 0.1 N $CoCl_2$.   Filter through a hardened filter to show the blue color of the solution.

Page 112.   Add 6 N NH_3 to 0.1 N $NiCl_2$ a little at a time so that both the formation of the precipitate and its solution in excess of NH_3 can be observed.

Add 6 N NaOH to another portion of NiCl$_2$ and show that the precipitate does not dissolve even in a very large excess of NaOH.

Add 3 N NH$_4$Cl to a portion of NiCl$_2$ solution to show that the color of the solution does not change.

Page 114. To 50 cc. of 0.25 N NiCl$_2$ add 10 cc. of 15 N NH$_3$ and 40 cc. of water. To another 50 cc. portion of the NiCl$_2$ add 50 cc. of 15 N NH$_3$. Compare the colors.

Add a sufficient excess of 6 N NH$_3$ to dissolve the precipitate to a 0.1 N CoCl$_2$ solution. Call attention to the color and set aside until the color change due to oxidation has taken place.

Add an equal volume of 15 N NH$_3$ to a 0.1 N solution of a chromic salt. Point out the lack of color of the liquid, and set aside until sufficient of the precipitate has dissolved so that the lavender color of the complex ion can be seen. Boil some of the lavender solution.

Page 115. Prepare a nickel-ammonia solution from 0.1 N NiCl$_2$ and a small excess of NH$_3$. Pass in H$_2$S and show the precipitate.

Add 4 volumes of 15-normal NH$_3$ to 1 volume of 0.1 N NiCl$_2$. Pass in H$_2$S and show that no precipitate appears.

Add 6 N HCl to a nickel-ammonia solution until the color changes to green.

Page 116. Prepare a nickel-ammonia solution from 0.1 N NiCl$_2$ and a small excess of NH$_3$. Add 6 N NaOH until the precipitation is complete.

Add 10 cc. of 6 N ammonium acetate to 50 cc. of 0.1 N NiCl$_2$, and show that the addition a very little at a time of NH$_3$ produces no precipitate but converts the nickel ion directly to the ammonia complex.

Page 117. Add 6 N NH$_3$ to a 0.5 N solution of a magnesium salt and show that the precipitate does not dissolve in excess. To another portion of magnesium salt add one quarter its volume of 6 N ammonium acetate and then add NH$_3$ to show that no precipitate appears.

Repeat the preceding experiment with a manganous salt and with a ferrous salt. Let the manganous solutions stand to demonstrate the effect of air oxidation.

Precipitate some AgCl and demonstrate its solubility in NH$_3$ and its reprecipitation with HNO$_3$.

Page 118. Add 6 N NH$_3$ to 0.1 N Hg(NO$_3$)$_2$.

Add normal KCN to 0.1 N AgNO$_3$ a little at a time so that both the formation of the precipitate and its solution in excess can be noted. Add a little NaCl solution and show that no AgCl precipitates. Add a few drops of 3 N Na$_2$S. Reserve the solution with the Ag$_2$S precipitate for a later experiment.

Page 119. In a migration setup such as that used on page 19 the solution in the bend of the U tube is N K$_3$Fe(CN)$_6$, the superimposed liquid is N Na$_2$SO$_4$. Electrolysis is continued until a marked motion of the boundary has taken place.

Page 121. Add solid KCN to the solution of KAg(CN)$_2$ with suspended Ag$_2$S remaining from the experiment on page 118 until the precipitate dissolves.

Page 122.   Pass H_2S into one portion of a solution containing 0.1 N Cu^{++} and 0.1 Cd^{++}. Note the complete masking of the color of CdS.   To another portion of the same solution add 6 N NH_3 until the precipitate redissolves, then N KCN until the blue color just disappears.   Pass in H_2S to precipitate yellow CdS.

Page 123.   Add 3 N Na_2S to 0.1 N K_2SnCl_6 a little at a time so both the formation and the solution of the precipitate can be observed.   Pass H_2S to saturation into another portion of the K_2SnCl_6 solution.   Add 6 N HCl to the sulfostannate solution to show the precipitation of SnS_2 and its solution in excess of HCl.

Page 124.   Add 6 N $(NH_4)_2S$ to 0.1 N $Hg(NO_3)_2$ to show that HgS does not dissolve in $(NH_4)_2S$.   Repeat with the sodium sulfide-hydroxide reagent of the laboratory to show the solution of HgS in this reagent. To the Na_2HgS_2 solution thus obtained add 6 N ammonium acetate until the HgS again precipitates.

Add the sulfide-hydroxide reagent to 0.1 N $SnCl_2$ to show that SnS does not dissolve to form a complex sulfide ion.

Add 10 cc. of the sulfide-hydroxide reagent to 10 cc. of 0.01 N bismuth salt.   Boil, and filter.   To the filtrate add 10 cc. of 6 N ammonium acetate.

Page 125.   Saturate a 0.1 N $CdCl_2$ solution with NaCl.   Actual saturation is necessary, and this requires time.   Pass in H_2S.   No precipitate should appear.   If there is one, remove it by filtration.   Dilute with several volumes of water and saturate with H_2S.   CdS precipitates.

Add first a small amount, then an excess of a concentrated solution of KI to solutions of mercuric, lead, bismuth, and silver salts to show the formation of complex iodides.

Page 129.   Add 6 N HNO_3 to a solution of $Fe(NO_3)_3$ to demonstrate lack of color of Fe^{+++}.   Repeat with $FeCl_3$ and HCl to show yellow color of molecular $FeCl_3$.

Add 0.1 N NH_3 a little at a time to a N $Fe(NO_3)_3$ solution.   After each addition stir until the precipitate disappears.   Stop before a permanent precipitate forms.   Call attention to the color.

Add a few cubic centimeters of normal $Fe(NO_3)_3$ to 200 cc. of boiling water, and call attention to the deep red color.

Add 10 cc. of 6 N ammonium acetate to 50 cc. of 0.1 N $Fe(NO_3)_3$. Call attention to the color, and compare with the color obtained in the two previous experiments.   Heat part of the solution to boiling and exhibit the precipitate.

Chapter VI

Page 133.   Add a little 0.2 N $KMnO_4$ to a portion of 0.1 N $FeSO_4$ acidified with H_2SO_4.

Page 139.   Two test glasses contain 0.1 N KBr and 0.1 N KI, respectively. Both solutions are acidified by the addition of a few cubic centimeters of 6 N acetic acid.   A few cubic centimeters of 0.2 N $KMnO_4$ are added to each solution.   The MnO_4^- color persists in the bromide solution, but disappears and is replaced by the brown of I_2 in the iodide solution. A few cubic centimeters of 6 N H_2SO_4 are now added to the bromide solution and the permanganate is now reduced here also. The Br_2 may be recognized by its color.

Page 142. Mix equal portions of 0.1 N KI and 0.1 N $CuSO_4$. Note the precipitate and the color of I_2 in the solution. Dilute part of the solution and add starch solution to confirm the I_2.

Add ten volumes of 12 N HCl to one volume of normal $CuSO_4$. Pass in H_2S and note the sulfur precipitate.

Page 143. Prepare a sodium stannite solution by diluting a portion of the stannous chloride reagent four times, and adding 6 N NaOH slowly with careful cooling until the precipitate dissolves. Boil a portion of this to show the precipitation of Sn.

Page 144. Precipitate $Bi(OH)_3$ by adding 6 N NaOH to 0.1 N $Bi(NO_3)_3$. Add to the suspension a portion of the sodium stannite solution.

Add 0.1 N $KMnO_4$ to 0.1 N $Mn(NO_3)_2$, and note the disappearance of the MnO_4^- color and the precipitate of MnO_2.

Page 145. Add BiO_2 to a portion of 0.1 N $MnCl_2$ and stir until the permanganate color is well developed.

Page 146. Neutralize a portion of 0.1 N $Hg_2(NO_3)_2$ and add 3 N KCN. Note the precipitate of Hg.

Precipitate some Hg_2Cl_2 from 0.1 N $Hg_2(NO_3)_2$ with NaCl, then add excess of 6 N NH_3.

Page 148. To a 0.5 N $NiCl_2$ solution add a few drops of 6 N acetic acid, and about one-tenth its volume of 6 N KNO_2. Repeat with a 0.5 N $Sr(NO_3)_2$. After noting that both solutions are free from precipitate mix equal volumes and stir until the yellow precipitate appears. Compare with $K_3Co(NO_2)_6$ precipitated from a 0.1 N $CoCl_2$ solution by KNO_2 and acetic acid.

Page 149. Add enough 6 N NaOH to a portion of 0.1 N $NiCl_2$ to produce a precipitate. Add 3 N KCN just sufficient to dissolve the precipitate completely. Now add Br_2 water until the black precipitate of $Ni(OH)_3$ appears. Repeat with 0.1 N $CoCl_2$ instead of the 0.1 N $NiCl_2$.

Page 151. Add Na_2O_2 to a portion of 0.1 N $CrCl_3$ until the oxidation is complete. This may be recognized by the color change. Divide into two parts. Acidify one immediately with HCl, then make alkaline with NH_3, and note the precipitate of $Cr(OH)_3$. Boil the other portion 2 or 3 min., cool, and acidify carefully with cooling. Make alkaline with NH_3 and note absence of precipitate, showing that no CrO_4^- has been reduced.

Acidify a 3 per cent solution of H_2O_2 with H_2SO_4 and add 0.2 N $KMnO_4$. Note the disappearance of the permanganate color and the evolution of O_2.

Chapter VII

Page 156. The galvanic cells used in these experiments may be made up from 250 or 400 cc. beakers. These are half-filled with normal NaCl so that the conductivity will be large, and junction potentials will be negligible.   Other reagents are added in small amounts in relatively concentrated solutions.   The salt bridges are U-tubes filled with the same NaCl solution and plugged at the ends with cotton.   The electrodes when platinum are foil or gauze of the sort used for copper determinations by electrolysis.   Some sort of lecture table potentiometer is almost indispensable if the true significance of the oxidation potential is to be brought home.   Such an instrument is described by Gucker and van Atta, *J. Chem. Education* **8**, 1157 (1931), who also describe convenient half-cells which may be used instead of the beaker setup just described.   The voltmeter potentiometer mentioned in the text and described for instance in Clark "Determination of Hydrogen Ions," page 324, is also easily adapted to lecture table use.   Table-type or wall-type galvanometer and voltmeter are used and the resistance AB may suitably be a radio potentiometer of 100 ohms.

In the present case the beakers are set up with the NaCl solution. To one beaker enough normal ferric nitrate and normal ferrous sulfate are added to make the concentrations about 0.01 N, to the other add a solution of I_2 in KI in corresponding amount.

Page 159.   The ferric-ferrous half-cell and the iodine-iodide half-cell may be measured against a normal hydrogen electrode, which may be constructed from any of the usual types of hydrogen half-cell and fed with tank hydrogen.   The potentials thus obtained should be compared with the value obtained by measuring the ferric-ferrous half-cell directly against the iodine-iodide one.

Page 165.   The half-cells contain approximately 0.01 N CuSO$_4$ in N Na$_2$SO$_4$. The electrodes are of sheet copper.   Note that the intial potential is zero.   Add a small amount of NaOH solution to one half-cell, and observe the potential.   Then add Na$_2$S solution, and again observe the potential.   Now add solid KCN and stir, rubbing the electrode to remove the film of CuS, until a clear solution is obtained.   Again observe the potential.

Page 168.   Set up two hydrogen electrode half-cells with normal NaCl solution.   Make the solution about 0.1 N HCl in one, about 0.1 N NaOH in the other.   Observe the potential.

Page 169.   Set up a copper electrode in a 0.01 N CuSO$_4$ solution, a zinc electrode in a 0.01 N ZnSO$_4$ solution, both solutions being also normal in Na$_2$SO$_4$.   Add successively NaOH, Na$_2$S, and KCN, as in the experiment on page 165, to the CuSO$_4$ solution, observing the potentials. Then add first NaOH, then KCN to the ZnSO$_4$ solution.

Page 174.   A solution of nearly pure ferrous salt may be made by adding iron nails to a solution 0.1 N in ferrous sulfate and normal in H$_2$SO$_4$, and allowing to stand for some hours.   Add 6 N NH$_3$ in excess to a portion of this solution and note the gradual change in color which accompanies the oxidation.

Add normal KSCN to a portion of 0.1 N FeCl$_3$.   Add to this a normal solution of Na$_4$P$_2$O$_7$ acidified with acetic acid until the red color disappears or nearly so. This is to demonstrate the stability of the ferric-pyrophosphate complex.

Mix equal volumes of 0.1 N FeCl$_3$ and 0.1 N KI. The solution takes on the brown color of I$_2$. Add the acidified pyrophosphate solution and the solution becomes colorless. The addition of starch solution gives a blue which shows that some iodine is left.

APPENDIX B

THE LABORATORY

THE SCHEDULE OF LABORATORY WORK

One careful analysis of a solution is of much greater value than three or four hasty ill-considered attempts to rush through the analysis, with the idea that if a mistake is made it can be rectified by repeating the analysis. In general, the laboratory work in a course of qualitative analysis is of much better quality when a schedule is posted and rigidly insisted upon which easily permits the one careful analysis, but makes the three hurried attempts impossible.

It may be recommended therefore that Unknown No. 1 be completed by the end of the second laboratory period of 3 hours, that Unknown No. 2 be completed by the end of the fifth such period, Unknown No. 3 by the end of the ninth period, Unknown No. 4 by the end of the sixteenth period, Unknown No. 5 by the end of the twenty-third period, and Unknown No. 6 by the end of the twenty-seventh period.

REAGENTS

Acetic acid, 6 N .... 300 cc.
    Mix 350 cc. of 99.5 per cent acid with 650 cc. water
Alcohol, ethyl, 95 per cent .... 200 cc.
Aluminum chloride, N .... 15 cc.
    Dissolve 80.5 g. $AlCl_3(H_2O)_6$ in water to make 1 liter.
Ammonium acetate, 6 N .... 200 cc.
    Dissolve 460 g. of the solid salt in water to make 1 liter.
Ammonium carbonate-ammonia reagent .... 200 cc.
    Dissolve 250 g. of ammonium carbonate in 6 N NH_3 to make
    1 liter.
Ammonium chloride, solid .... 5 g.
Ammonium chloride, 3 N .... 200 cc.
    Dissolve 160 g. of NH_4Cl in water to make 1 liter.
Ammonia, 6N .... 300 cc.
    Mix 400 cc. of 15 N NH_3 with 600 cc. of water.
Ammonia, 15 N .... 100 cc.
    This is aqua ammonia, specific gravity 0.90.
Ammonium thiocyanate, N .... 90 cc.
    Dissolve 76 gr. NH_4SCN in water to make 1 liter.
Antimony chloride, N, in 6 N HCl .... 10 cc.
    Dissolve 76 g. $SbCl_3$ in 6 N HCl to make 1 liter.

Antimony, powder.. 15 g.

Arsenic acid, *N*.. 10 cc.

    Dissolve 23 g. As_2O_5 in water to make 1 liter.

Aurin tricarboxylic acid, ammonium salt, 0.1 per cent......... 60 cc.

    Dissolve 1 g. of the dye in water to make 1 liter.

Asbestos soup...

    50 g. asbestos in about 100 cc. water.

Barium chloride, *N*.. 90 cc.

    Dissolve 122 gr. $BaCl_2(H_2O)_2$ in water to make 1 liter.

Bismuth nitrate, *N*, in 3 *N* HNO_3........................ 15 cc.

    Dissolve 162 g. $Bi(NO_3)_3(H_2O)_5$ in 3 *N* HNO_3 to make 1 liter.

Bromine water... 15 cc.

    A saturated solution of Br_2 in water. Each bottle should contain a small excess of liquid Br_2.

Cadmium nitrate, *N*....................................... 15 cc.

    Dissolve 154 g. of $Cd(NO_3)_2(H_2O)_4$ in water to make 1 liter.

Calcium nitrate, *N*.. 30 cc.

    Dissolve 118 g. $Ca(NO_3)_2(H_2O)_4$ in water to make 1 liter.

Chromic chloride, *N*....................................... 15 cc.

    Dissolve 89 g. $CrCl_3(H_2O)_6$ in water to make 1 liter.

Cobalt nitrate, *N*... 20 cc.

    Dissolve 145 g. $Co(NO_3)_2(H_2O)_6$ in water to make 1 liter.

Copper nitrate, *N*... 20 cc.

    Dissolve 121 g. $Cu(NO_3)_2(H_2O)_3$ in water to make 1 liter.

Dimethyl glyoxime, 0.1 *N*.................................. 30 cc.

    Dissolve 12 g. of the solid substance in 1 liter 95 per cent ethyl alcohol.

Ferric nitrate, *N*.. 75 cc.

    Dissolve 135 g. $Fe(NO_3)_3(H_2O)_9$ in water to make 1 liter.

Ferrous sulfate, solid...................................... 5 g.

Hydrochloric acid, 12 *N*................................... 300 cc.

    This is hydrochloric acid, specific gravity 1.19.

Hydrochloric acid, 6 *N*.................................... 300 cc.

    Mix 500 cc. 12 *N* HCl and 500 cc. water.

Iron, powder... 10 g.

Iron sulfide, lump, for H_2S.............................. 100 g.

Lead nitrate, *N*... 90 cc.

    Dissolve 166 g. $Pb(NO_3)_2$ in water to make 1 liter.

Magnesium nitrate, *N*..................................... 30 cc.

    Dissolve 128 g. $Mg(NO_3)_2(H_2O)_6$ in water to make 1 liter.

Manganese nitrate, *N*..................................... 15 cc.

    Dissolve 144 g. $Mn(NO_3)_2(H_2O)_6$ in water to make 1 liter.

Mercuric chloride, 0.2 *N*.................................. 15 cc.

    Dissolve 27 g. $HgCl_2$ in water to make 1 liter.

Mercuric nitrate, *N*, in *N* HNO_3....................... 15 cc.

    Dissolve 162 g. $Hg(NO_3)_2$ in *N* HNO_3 to make 1 liter.

Mercurous nitrate, N **in** HNO_3............................ 15 cc.
Dissolve 262 g. $HgNO_3$ in N HNO_3 to make 1 liter.   Add a
drop of Hg to each bottle.

Nickel nitrate, N....................................... 20 cc.
Dissolve 145 g. $Ni(NO_3)_2(H_2O)_6$ in water to make 1 liter.

Nitric acid, 16 N....................................... 125 cc.
This is nitric acid, specific gravity 1.42.

Nitric acid, 6 N.. 300 cc.
Mix 380 cc. 16 N HNO_3 with 620 cc. water.

p-nitrobenzene azo resorcine reagent..................... 15 cc.
Dissolve 1.2 g. of the solid dyestuff in 10 cc. 6 N NaOH and
dilute to 2,500 cc.

Potassium antimonate reagent............................ Side bench
Add 22 g. of commercial potassium antimonate to 1,000 cc.
boiling water, boil for a minute or two until nearly all is dissolved, cool quickly, add 35 cc. 6 N KOH, let stand over
night and filter.   The solution is approximately 0.1 M
$KSb(OH)_6$ and 0.5 N KOH.

Potassium chlorate, solid................................. 20 g.
Potassium chloride, solid................................. 15 g.
Potassium chromate, 3 N................................ 125 cc.
Dissolve 292 g. K_2CrO_4 in water to make 1 liter.

Potassium ferricyanide, solid............................. 5 g.
Potassium ferrocyanide, N.............................. 60 cc.
Dissolve 105 g. $K_4Fe(CN)_6(H_2O)_3$ in water to make 1 liter.

Potassium nitrate, N................................... 30 cc.
Dissolve 101 g. KNO_3 in water to make 1 liter.

Potassium nitrite, solid.................................. 50 g.
Potassium oxalate, 3 N................................. 100 cc.
Dissolve 280 g. $K_2C_2O_4(H_2O)$ in water to make 1 liter.

Silver nitrate, N...................................... 15 cc.
Dissolve 170 g. $AgNO_3$ in water to make 1 liter.

Sodium arsenite, N.................................... 10 cc.
Dissolve 33 g. As_2O_3 in 60 cc. 6 N NaOH and dilute with
water to 1 liter.

Sodium carbonate, 3 N................................. 30 cc.
Dissolve 160 g. Na_2CO_3 in water to make 1 liter.

Sodium chloride, solid................................... 100 g.
Sodium cobaltinitrite reagent............................ 60 cc.
Dissolve 230 g. $NaNO_2$ in 500 cc. water, add 165 cc. 6 N
acetic acid, and 30 grams $Co(NO_3)_2(H_2O)_6$, let stand over
night, filter, and dilute to 1 liter.   This is 0.3 N
$Na_3Co(NO_2)_6$, 3 N $NaNO_2$, N acetic acid.

Sodium hydroxide, 6 N................................. 300 cc.
Dissolve 250 g. NaOH in water to make 1 liter.

Sodium nitrate, N..................................... 30 cc.
Dissolve 85 g. $NaNO_3$ in water to make 1 liter.

Sodium nitrite, solid...................................... 5 g.
Sodium peroxide, solid..................................... 10 g.
Sodium phosphate, secondary, N......................... 200 cc.
    Dissolve 120 g. $Na_2HPO_4(H_2O)_{12}$ in water to make 1 liter.
Sodium silicate, concentrated............................. 15 cc.
    This is the water glass of commerce.
Sodium sulfide-hydroxide reagent......................... 100 cc.
    Dissolve 480 g. $Na_2S(H_2O)_9$ and 40 g. NaOH in water to
    make 1 liter. This is 4 N Na_2S and N NaOH.
Stannous chloride, N, in 2 N HCl....................... 15 cc.
    Dissolve 115 g. $SnCl_2(H_2O)_2$ in 170 cc. 12 N HCl, and dilute
    with water to 1 liter. Add a small piece of tin metal to
    each bottle.
Strontium nitrate, N.................................... 20 cc.
    Dissolve 106 g. of $Sr(NO_3)_2$ in water to make 1 liter.
Sulfuric acid, 36 N...................................... 50 cc.
    This is 95 per cent H_2SO_4, specific gravity 1.84.
Sulfuric acid, 6 N....................................... 125 cc.
    Pour 200 cc. 95 per cent H_2SO_4 carefully into 1 liter of water.
Zinc nitrate, N... 15 cc.
    Dissolve 150 g. $Zn(NO_3)_2(H_2O)_6$ in water to make 1 liter.

The late Prof. Thomas B. Freas instituted about 1913 the system of giving to each student in a course in chemistry a complete individual outfit of chemicals. This outfit contains an amount of each reagent which is sufficient in the hands of the average student for the whole work of the term. The quantities listed after each reagent in the above table are those which have been found to be suitable for issuance in such individual outfits for the laboratory work outlined in this book.

This system has particular advantage in a course of qualitative analysis in that each student becomes responsible for the care of his own reagents, and the inevitably unclean reagent side shelf is eliminated. The previous difficulty of the large and well-organized stockroom force necessary is eliminated by the fact that such outfits can now be purchased ready for issuance.

UNKNOWN SOLUTIONS

The unknown solutions issued to the students should be made up to definite concentrations, each ion present being at a concentration of either 0.5 N, 0.1 N, or 0.01 N. 25 or 50 cc. may be issued of each.

It will be found convenient to use silver, mercurous, lead, bismuth, copper, cadmium, mercuric, zinc, manganous, cobalt, nickel, barium, strontium, calcium, magnesium, potassium, sodium, and ammonium nitrates; antimonous, ferric, aluminum, and chromic chlorides; arsenic acid, sodium arsenite, and potassium chlorostannate. Of these the solutions of mercurous, mercuric, and bismuth nitrates, and of arsenic acid should be acidified strongly with nitric acid; and the solutions of antimonous, ferric, aluminum, and chromic chlorides and of sodium arsenite and potassium chlorostannate should be acidified strongly with hydrochloric acid.

APPARATUS

Returnable

1 beaker, resistance glass, 100 cc.
1 beaker, resistance glass, 150 cc.
1 beaker, resistance glass, 250 cc.
1 beaker, resistance glass, 400 cc.
1 beaker, resistance glass, 600 cc.
1 beaker, resistance glass, 800 cc.
2 bottles, glass stoppered, narrow neck, 250 cc.   For unknowns
2 burners, Tyrell
1 calcium chloride tube
2 casseroles, porcelain, 7 cm.
2 casseroles, porcelain, 11 cm.
1 crucible and cover, porcelain, 3.5 cm.
1 filter bar, wood, four holes, iron clamp
1 filter pump
1 flask, Erlenmeyer, resistance glass, 25 cc.
4 flasks, Erlenmeyer, resistance glass, 50 cc.
4 flasks, Erlenmeyer, resistance glass, 100 cc.
2 flasks, Erlenmeyer, resistance glass, 250 cc.
1 flask, Erlenmeyer, resistance glass, 500 cc.
1 flask for filtering, side neck, thick-walled, resistance glass, Erlenmeyer, 500 cc.
1 funnel, 4 cm.
2 funnels, 7 cm., long stem
1 generator for H_2S
1 gold cone, perforated, for suction filtration
1 graduated cylinder, 10 cc.
1 graduated cylinder, 50 cc.
1 ringstand, 18-in. rod, with 2- and 3-in. rings
1 spatula, horn, 12.5 cm.
12 test tubes, 4 × ½ in.
24 test tubes, 6 × ¾ in.
1 test-tube rack
1 tripod, 4½ in. diameter
1 wash bottle, 700 cc. with glass bends, but without rubber stopper
4 watch glasses, 2 in.
2 watch glasses, 3 in.
2 watch glasses, 4½ in.
1 wing top for burner

Non-returnable

1 asbestos disk, 5 in.
2 boxes safety matches

1 corkscrew
4 g. absorbent cotton
1 file, triangular, 5 in.
100 filter papers, HCl washed
12 filter papers, hardened, 9 cm.
5 feet glass rod, soft, 4 mm.
5 feet glass tubing, soft, 6 mm.
3 grams glass wool
1 box labels, gummed, 1 × 1½ in.
2 dozen labels, gummed, round, ½-in. diameter
1 rubber stopper, two-hole, to fit wash bottle
1 rubber stopper, one-hole, to fit filter flask
1 rubber stopper, one-hole, to fit calcium chloride tube
2 rubber stoppers, two-hole, No. 5
2 rubber stoppers, two-hole, No. 6
2 feet rubber tubing, black, ³⁄₁₆ in.
7 feet rubber tubing, white, ¼ in.
1 sponge
1 test-tube brush
1 test-tube cleaner
1 test-tube holder
1 triangle, pipe stem, 5-cm. side
2 towels
1 vial litmus paper, blue
1 vial litmus paper, red
3 wire gauze squares, 4 in.

INDEX

A

Acetic acid, solutions in, 16, 17
Acidity, 82–84
Acids and bases, 15–17, 46–48
    catalysis by, 49, 92
Activity coefficients, 63–64
Additivity of properties, 10–11, 59–60
Adsorption, 44
Alcohol, 44, 190–192, 204, 205
Alkali group, 75, 76, 201, 204, 206–207
Alkaline-earth group, 75, 76, 100, 117, 201, 204–206
Aluminum group, 201–203
Aluminum ion, 75, 98–101, 109–112, 117, 123, 129–132, 148, 192, 193, 201, 202, 210
Amides, 14, 16, 48, 118, 132, 146, 197
Ammonia, 16, 47, 51, 65, 78, 112–118
    solutions in, 9, 13–14, 16, 17, 118
Ammonia complex ions, 112–117, 147
Ammonium ion, 13, 14, 16, 17, 77, 115, 207
Amphoteric hydroxides, 105–112, 131, 132
Anion concentration, control of, 69–76, 89, 95
Antimony, ions of, 27, 45, 76, 110, 111, 123–125, 162, 197–201, 207–208
Atomic number, 4, 5
Atomic structure, 4
Aqua regia, 149–150, 188
Arsenic, ions of, 65, 76, 97, 111, 123–125, 131, 197–200, 207–208
Aurin tricarboxylic acid, 193, 202, 210

B

Barium ion, 40, 42, 69–71, 76, 79, 162, 189–191, 204–205
Basic-acetate separation, 99, 101, 211
Bismuth dioxide, 145
Bismuth ion, 76, 101, 124–125, 144, 198
Blank test, 186
Buffer solutions, 68–69, 71, 75, 79

C

Cadmium ion, 40, 42, 75–76, 114, 116, 121–122, 125, 162, 177, 178, 189, 199
Calcium ion, 40, 44, 79, 162, 186, 191–192, 205, 211
Calculation, of hydrolysis, 86–90, 95–96, 101–102
    of ionization, 65–68
    of ionization constants, 56–62, 78–79, 86
    of solubility products and solubilities, 32–36, 44–45, 70
Calomel electrode, 169
Carbonate ion, 7, 65, 89–90, 189, 192, 215
Chlorate ion, 144
Chloride complex ions, 122, 125–127, 143, 149–150
Chloride ion, 214
Chromium, ions of, 40, 44, 69–71, 75, 77, 98, 100–101, 110–111, 114, 116, 123, 128, 130–131, 151–152, 162, 189–192, 201–202, 209–210
Cleanliness, 185–186